First Edit...

MW01098023

Fireground
Support
Operations

Carl Goodson, Author
Cynthia Brakhage, Editor

Validated by the
International Fire Service Training Association

Published by
Fire Protection Publications
Oklahoma State University

RECYCLABLE

The International Fire Service Training Association

The International Fire Service Training Association (IFSTA) was established in 1934 as a "nonprofit educational association of fire fighting personnel who are dedicated to upgrading fire fighting techniques and safety through training." To carry out the mission of IFSTA, Fire Protection Publications was established as an entity of Oklahoma State University. Fire Protection Publications' primary function is to publish and disseminate training texts as proposed and validated by IFSTA. As a secondary function, Fire Protection Publications researches, acquires, produces, and markets high-quality learning and teaching aids as consistent with IFSTA's mission.

The IFSTA Validation Conference is held the second full week in July. Committees of technical experts meet and work at the conference addressing the current standards of the National Fire Protection Association and other standard-making groups as applicable. The Validation Conference brings together individuals from several related and allied fields, such as:

- Key fire department executives and training officers
- Educators from colleges and universities
- Representatives from governmental agencies
- Delegates of firefighter associations and industrial organizations

Committee members are not paid nor are they reimbursed for their expenses by IFSTA or Fire Protection Publications. They participate because of commitment to the fire service and its future through training. Being on a committee is prestigious in the fire service community, and committee members are acknowledged leaders in their fields. This unique feature provides a close relationship between the International Fire Service Training Association and fire protection agencies which helps to correlate the efforts of all concerned.

IFSTA manuals are now the official teaching texts of most of the states and provinces of North America. Additionally, numerous U.S. and Canadian government agencies as well as other English-speaking countries have officially accepted the IFSTA manuals.

ISBN 0-87939-203-7   Library of Congress Control Number # 2001098939

First Edition, First Printing, March 2002   Printed in the United States of America

If you need additional information concerning the International Fire Service Training Association (IFSTA) or Fire Protection Publications, contact:

Customer Service, Fire Protection Publications, Oklahoma State University
930 North Willis, Stillwater, OK 74078-8045
800-654-4055   Fax: 405-744-8204

For assistance with training materials, to recommend material for inclusion in an IFSTA manual, or to ask questions or comment on manual content, contact:

Editorial Department, Fire Protection Publications, Oklahoma State University
930 North Willis, Stillwater, OK 74078-8045
405-744-4111   Fax: 405-744-4112   E-mail: editors@ifstafpp.okstate.edu

Table of Contents

Preface vi

Introduction ix
   Purpose and Scope ix
   Notice on Gender Use x

1 Size-Up 3
   Size-Up 4
      What Has Happened? 4
      What Is Happening? 4
      What Is Likely To Happen? 4
      Safety Considerations 4
   NIOSH Model 5
      Time of Day 6
      Day of Week 6
      Weather 6
   Fire Behavior 7
      "Routine" Fires 7
      "Self-Vented Fires 9
      Rollover 10
      Flashover 10
      Backdraft 10
      Structural Collapse 10
   Building Construction 11
      Age of Building 11
      Type of Construction 12
      Collapse Potential 12
      Building Modifications 13
      Fire Characteristics 14
   Summary 17

2 Firefighter Survival 21
   Standard Safety Behaviors 21
      Phoenix Model 22
   Communication 23
   Accountability 23
   Structural Collapse 24
   Rapid Intervention 25
   Emergency Egress 26
      Firefighter Trapped 26
      Firefighter Lost 26
      Locating Windows and Doors 27
      Window Egress 27
      Door Egress 28
      Wall Breach 29
   Summary 29

3 Access to Structures 33
   Topography and Landscaping 33
      Overcoming Site Obstacles 34

Gates 36
      Manually Operated Gates 36
      Automated Gates 37
      Lockboxes 38
Fences 38
      Wire Fences 38
      Chain Link Fences 39
      Wooden Fences 40
      Vinyl Fences 41
      Decorative Metal Fences 41
      Masonry Walls 41
Security Measures 42
      Barbed Wire 42
      Razor Ribbon 42
      Fence Spikes 42
      Wall Tops 43
      Guard Dogs 43
      Booby Traps 43
Summary 44

4 Access Into Structures 47
Forcible Entry Tools 48
Doors 49
      Residential/Commercial Doors 50
      Industrial/Institutional Doors 54
      Door Security Systems 61
Windows 62
      Types of Windows 62
      Breaking Windows 63
      Residential/Commercial Windows 64
      Industrial/Institutional Windows .. 64
      Window Security Systems 64
Walls 66
      Types of Exterior Walls 68
Summary 71

5 Interior Operations 75
Search and Rescue 75
      Type of Building 75
      Primary Search 78
      Rescue 80
      Sheltering In Place 80
      Secondary Search 81
Heat Removal 81
      Vent As You Go 82
Salvage 82
      Attic Fires 82
      Water Removal 84
Summary 85

6 Ventilation Size-Up **89**

Ventilation Overview 89
Fire Behavior 91
   Growth Stage 91
   Flashover Stage 92
   Fully Developed Stage 93
   Decay Stage 93
   Fire Spread 95
Smoke Behavior 96
   Volume 96
   Color 96
   Density 97
   Pressure 97
Building Construction 98
   Age and Type of Building 98
   Features That Help 101
   Features That Hinder 103
   Features Related to the Occupancy 106
Coordination With Rescue and Fire
   Attack 107
   Timing 108
   Location 108
   Method 109
Other Ventilation Size-Up Considerations 110
   Exposures 110
   Weather 111
Summary 112

7 Horizontal Ventilation **115**

Horizontal Ventilation Tools and
   Equipment 115
   Ventilation Tools 115
   Ventilation Equipment 115
Building Construction Related to
   Horizontal Ventilation 119
   Walls 119
   Windows 122
   Doors 124
Establishing and Supporting
   Horizontal Ventilation 128
   Precautions Against Upsetting
     Established Horizontal Ventilation .. 129
Natural Horizontal Ventilation 132
   Doors 132
   Windows 132
Forced Horizontal Ventilation 136
   Using Smoke Ejectors 136
   Using Blowers 137
   Using Nozzles (Hydraulic Ventilation) 138
Summary 139

8 Vertical Ventilation **143**

Vertical Ventilation Tools 143
   Cutting Tools 143

Stripping Tools 146
Establishing and Supporting
   Vertical Ventilation 148
Vertical Ventilation Safety 148
   Identifying Vertical Ventilation
     Hazards 149
   Getting Firefighters to the Roof 149
   Reading a Roof 150
   Sounding a Roof 151
   Working on a Roof 152
   Working with Protective Hoselines 152
Existing Roof Openings 153
   Scuttle Hatches 153
   Penthouses (Bulkheads) 154
   Skylights 154
   Monitors 154
   Turbine (Rotary Vane) Vents 155
   Light and Ventilation Shafts 155
   Ridge Vents 156
   Clerestory Windows 156
Roof Construction 156
   Pitched Roofs 156
   Flat Roofs 164
   Arched Roofs 173
Lightweight Construction 176
   Panelized Roofs 176
   Trussed Roofs 176
   Wooden I-Beams 180
Roof Coverings 181
   Wooden Shingles and Shakes 181
   Composition Roofing/Shingles 182
   Tar and Gravel 183
   Urethane/Isocyanate Foam 183
   Single-Ply/Synthetic Membrane 183
   Tile/Slate 184
   Light-Gauge Metal/Fiberglass 185
   Steel Clad 186
Opening A Roof 186
   Cutting the Hole 188
   Louver Vents 189
   Trench (Strip) Ventilation 191
Summary 192

**9 Special Ventilation
   Operations** **195**

Fire Operations in High-Rise Buildings 195
   Staffing 195
   Fire Attack 195
   Elevators 196
   Fire Behavior 197
High-Rise Ventilation 198
   Vertical (Top) Ventilation 199
   Channeling the Smoke 200

Ventilating Below the Fire 204
Ventilating the Fire Floor 204
Ventilating Above the Fire 205
HVAC and Smoke-Control Systems 206
Built-In Ventilation Devices 206
Automatic Roof Vents 207
Atrium Vents 207
Monitors 208
Skylights 208
Curtain Boards 208
Underground Structures 208
Windowless Buildings 210
Highly Secure Buildings 210
Remodeled Buildings 210
Summary 211

10 Controlling Utilities 215
Fuel Control 215
Situational Differences 216
Controlling Natural Gas in
Structure Fires 216
Controlling LPG in Structure Fires 218
Controlling Fuel Oil in Structure Fires 219
Gas Leaks Without Fire 220
Approach................................. 221
Perimeter Control 221
Hazard Assessment 222
Hazard Mitigation 223
Electricity Control 225
Situational Differences 225
Controlling Electricity in
Structure Fires 225
Wires Down Without Fire 228
Perimeter Control 228
Water Control 231
Situational Differences 231
Water Control in Structure Fires 231
Water Leaks Without Fire 234
Summary 234

**11 Controlling Building
Systems 237**
Heating, Ventilating, and Air
Conditioning Systems (HVAC) 237
HVAC Systems and Their Hazards 237
Control of HVAC Systems 239

Lighting Systems 241
Lighting Systems and Their Hazards ..241
Control of Lighting Systems 241
Conveyance Systems 243
Conveyance Systems and Their
Hazards 243
Control of Conveyance Systems 243
Fire Detection and Suppression
Systems 246
Types of Systems and Their Hazards ..246
Control of Fire Detection and
Suppression Systems 252
Summary 255

12 Loss Control 259
Pre-Incident Loss Control Operations 259
Risk Identification 260
Risk Evaluation 260
Plans Development 261
Incident Loss Control Operations 262
Primary Loss Control 262
Secondary Loss Control 266
Post-Incident Loss Control Operations 269
Economic Loss Control 269
Psychological Loss Control 270
Summary 271

**13 Coordinated Fireground
Support Operations 275**
Fireground Priorities 275
Incident 275
Resources 276
Operational Modes 277
Offensive Mode 277
Defensive Mode 278
Rescue Mode 278
Coordinated Fireground Operations 280
Command Options 280
Structure Fire Scenarios 282
Summary 288

Appendix A 291

Appendix B 305

Glossary 309

Index 317

Preface

This first edition of **Fireground Support Operations** replaces the IFSTA **Ventilation** and **Forcible Entry** manuals. It is intended to build a bridge of information between the IFSTA **Essentials** and the IFSTA **Company Officer** manuals.

A work of this size and complexity could not have been created without the expertise, dedication, and hard work of the members of the validation committee. Profound thanks are extended to them.

IFSTA Fireground Support Operations Committee

Committee Chair
Wes Kitchel
Santa Rosa (CA) Fire Department

Dan Brown
Spokane (WA) Fire Department

David Douglas
Greensboro (SC) Fire Department

John Hinton
Phoenix (AZ) Fire Department

Alan Joos
Utah Fire and Rescue Academy

Bob Madden
Bend (OR) Fire and Rescue

Robert Miller
Mesa (AZ) Fire Department

Mark Pare
Providence (RI) Fire Department

Peter Sells (Secretary)
Toronto (ONT) Fire Services

Jerry Shacklett
Orange County (CA) Fire Authority

Steve Taylor (Vice Chair)
Rescue Engineering Institute (IN)

Greg Terrill
Los Angeles (CA) Fire Department

Bob Waldron
Spokane County (WA) Fire District #9

In addition, numerous individuals and organizations contributed photographs and/or other assistance without which this manual could not have been completed. Gratitude is extended to this group.

Wayne Bennett
Sand Springs (OK) Fire Department (Ret.)

Mark Biedenharn
Shawnee (OH) Fire Department

Ronnie Boedicker
Lima (OH) City Schools

Ray Brown
Oklahoma Natural Gas
Tulsa, OK

Cedar Rapids (IA) Fire Department
Fire Chief Steve Havlik
Training Chief Mark English

District Chief George Bockenstedt
Capt. Lenny Drake
Capt. Dan Drexler
Capt. Tom Mackey
Lt. Vern Sebetka
FF Brian Hibbs
FF Randy Hook
FF Bryan Johnson
FF Rick Larson
FF Jason Lopez
FF Rob McAllister
FF Pat Mick
FF Tom Moats

Dexter Coffman
Tempest Technology
Fresno, CA

Randy Crossley
Lima (OH) Education Center

Francine DeLanty
Santa Rosa, (CA) Fire Department

Keith Flood
Santa Rosa (CA) Fire Department

Donna Gill
Wilton, CA

Ron Jeffers
Union City, New Jersey

Bill Lellis
Larkspur (CA) Fire Department (Ret.)

Lima (OH) Fire Department
Fire Chief Theodore Bookman
Assistant Chief Tony Depalma
Assistant Chief James Foust
Assistant Chief Rick Robinson
Inspector Christopher Jackson
Platoon Chief Mark Hefner
Platoon Chief David McDermott
Platoon Chief Kevin Rader
Lt. Bruce Black
Lt. Robert Dershem
FF Toby Atkinson
FF Eric Hayes
FF Bryan Malsam
FF Mark Rudasill
FF John Seleski

Danny Lynchard
Tulsa (OK) Police/Fire Chaplaincy Corps

Jeff Lara
Yukon (OK) Fire Department

Jennifer Marsh
Bullard Safety Products
Cynthiania, KY

Ron Meyer
Johnson County (IA) Sheriff's Office

Leslie Miller
Oklahoma State University
Stillwater, OK

Rick Montemorra
Mesa (AZ) Fire Department

Sand Springs (OK) Fire Department
Fire Chief Bradd Clark
Assistant Chief Mark Joslin
Capt. Dan Call
Capt. Robert Chailer
Capt. Rick Pate
Capt. Rick Portilloz
Capt. Mike Wood
FF Wes Ashford
FF Shelby Baughn
FF Stephen Brewer
FF Mark Davis
FF James Evans
FF Larry Fisher
FF Charlie McGee
FF Justin Melton
FF Jim Mock
FF Molencupp
FF Brad Newport
FF Stan Smith
FF Jason Sprouse
FF Matt Tavaglione
FF Jeremy Wade

Scott Health and Safety
Monroe, NC

Super Vacuum Manufacturing Co., Inc.
Loveland, CO

Thermal Windows, Inc.
Tulsa, OK

Rob Thompson
Public Service Company
Tulsa, OK

Tulsa (OK) Fire Department
Fire Chief Tom Baker
Frank Mason, Visual Communications Officer
A. P. Romero, Training Officer
Capt. Bill Kaiser
Capt. Stan May
Capt. Rick Powell
Capt. Randy Steede
Capt. Mike Whitten
FF Steve Abernathy
FF Dicus Benton
FF Scott Clark

FF R.B. Ellis
FF Jeff Fry
FF Sean Lawless
FF Eddie Mangold
FF Kevin McLarty
FF Martin Noah
FF Melissa Pendergraft
FF Jerry Roberts
FF Matt Saint
FF George Surrell
FF Joe Youngblood

Chuck Wehrli
Naperville (IL) Fire Department

Grady Whitaker, Jr.
Whitaker Architects
Sand Springs, OK

Last, but certainly not least, gratitude is extended to the members of the Fire Protection Publications staff who contributed their time and talent to the completion of this manual.

Barbara Adams, Associate Editor
Tara Gladden, Editorial Assistant
Don Davis, Production Coordinator
Ann Moffat, Graphic Design Analyst
Ben Brock, Senior Graphic Designer
Desa Porter, Senior Graphic Designer

Brien McDowell, Graphic Technician
Susan F. Walker, FPP Librarian
Shelly McGee, Library Assistant
Kayla Moorman, Library Assistant
Jay Nelson, Research Technician

Introduction

When a fire breaks out inside a structure, certain predictable things occur. Given an adequate supply of oxygen, the fire will continue to burn until one of two things happens — the fire is extinguished by some external intervention (fire attack or extinguishing system activation), or it goes out when all of the available fuel has been consumed. While the fire burns, it produces heat that helps to propagate and sustain the process. The fire also produces varying amounts of smoke and other toxic products of combustion that may fill the building. The smoke obscures vision and makes respiration difficult for the occupants of the building. A burning building filled with smoke and superheated toxic gases is a hostile and potentially life-threatening environment for firefighters as well. To survive in this environment, firefighters must learn to accurately assess the situation and then compare the risks involved to the benefits to be gained from each action being considered.

Firefighters have been and continue to be injured or killed in so-called "routine" fires, or those that have "self-vented" by breaking a window or burning through the roof. In addition, any number of nonfire hazards may be present on the fireground. There may be charged electrical wires down, gaseous or liquid fuel leaks, or toxic or explosive materials present. Firefighters must learn how to recognize the potentially lethal conditions in these seemingly innocuous situations, and how to mitigate those conditions.

In situations where the oxygen supply is limited, potentially explosive backdraft conditions can develop. If these conditions go unrecognized by the first-arriving fire crews, and if ventilation is not performed before entry is attempted, the results can be catastrophic.

Therefore, if firefighters are to quickly but safely enter a burning building to search for trapped occupants and extinguish the fire, a number of other things need to happen — sometimes sequentially, sometimes simultaneously. These things include sizing-up the structure and the fire, gaining access to the building's interior, ventilating the building, and controlling the building's utilities. And, as soon as the situation and available resources allow, steps should also be taken to minimize collateral damage.

Since they are performed in support of the rescue and fire suppression efforts, these other functions are commonly known as *fireground support operations.* However, considering that properly performed fireground support operations can and often do prevent or reduce the loss of life in working structure fires, the term "support" should not be taken to mean "subordinate to" or "less important than" the fire suppression operations. In fact, they are as critical as any other fireground function. Fireground support operations should be performed as part of a coordinated attack involving rescue, fire suppression, and support functions executed in the manner and sequence dictated by the situation.

In many fire departments throughout North America, fireground support operations are performed by truck companies. However, when these operations are needed, they must be performed quickly and safely regardless of whether there is a truck company on scene or not — even if the department doesn't have a ladder truck. All firefighters should have a working knowledge of fireground support activities; therefore, this manual focuses on the operations that need to be performed without specifying who performs them.

Purpose and Scope

This manual is intended to serve as a reference in formal training courses on fireground support operations, and in self-study by individual firefighters. The material in this manual combines and updates information previously contained in the IFSTA **Forcible Entry**, **Fire Service Ventilation**, and **Fire Service Loss Control** manuals. The knowledge, skills, and abilities discussed in this manual are critical to safe and efficient structural fire fighting.

It is assumed that the readers of this manual will have read the IFSTA **Essentials of Fire Fighting** manual and will have successfully completed a recognized training course in basic fire fighting theory and practice. Therefore, this manual focuses on fireground support operations in greater depth than presented in **Essentials**.

NOTICE

No one should expect to become proficient at performing fireground support operations simply by reading this or any other book on the subject. The information contained in this manual must be combined with hands-on training delivered by qualified instructors and with experience on working structure fires.

The text begins with a discussion of fireground safety through proper size-up of structure fires and a series of firefighter survival techniques. Next, gaining access and interior operations are discussed. In the chapters on ventilation, size-up for ventilation operations, ventilation tool selection and application, and ventilation methods are discussed. The chapter on utilities control discusses gas control, electricity control, water control, and the control of building systems. The loss control chapter discusses pre-incident loss control activities as well as operations that are performed on the fireground, both during and after fire suppression. Finally, the chapter on coordinated fireground support operations discusses how all of the various fireground functions are combined into a safe and effective operation.

Throughout this book, a number of case histories of actual incidents in which firefighters were injured or killed are cited. This is done to provide examples of what has happened in various locations, and what may happen again if safe and effective techniques are not used. The cases cited are all ones that have been investigated and analyzed by neutral third parties such as NFPA, NIOSH, or USFA. More information on these and other case histories can be obtained from the following web sites:

NFPA = www.nfpa.org

NIOSH = www.cdc.gov/niosh

USFA = www.usfa.fema.gov

Notice on Gender Use

The English language has historically given preference to the male gender. In standard English, the pronouns, "he" and "his" are commonly used to describe both genders. IFSTA/Fire Protection Publications has made great effort to treat both genders equally, recognizing that a growing number of fire service personnel are female. However, in some instances, male pronouns are used to describe both males and females solely for the purpose of brevity. This is not intended to offend readers of the feminine gender.

Chapter 1
Size-Up

Chapter 1
Size-Up

On an April evening in 1978, a candle started a fire on the second floor of a partially sprinklered, three-story, wood frame apartment house in Upstate New York. The fire spread into the wall and before this fire was extinguished the following morning, four firefighters had lost their lives and several more were injured.

According to the post-fire analysis conducted by NFPA, the deaths were the result of a combination of how the building was constructed and delayed ventilation. The building was of balloon frame construction that allowed the fire to spread inside the wall from the second floor into the attic space above the third floor. Ventilation was delayed, apparently because the fire situation was not accurately assessed by those first on the scene. The results were that water from the attic sprinklers turned to steam and forced fire and superheated gases from the unvented attic down into the third floor rooms. Water from the sprinklers was also heated to scalding temperatures and helped to cut off the means of egress for the firefighters trapped on the third floor.

ings may be affected by the age of the building and the type of construction, as well as the materials in them.

All too often firefighters fail to understand how a fire inside a structure is behaving because they are unfamiliar with the type of construction and its characteristics or with remodeling that the structure has undergone over the years. Both of these problems can be mitigated by firefighters studying the types of construction common to their response districts and by an ongoing program of pre-incident planning inspections to keep the firefighters current on any remodeling taking place in the buildings they are assigned to protect (**Figure 1.1**).

This chapter begins with a discussion of the general characteristics of the size-up process and how the process applies to fireground support operations. Also discussed are some general descriptions of fires that have all too often resulted in firefighters being injured or killed. The chapter continues with

This tragic incident is just one example of firefighters being injured or killed because, at least in part, the fire situation was not accurately sized-up upon arrival. While the size-up of interior structure fires is an inexact science, there are things that firefighters can and should do to increase the accuracy of their size-ups and thereby decrease the chances of firefighter fatalities such as occurred in this case. In addition to understanding basic fire behavior as presented in the IFSTA **Essentials of Fire Fighting** manual, firefighters need to have a thorough knowledge of the structures within their response districts and how fires inside these build-

Figure 1.1 Firefighters need to stay current on new construction and remodeling within their districts.

discussions of various fire conditions that have the potential for injuring or killing unwary firefighters. Finally, various types of building construction are discussed along with how fires may behave in each type.

Size-Up

In general, size-up is a relatively simple process. Although it can be and has been described in many different ways, it is simply the continual and ongoing process of making careful observations and drawing reasonable conclusions from those observations. However, because the process is simple, does not mean that applying it is always easy. In fact, from a life safety standpoint, accurately sizing-up a fire situation is sometimes one of the most difficult functions, but always one of the most important functions.

> For purposes of this manual, *size-up* is defined as the continual and ongoing assessment of an emergency situation from initial alarm to incident termination.

Regardless of the nature of the incident, every size-up involves answering the following fundamental questions.

- What has happened?
- What is happening?
- What is likely to happen?
- What safety considerations are involved?

What Has Happened?

Identifying what initially happened to create the emergency situation can be a critical step in sizing-up that situation. Among the questions that need to be answered are the following:

- Was anyone injured?
- How long has it been burning?
- Did it start as a result of an earthquake or other natural occurrence?
- Was there an explosion, and if so, what exploded?
- Was the scene contaminated with some hazardous material?

What Is Happening?

Identifying what is happening at any given moment is obviously critical information. Some of the questions that need to be answered are these:

- Is the situation stable or getting worse?
- Are there trapped victims?
- Is the fire threatening those victims?
- Are exposures being threatened?
- Is the fire getting bigger?
- Are there signs of backdraft conditions developing?
- Is the building losing structural integrity?

What Is Likely to Happen?

Estimating what is likely to happen is a key element in the development of an Incident Action Plan (IAP). Questions that need to be answered might be the following:

- Is the fire likely to get bigger without additional resources being used?
- Is there a possibility of a secondary explosion or a backdraft?
- Is the structure likely to collapse?
- Will firefighters or others be at risk from toxic residue or other hazards?

Safety Considerations

While all of the foregoing questions relate directly or indirectly to fireground safety, the officer conducting the initial and subsequent size-ups should continually and consciously address the question of safety. Addressing safety issues is often a process of weighing the risks involved in various courses of action against the possible benefits to be gained by those actions. These considerations must take into account the risks to building occupants and firefighters alike. Some of the questions that need to be answered are as follows:

- Is immediate intervention needed to save lives?
- What are the risks to firefighters and other emergency responders?
- Are there electrical wires down that represent an electrocution hazard?

- Is vehicular traffic putting firefighters or others at risk?
- Are gaseous or liquid fuels leaking and contaminating the scene?
- Can these and any other safety considerations be handled with the resources currently on scene or en route?

All fireground personnel, including those assigned to fireground support operations, must consider the foregoing and make appropriate decisions based upon the answers to those questions. However, the incident commander (IC) and others in command and/or supervisory positions must also consider the following during initial size-up:

- What resources will be required to mitigate this situation?
- Are those resources immediately available or will their responses be delayed?
- How should the available resources be deployed to best advantage?
- What are the risks and benefits of each possible deployment mode?

The main reason that making an accurate initial size-up is so important is that the initial "report on conditions" and the IAP are based on it (**Figure 1.2**). It is also the basis for the initial incident decisions, and for one of the most critical decisions facing the first-arriving officer: "Are the resources that are on scene or en route sufficient to handle this incident?" If the answer is "no," or even "maybe," then additional resources must be requested *immediately*. If the request for additional resources is delayed, by the time they arrive at the scene the fire may have progressed to the point that, even with these additional resources, the total number of resources on the scene is still insufficient. Therefore, the initial size-up often sets the tone for the entire incident. If the initial size-up is accurate, the incident is more likely to be handled in a safe and timely manner. If the initial size-up is inaccurate, the incident is more likely to deteriorate and the chances of firefighter injuries or fatalities are increased.

The main reason that making an accurate initial size-up of a structure fire is difficult is that it requires not only a knowledge of fire behavior, building construction, and resource availability and capability,

Figure 1.2 An accurate size-up is the basis for both the report on conditions and the incident action plan.

it requires the necessary experience and judgment to understand how all of those factors may affect the situation at hand. The more that is known about each of these factors and of the particular building involved, the more likely an accurate size-up will be made and the incident handled safely and efficiently. Therefore, it is not only necessary for the first-in officer to know fire behavior and building construction, it is also very important for him to know the particular building involved. He needs to know the type of construction, the era in which the building was constructed, whether the building has been remodeled (how and to what extent), what the building contains, and whether the building is likely to be occupied at the time of the incident.

NIOSH Model

As mentioned earlier, the initial size-up of a structure fire can be described in a number of different ways. From a fireground support operations standpoint, the size-up recommended by the National Institute for Occupational Safety and Health

(NIOSH) is excellent. NIOSH recommends that the initial size-up of a structure fire include the following information:

- Fire size and location (room/contents, fully involved, floor(s), front/rear)
- Length of time the fire has been burning (estimated)
- Conditions on arrival (nothing showing, light smoke, heavy involvement)
- Size of the building (single/multistory, floor area, and height)
- Age of building (obvious weathering or other deterioration, modern construction materials)
- Presence of combustible materials (wooden structure, wooden roof assembly)
- Occupancy (residential, commercial, high hazard)
- Renovations or modifications (facades, false ceilings, additions)
- Previous fires (if known)
- Dead loads that might affect structural integrity (HVAC, water tank on roof)
- Adjacent exposures (fire extension, smoke contamination)
- Resources at scene or available (mutual aid)

In addition to the items on the NIOSH list, in some jurisdictions the availability of a reliable water supply is another factor that must be considered during size-up. Some rural areas may depend partially or entirely on mobile water supply. The time needed to establish the needed water supply under these conditions must be factored into the IAP.

Even though the size-up of any given structure fire starts even before the initial alarm (because of pre-incident planning), there are a number of other factors that can affect the initial size-up. Some of these additional factors are time of day, day of week, and weather.

Time of Day

This factor has a number of possible effects on the size-up of a structure fire. The time of day may increase or decrease the likelihood of the building being occupied. For example, during the late night and early morning hours, a residential structure is more likely to be occupied, and the occupants may be asleep. On the other hand, a small retail store (or similar occupancy) is unlikely to be occupied unless there is an apartment above it. The time of day can also affect the volume of vehicular and pedestrian traffic, such as children walking to or from school, crowds gathering at places of entertainment, or rush hour traffic obstructing response routes (**Figure 1.3**). Such traffic can affect the response times of additional resources.

Figure 1.3 The time of day can seriously affect response to emergencies.

Day of Week

The day of the week can also affect the size-up of a structure fire. School buildings are often (but not always) vacant on weekends. However, movie theaters and other places of entertainment, health clubs and sports facilities, and places of worship are often occupied on weekends — sometimes by large numbers of people. Many retail businesses are very crowded during business hours on weekends but may be closed on Sundays (**Figure 1.4**). Daylight hours on weekdays may involve heavy traffic congestion in business and commercial districts. These factors may increase or decrease the need for laddering buildings, conducting search and rescue operations, and/or may delay the response of additional resources.

Weather

Even though weather is less a factor in interior structure fires than in wildland operations, it can affect structure fire behavior and therefore make a difference in the size-up of such a fire. High ambient temperature and humidity take a toll on firefighters encapsulated in modern turnout gear. This may require more frequent crew relief and may increase

Figure 1.4 The day of the week can either help or hinder responses.

Figure 1.5 Inclement weather can slow responses significantly.

the need for medical monitoring and the establishment of a Rehab Unit. On the other hand, inclement winter weather can slow the response of emergency vehicles because of wet, snowy, or icy roads (**Figure 1.5**). Access to buildings may be more difficult in winter, and roof operations may be more difficult and dangerous. Strong winds may accelerate fire spread and affect ventilation operations. Firefighters working outside may be vulnerable to frostbite or hypothermia on protracted incidents. Sidewalks and driveways may be covered with ice creating slippery conditions. Roofs may be slippery or snow covered making ventilation very difficult.

It is sometimes more difficult for firefighters to function in extremely cold conditions, and the weight of protective clothing can add to firefighter fatigue.

Those assigned to fireground support operations must continually evaluate how each of the factors involved in sizing-up a structure fire may apply in a given situation. They must carefully observe the situation at hand and decide which of the factors apply, in what way, and to what extent. While no one can always observe every critical factor or anticipate every possible contingency, the skill and diligence with which these observations and decisions are made will determine how successful the operation is likely to be and, more importantly, how safe it is likely to be. From a safety standpoint, one of the most critical factors to evaluate in a structure fire is fire behavior.

Fire Behavior

To increase their chances of surviving interior structure fires unscathed, firefighters must apply all the knowledge of fire behavior they gained from training and experience when sizing-up specific situations. Interior structure fires have and continue to injure and kill firefighters who lack the necessary knowledge and skills to function safely in these unsafe environments. Among the specific situations that often lead to firefighter injuries or deaths are "routine" fires, "self-vented" fires, those that rollover or flashover unexpectedly, those in which backdraft potential is not handled correctly, and those involving unexpected structural collapse.

"Routine" Fires

In this context, "routine" refers to fires that appear to be relatively innocuous and easy to control. In the majority of relatively small interior structure fires, all is as it first appears, and all goes according to plan. Therefore, when firefighters have been involved in a series of these fires and nothing unusual happens and there are no serious injuries, it is easy for them to become complacent and begin to view these fires as "routine." However, in all too many of these "routine" fires, all is not as it first appears, and if firefighters fail to recognize the signs that something is seriously wrong — the results can be catastrophic (**Figure 1.6**). The quadruple fatality fire discussed earlier is a prime example of the sort of "routine" fire that kills firefighters.

When the first units arrived on scene, there was light smoke issuing from the second and third floors and from the eaves, but the only visible fire was in a section of wall on the second floor. When the firefighters opened up the wall, the fire in the attic above the third floor was provided with an increased oxygen supply because of the balloon frame construction. When the search crew arrived on the third floor, they saw no fire and felt no heat. However, heat and smoke from the fire above the third floor ceiling, intensified by the abundant oxygen supply coming up through the wall voids, quickly began to fill the third floor. When a hoseline was stretched to the third floor, the firefighters donned their SCBA and began fighting the fire that was intensifying in the walls and above the ceiling.

At that point, the firefighters were ordered to leave the third floor because of deteriorating conditions but only part of the crew did so — four firefighters remained. When other firefighters attempted to reenter the third floor to fight the fire there, they could not get through the wall of extremely hot water and steam that was cascading into the hallway. Since the roof was still unvented, the heat continued to build downward from the fire in the attic.

The first ventilation opening was cut at the peak of the roof but directly over an operating sprinkler. The water spray from the sprinkler kept smoke and heat from rising through the ventilation opening in the roof. A second opening was cut in the roof some distance from the first. This vent opening also was apparently ineffective. Finally, a third ventilation opening was cut in the roof nearer the point of origin. But, by this time, the attic and the third floor rooms were heavily involved in fire. Trapped on the third floor by the fire and a wall of scalding hot water, the four firefighters ran out of breathing air. In addition, because several firefighters had been sent to a nearby hospital with various injuries, the four missing firefighters were assumed to be among those that went to the hospital. Therefore, the search for them was delayed, and their bodies were not found until after the fire was extinguished.

Figure 1.6 There are no "routine" structure fires. *Courtesy of Ron Jeffers.*

The chain of events that lead to these firefighter fatalities had several links. According to the NFPA analysis, the fire was not accurately sized-up, and ventilation was delayed. But, in addition, the crew sent to search the third floor did not have a charged hoseline, and they apparently didn't try any avenue of escape other than the way they had come in. The firefighters did not have PASS devices since they were not widely available at that time. In addition, the trapped firefighters were probably suffering from impaired judgment due to oxygen deprivation (carboxyhemoglobin), so it is understandable that it might not have occurred to them to break through a window or wall to escape.

Similar fire conditions and similar fire behavior are typical of structure fires everywhere. Despite the fact that this fire occurred decades ago, the lessons to be learned are just as important today.

Another incident that resulted in four firefighter fatalities was a January 1995 arson fire in a Chinese food warehouse in Washington state. As in the fire described earlier, the chain of events that led to the deaths of the firefighters in this incident had many links. However, according to the U.S. Fire Administration investigative report, one of the most important contributing factors was that the building had been altered in a way that made it vulnerable to collapse if there were a fire in the basement. The decades old brick and heavy-timber building had been modified so that one end of the main floor beams were supported only by an unprotected wood frame "pony wall" (a lightweight support wall made of 2- × 4-inch [50 mm by 100 mm] lumber) that failed during the fire. Unfortunately, the four firefighters were standing on the floor above when it collapsed, dropping them into the fire.

Other contributing factors in this tragic incident were the layout of the building and its situation on the property. Because it was difficult for the IC to make a complete lap around the structure, he had an incomplete (and inaccurate) view of what was happening inside the building. Therefore, a strategy was devised that was based on inaccurate information. In addition, because of the unusual way the building was laid out, fire crews working in and around the building each saw the fire situation differently. Unfortunately, these differences in perception were not communicated to the IC. Therefore, he had no reason to suspect that the main floor of the building – where there was smoke but no fire – was about to collapse.

Earlier in this fire, a relatively new firefighter was on the main floor as a member of a crew and noticed that even though there was smoke on the main floor, there was little heat – except for the floor. He noticed that the concrete floor itself was quite hot. While a more experienced firefighter might have realized that the hot floor indicated that a fire was burning beneath it, the young firefighter did not, and he failed to bring his observation to his company officer's attention.

CAUTION

Everyone on the fireground should constantly monitor the situation with all his senses and report anything that seems unusual.

Structural firefighters can benefit from a well-established safety practice used by wildland firefighters. The practice is called "look up, look down, look around." This teaches firefighters to constantly monitor their surroundings for any sign that the situation is changing in a way that might put the crew in jeopardy.

There are other types of interior structure fires that injure and kill firefighters. One of the most common of these is the so-called "self-vented" fire.

"Self-Vented" Fires

When firefighters approach a working structure fire and flames and smoke are rising from the roof, they may breathe sighs of relief. This is because they think that the interior of the building will be relatively free of heat and smoke because the fire has "self-vented." Unfortunately, this is not always the case.

If firefighters are inside a structure where the heat and smoke forces them to crawl along the floor, regardless of whether fire is visible in the room or not, they should be aware that a flashover may be imminent. If the firefighters cannot stand up because of the tremendous heat, the combustibles in the room may be nearing their (nonpiloted) autoignition temperature.

Rollover

As described in **Essentials**, a rollover (also called *flameover*) is the ignition of superheated gases at or near the ceiling inside a structure. When a large volume of these gases suddenly ignite, a flame front rolls across the ceiling. A rollover can be a very dramatic and startling event and this is why rollovers are sometimes mistaken for flashovers.

To protect themselves in a rollover, firefighters must stay as low as possible and allow the fire and smoke to pass above them (**Figure 1.7**). Since a rollover rarely lasts for more than a few seconds, once it has passed over them, firefighters can resume their attack. Rollovers can usually be prevented with adequate and timely ventilation.

Flashover

As also described in **Essentials**, a flashover can be one of the most dramatic and frightening phenomena that most firefighters will ever witness. The speed with which the flames develop is part of what makes a flashover so dangerous to firefighters. If a fire has been burning inside a room for some time — and no one can tell exactly how long that is — the potential for the room to suddenly flashover and turn into an inferno should not be ignored. No building or its contents is worth a firefighter's life.

Backdraft

At least as lethal as any flashover, the only thing positive that can be said about a backdraft is that its potential is easier to recognize. From a size-up standpoint, the indications of possible backdraft conditions are as listed in **Essentials**, but because of their potential for saving firefighters' lives, they bear repeating here. The indications of backdraft potential are as follows:

- Pressurized smoke exiting small openings
- Black smoke becoming dense gray yellow
- Confinement and excessive heat
- Little or no flame visible inside
- Smoke leaving the building in puffs or at intervals (the appearance of breathing)
- Smoke-stained windows

However, in some newer, energy-efficient buildings these indications may not be as obvious as in older structures. In addition, because they are so well sealed, some modern structures are more likely to develop backdraft conditions. Firefighters should take this into account when they are sizing-up a modern building or an older one that has been brought up to modern standards. Once again, pre-incident planning can alert firefighters to a building's potential for developing backdraft conditions.

Structural Collapse

Over the years, the sudden and unexpected collapse of burning buildings has been the cause of numer-

Figure 1.7 Understanding fire behavior is essential to firefighter safety and survival.

ous firefighter deaths. In addition to the arson fire discussed earlier, the following case histories are two more examples of what can and does occur.

According to a NIOSH report, in March of 1996, two Virginia firefighters were killed when the roof of an auto parts store collapsed on them. While only light smoke was showing inside the store when the first unit arrived, fire was burning unseen between the dropped ceiling and the roof. The two firefighters took a 1-¾ inch (45 mm) hoseline inside with them as they investigated. The roof and the heavy HVAC units on it were supported by wooden roof trusses that were 50 feet (15 m) wide. Weakened by the fire, the roof assembly suddenly collapsed trapping the two firefighters. They died of burns and smoke inhalation.

In another incident, firefighters were not even in the building when a partial collapse proved fatal for one of their members. The necessity for "look up, look down, look around" cannot be overemphasized.

Also reported by NIOSH, in September of 1998, a nineteenth century brick and heavy timber warehouse was fully involved in fire. A Vermont firefighter was attempting to prop the self-closing warehouse doors open to allow a defensive attack from the outside when the parapet wall above collapsed on him. He died of crushing injuries.

But it is not only the roof and walls of a building that can collapse and endanger firefighters. As in the warehouse fire discussed earlier, and many others, collapse of a fire-weakened floor can drop firefighters into an inferno in the basement. Even if the basement fire has been extinguished, firefighters can die from injuries suffered in the fall, be asphyxiated by toxic black smoke, or even drown in water collected in that area.

Building Construction

It is vitally important for firefighters to understand the relationship between building construction and fire behavior. They must understand that, as in the fire described at the beginning of this chapter, an operating fire sprinkler can reduce the effectiveness of a ventilation opening cut directly above the sprin-

kler. They must also be aware of how various building designs — such as those that are tightly sealed for energy conservation — can affect fire behavior inside those buildings. They must be aware of the effects of various building materials. Some new materials change the fire environment by keeping the heat and other products of combustion confined within the building, rather than allowing them to be vented to the outside by breaking windows or by burning through the roof. Or these materials may add massive volumes of fuel and/or toxic products as they deteriorate due to the heat of the fire.

There are many ways in which the construction of a building that is on fire can affect fireground support operations, and firefighters must include these factors in their overall size-up of a fire situation. Among the factors that can impact these operations are the age of the building, the type of construction, its collapse potential, the nature and extent of any modifications, and how the fire is likely to behave in this particular building.

Age of Building

The age of a burning building can be a very critical thing for firefighters to assess in their size-up of the building. Buildings in a given neighborhood tend to be of generally the same age and have similar construction features and characteristics (**Figure 1.8**). Depending upon the geographic region in which the building was constructed, very old wood frame buildings may be of balloon frame construction that allows fire to travel unseen inside the walls from the basement to the attic. Older wood frame

Figure 1.8 Buildings of the same type usually have the same construction features. *Courtesy of Mark Pare.*

buildings are likely to have substandard wiring, and the adjacent combustibles are likely to be tinder dry — characteristics that lend themselves to fires starting and spreading rapidly. Older brick (unreinforced masonry [URM]) buildings often trap heat and smoke inside and are sometimes prone to wall collapse. Some older buildings may have unsupported truss roofs, such as the bowstring truss type, and be covered with many layers of composition shingles or other roofing materials. Older residential structures may have extraordinarily high ceilings unless they have had false ceilings installed at some point — a common practice.

On the other hand, newer wood frame buildings are more likely to have some type of lightweight construction that may fail early in a fire. Newer buildings of all types may contain building materials that liberate toxic products when subjected to the heat of a fire. However, in many jurisdictions, newer buildings are much more likely to be fully sprinklered so the likelihood of full fire involvement is reduced. The more that firefighters know about the requirements of the local building code, the more likely they are to identify exceptionally dangerous buildings within their response district.

Type of Construction

In sizing-up a burning building, firefighters need to take into account the type of construction. Obviously, wood frame buildings of any age may contain large quantities of highly combustible wooden structural members. Masonry buildings may resist the effects of fire but add to the risk of wall collapse. Buildings with arched roofs, lightweight roofs, or similar assemblies may be prone to sudden and unexpected roof collapse when subjected to a major fire within. Metal buildings, especially if well insulated, may contain a fire long enough that it can develop into major proportions before it is discovered. In addition, unprotected steel members are likely to distort and fail earlier in a fire than would wooden beams. For more information on the types of construction, refer to the IFSTA **Building Construction Related to the Fire Service** manual.

Collapse Potential

As described in the case histories discussed earlier, one of the things that firefighters need to assess in their initial and ongoing size-up of a burning building is its collapse potential. Assessing the collapse potential of a building that is on fire involves each of the foregoing factors as well as the effects of the fire itself. The age of the building may indicate the amount and type of reinforcing material used in its construction. The mortar in older brick (URM) buildings may have deteriorated to the point where the potential for wall collapse during a fire or earthquake is greatly increased **(Figure 1.9)**. Reinforced concrete buildings are designed to be both fire and collapse resistant. Many newer buildings, or older buildings that have been retrofitted to meet current standards, are likely to have structural components and assemblies designed to reduce collapse potential. However, regardless of the age of a building or its construction, almost any building may collapse if it is given a sufficient volume of fire over long enough time.

Figure 1.9 Unreinforced masonry buildings have a high collapse potential.

Building Modifications

According to an NFPA report, in 1978 a fire of unknown origin broke out in a 100-year-old hotel in Massachusetts. The hotel was undergoing extensive renovation at the time. The fire department responded with sufficient resources to extinguish the fire in a timely manner. However, during overhaul operations approximately three hours after the fire was reported, the building suddenly collapsed killing nine firefighters and injuring nine others. While the building may have been weakened by the fire, the most serious weakness was created by unauthorized structural changes made during the renovation. The collapse appeared to have been triggered by the extra weight of the fire crews and the water used to extinguish the fire.

Assessing how and to what extent a building has been modified (remodeled) can be a challenge when arriving at the scene of a structure fire. Remodeling in older buildings using lightweight construction materials and methods may be disguised in the finishing process, and this can sometimes lull firefighters into a false sense of security. Identifying how and to what extent buildings have been remodeled is most effectively done during pre-incident planning inspections. Frequent pre-incident inspections are the best way for firefighters to become familiar with the characteristics of the buildings within their response districts and to keep that knowledge up to date (**Figure 1.10**).

Had the firefighters in Washington been aware of the structural deficiencies in the Chinese food warehouse, they might have been able to prevent the collapse of the floor by protecting the "pony wall." Or, they may have known to keep firefighters from entering the collapse-prone area of the building.

Both residential and commercial buildings constructed before the middle of the twentieth century commonly had high ceilings, some 10 feet (3 m) or more, but many of them have had dropped (false) ceilings installed (**Figure 1.11**). A fire burning between a false ceiling and the original ceiling may be unaffected by a fire in the attic venting itself by burning through the roof.

CAUTION

If a firefighter crawling on the floor of a smoke-filled Victorian-style residence can touch the ceiling with a 6-foot (2 m) pike pole, there is probably a false ceiling in that room.

Figure 1.10 Pre-incident inspections provide critical information about occupancies within the district.

Figure 1.11 Many Victorian-type residences have false ceilings.

Other structural modifications, many of them in violation of local codes, often result in unsprinklered rooms being created in otherwise fully sprinklered buildings. This happens when someone divides an existing room with one or more interior walls but does not modify the sprinkler system to cover each of the separate spaces created by the modification. When firefighters observe heavy fire involvement in one area of a fully sprinklered building, it may be because of some accelerant causing the fire to overwhelm the sprinkler system, or it may be because of some unauthorized modification to the structure.

Other unauthorized modifications involve rooms being added to the exterior walls of a building. Access into such a room from inside the building may be through what was formerly a required exit door. Obviously, anyone trying to exit the building through that door would find himself in another room — which may or may not have an exit door to the outside. Often, these add-ons can be identified from the outside because they do not match the construction of the original building.

Another common modification is for building occupants to add deadbolts, pad locks, metal security doors or windows, or other security devices to keep intruders from entering the building. However, in total darkness and/or heavy smoke from an interior fire, these devices may make it virtually impossible for people (including firefighters) to escape through these exit doors. Even if firefighters are unable to get these dangerous conditions changed through the code enforcement process, and they know of these situations when they arrive at the scene, they can take appropriate steps to protect themselves and others. Some of these steps are discussed in Chapter 2, Firefighter Survival.

Fire Characteristics

If firefighters are to accurately size-up interior structure fires, they must not only understand basic fire behavior and basic building construction, they must also understand how these two major components of interior structure fires interact with each other. While the physics and chemistry of fire behavior remain the same, understanding how fire may behave when confined in various types of structures or parts thereof is critical to accurately

sizing-up these fires. Therefore, fire behavior in attics, basements, townhouses, Victorians, warehouses, and office buildings is discussed in the following section.

Attics

These confined spaces are constructed in a wide variety of sizes and configurations. However, regardless of whether it is the typical small crawl space between the ceiling and roof of a suburban tract home, the common attic in a strip mall, or the cavernous cockloft or interstitial space above a large commercial or manufacturing occupancy, most attics have certain characteristics in common. In most cases, there are no openings between the attic and the occupied space below except the covered access opening. Most, but not all, attics are vented to the outside in some way. During a fire, attic vents allow air in — feeding the fire — and also provide a means for the products of combustion to escape. Therefore, attic fires can grow to significant proportions before creating enough internal pressure to force smoke down into the occupied space below. Because the occupied space may be completely clear of smoke or unusual odors, the occupants may be unaware that a fire is burning above their heads.

In general, attic fires in single-story residences are relatively easy to size-up. When smoke and/or fire is issuing from attic vents or from under roof shingles, but there is little or no evidence of fire or smoke in the space below, a fire in the attic is a reasonable conclusion. On the other hand, multistory residential structures, especially very old ones, may be of balloon frame construction that will allow smoke and fire to travel upward through the walls into the attic. This can give the outward appearance of a typical attic fire when there is actually fire throughout the shell of the building. Fires in the attics of large commercial buildings can be very difficult to pinpoint because the smoke may travel some distance within the attic before escaping through a vent or scuttle. In these situations, the fire may be a great distance from the point where the smoke is showing.

Basements

Fires in basements may or may not be difficult to size-up, but they are almost always difficult to extinguish. As in the New York fire discussed earlier, basement fires in buildings with balloon frame construction can and often do quickly spread throughout the structure. The key to accurately sizing-up fires in these buildings is knowing beforehand (because of pre-incident planning inspections) which buildings or types of buildings in the jurisdiction have or are likely to have balloon frame construction. Because of its fire spread characteristics, balloon frame construction has been prohibited in many jurisdictions for so many years that few if any of these old, pre-code buildings are still standing. Other jurisdictions still have many older buildings with this type of construction.

In buildings of more modern design, basement fires may be somewhat easier to size-up. With the exception of buildings with one or more sub-basements, basement fires have only one way to spread — up. Basement fires will usually reveal themselves by smoke and/or fire issuing from ground level windows, dead lights, cellar doors, vents, cracks in the exterior walls, or from the interior wall/floor junction. Smoke on the first floor may be relatively cool from floor to ceiling without obvious layering. The floor may be noticeably hot, but with no sign of fire. In some cases, vent pipes run up from the basement to and through the roof. Therefore, if smoke is issuing from a roof vent but there is no evidence of fire in the attic or the occupied spaces, the basement should be checked.

Certain building features may also make sizing-up a basement fire difficult. For example, smoke from a basement fire may spread throughout the building through the ventilation system. It may also spread from floor to floor in a trash or laundry chute. And, as discussed earlier, smoke can also spread through the walls of buildings with balloon frame construction.

Townhouses

Because they make efficient use of space, townhouse condominiums and apartments can be found in most cities and towns in North America. Most are two-story, wood-frame, multiple-residential buildings that may or may not have fire walls separating the units (**Figure 1.12**). Some not only do not have fire walls, but they have common attics or attics in which the smoke barrier has been com-

promised. Such deficiencies allow fires to spread through the attic beyond the unit of origin to involve the entire building. However, the most common fire spread problem related to the typical townhouse design is the open stairway that allows fire to spread from the ground floor to the second floor.

Typically, the kitchen and living room are on the ground floor and the bedrooms are on the second floor. A fire that develops on the ground floor, especially during the late night or early morning hours, is likely to trap those sleeping in rooms on the second floor. This is because their primary exit (the stairway) acts as a chimney that channels fire and smoke upward into the second floor hallway. Because the two-story design makes vertical ventilation of a ground-floor fire problematic, horizontal ventilation is most often used. However, this can allow fire on the ground floor to lap up the outside of the building and spread to the second floor and/or the attic. Because townhouse units often have skylights that are covered by a plastic bubble, the bubble will often melt and fall out creating a vertical opening through which smoke and heat from a fire on the ground floor can issue from the roof.

From a size-up standpoint, smoke from a ground-floor fire can also issue from openings on the second floor because that is where the highest internal pressure is. Sizing-up a fire on the second floor, or in the attic, is no different than sizing up a similar fire in a single-story residence. From a life safety standpoint, laddering the second floor windows, front and rear, is usually a high priority.

Figure 1.12 Some townhouse units are separated by fire walls.

Victorians

Many older neighborhoods have Victorian-style residences in them. While many of these ornate buildings are still single-family dwellings or have been converted to office or retail space, many of the larger ones have been converted to apartment houses such as the one in the case history cited at the beginning of this chapter (**Figure 1.13**).

From the standpoint of size-up, Victorians contain one or more of each of the undesirable characteristics already discussed. In general, they have many features that make them vulnerable to fires starting and, once started, spreading rapidly. These features may include old substandard wiring inside walls made of wood that is completely dehydrated. Victorians are typically of balloon frame construction which lends itself to rapid fire spread. Most have been remodeled to a greater or lesser extent creating hidden spaces in which fire can burn for a considerable time before being discovered. In short, they can be highly problematic for firefighters.

Warehouses

Depending upon when, where, and how they were constructed, warehouse buildings have the potential to produce some of the largest and most dangerous structure fires that many firefighters will ever face (**Figure 1.14**). And given that they may be packed full of highly flammable, toxic, or explosive materials, warehouses can produce some of the most spectacular and deadly blazes.

Since these buildings typically have large open spaces within them, any fire that starts inside has a virtually unlimited supply of oxygen. In order to create these large open interior spaces, the roof assemblies often span great distances — sometimes unsupported by columns or posts — making the collapse potential extremely high. Even though many warehouses are fully sprinklered, if the contents are stacked too close to the sprinklers, they can reduce the system's effectiveness. Likewise, if the sprinkler system has been disabled — intentionally or through lack of maintenance — the fire may grow to such proportions that it may be deemed necessary to allow the building to burn completely down.

From a size-up standpoint, one of the first determinations that must be made is if it is merely a small fire in a big building — such as a fire in a waste basket that could be handled with a portable extinguisher — or if it is a big fire that is likely to get bigger. If it is the latter, the incident commander may order a defensive attack from outside the building. Even though it may be embarrassing if, while firefighters are setting up master streams, a warehouse employee suddenly emerges from the smoke carrying a burning trash barrel on a forklift, it is better to be embarrassed than dead. Always err on the side of caution.

Figure 1.13 Many large older residences have been divided into small apartments.

Figure 1.14 Warehouses can produce very large fires.

Office Buildings

Whether single-story or high-rise, fires in office buildings can often be difficult to accurately size-up (**Figure 1.15**). Most of the fires that occur during office hours are relatively small because they are discovered early and perhaps even extinguished before firefighters arrive. However, after office hours, fires often go undetected until they have

Figure 1.15 Because of the potential for fire spread, office-building fires may be difficult to size up.

reached major proportions. Just as in warehouses, an office building full of smoke may or may not indicate the existence of a big fire within. It may only be a small, well-contained fire that has smoldered for many hours. But it may also be a potential backdraft situation. Carefully checking the doors and windows as described earlier in this chapter can help to confirm or rule out backdraft conditions. If conditions allow entry, finding the seat of the fire in a maze of cubicles and offices in a smoke filled building can be tedious and time-consuming. Otherwise, fires in offices generally behave as they do in any other structure of similar size and construction.

Summary

Size-up is defined as the continual and ongoing assessment of an emergency situation from initial alarm to incident termination. Accurately sizing-up a working structure fire is one of the most critical functions during the incident. How the initial size-up is performed sets the tone for the entire incident. Depending upon the nature and scope of the incident, size-up can be a relatively straightforward process, or it can be very difficult.

Performing an accurate size-up of a working structure fire requires knowledge of fire behavior, building construction, and resource availability and capability. But it also requires the experience and judgment to determine how these individual factors combine to affect the plan of attack on the incident at hand.

Chapter 2
Firefighter Survival

Chapter 2
Firefighter Survival

In December of 1983, a New York fire department received a call reporting a propane leak. A large propane tank had fallen from a forklift that was moving it inside a three-story warehouse. When the tank struck the concrete floor, the valve broke off. The forklift driver called the fire department. Just as the firefighters arrived, the propane vapors reached an ignition source and a tremendous explosion occurred. The explosion blew a ladder truck and two engines across the street. Five firefighters were killed, and nine others were seriously injured. Two civilians were killed and dozens more were injured.

This incident reinforces the point that there are no "routine" calls. Every emergency call is potentially lethal for the firefighters responding to it. As discussed in Chapter 1, Size-Up, fighting an interior structure fire is a very dangerous undertaking. If firefighters are to safely and effectively fight fires inside of structures, they need to understand that their safety and that of all other fireground personnel is dependent upon several equally important elements:

- Adequately sizing-up the situation
- Doing a risk/benefit analysis
- Employing safe and effective strategy and tactics
- Using some form of personnel accountability system
- Having one or more rapid intervention crews (RIC) standing by
- Setting up a Rehab Unit on all working fires
- Using appropriate emergency escape techniques when needed.

The interior of a burning building is a hostile and sometimes lethal environment. However, this is where firefighters are expected to function when necessary. Therefore, it is vitally important for firefighters to learn to survive in this environment. The case histories cited in Chapter 1 are clear examples of what can happen when things go wrong. From a personal survival standpoint, firefighters need to develop the ability to recognize hazards and avoid them.

This chapter begins with a discussion of some standard safety behaviors that have proven successful in many incidents. A discussion follows on the safety/survival techniques that have been developed and widely adopted because negative experiences on many fires in many jurisdictions made them necessary. Finally, specific techniques that firefighters can use to escape if they are trapped in a burning building are discussed.

Standard Safety Behaviors

It is vitally important for all emergency response personnel, including firefighters, to understand incident scene priorities because they translate into how personnel and other resources are deployed on scene. Certain universal priorities apply on every emergency response. In order of importance, these priorities are as follows:

- Life safety
- Incident stabilization
- Property conservation

In every emergency incident, life safety is always the highest priority. However, firefighters need to understand that life safety includes *their* lives as well as those of any other people, pets, or livestock that are at risk because of the emergency situation. This fundamental principle can be stated as follows:

> Firefighters must remember that they did not start the fire, nor did they put the victims in that situation, and they are not obligated to sacrifice themselves in a heroic attempt to extinguish a fire or save a victim – and especially not to recover a body.

In fact, it can be argued that protecting the lives of the firefighters is the highest fireground priority. The logic behind this position is simple — if a firefighter suffers a disabling injury while attempting to extinguish a fire or save a victim, this renders him unable to help others who may be in mortal danger.

Phoenix Model

The Phoenix (AZ) Fire Department (PFD) has translated the foregoing into an emergency response decision model that helps its firefighters keep things in the proper perspective. According to its decision model, all PFD personnel are guided by the following principles:

- They begin every response with the assumption that they can make a positive difference in the outcome.
- They will risk their lives a lot to save savable lives.
- They will risk their lives a little, and in a calculated manner, to save savable property.
- They will *not* risk their lives at all trying to save lives or property that are already lost.

This mind-set is also translated into a general set of expectations that the PFD has for every emergency response. In addition to the four items just listed, all PFD personnel are expected to do another four things on every call – emergency or not. These expectations are as follows:

- Respond quickly.
- Take care of the problem.
- Be nice.
- Come back safe.

As a way of helping its personnel accomplish these goals, the PFD has also developed a list of

key safety behaviors. All PFD personnel are expected to apply these behaviors whenever they are on duty. These key behaviors are as follows:

- Think.
- Drive defensively.
- Drive slower rather than faster.
- At intersections: if you can't see, stop.
- Don't run for a moving rig.
- Always wear your seat belt/safety strap.
- Wear full protective clothing and SCBA.
- Don't *ever* breathe smoke.
- Attack with a sensible level of aggression.
- Always work under sector command – no freelancing.
- Keep crew intact.
- Maintain a communications link to command.
- Always have an escape route (hoseline/lifeline).
- Never go beyond your air supply.
- Use a big enough and long enough hoseline.
- Evaluate the hazard – know the risk you're taking.
- Follow standard fireground procedures – know and be a part of the plan.
- Vent early and vent often.
- Provide lights for the work area.
- If it's heavy, get help.
- Always watch your fireground position.
- Look and listen for signs of collapse.
- Rehab fatigued companies – assist stressed companies.
- Pay attention at all times.
- Everybody takes care of everybody else.

While some of the foregoing points apply to nonfireground activities, even they serve to help instill and maintain a *safety first* mind-set. That mind-set is critically necessary if firefighters are to survive until retirement and to enjoy a service retirement and not a disability retirement.

In addition, one of the most important ways that these safety behaviors become a part of the departmental culture and of individual behavior is through training (**Figure 2.1**). When the department develops SOPs that reflect these safety behaviors, the

Figure 2.1 For firefighters to function safely, they must be trained to do so.

firefighters must then be trained to function according to those SOPs *instinctively* — that is, without having to consciously consider which is the safest way to perform in any given situation. In other words, functioning safely becomes second nature.

Communication

Communication is one of the most important safety behaviors on any emergency scene. One of the reasons for keeping a crew intact is to maintain communication between crew members and between the members and their supervisor. The OSHA two-in/two-out rule requires that those inside the hazard zone stay together and remain in visual or voice contact at all times. They must also be in visual, voice, or radio contact with the *rapid intervention crew* (RIC), sometimes called a *rapid intervention team* (RIT), standing by outside of the hazard zone.

One of the most fundamental rules of firefighter survival is that *everyone looks out for everyone else.*

And what makes this rule work is communication — between crew members, between crews, and between operational units (divisions, groups, sectors) and command. If one firefighter sees a threat to the crew's safety and communicates it to the other crew members and the supervisor, the crew can then either avoid the threat or mitigate it, and they can inform other crews of the danger. This increases everyone's chances of survival.

Accountability

As described in **Essentials**, the purpose of using an accountability system on the fireground is to ensure that only those who are authorized and properly equipped to enter a hazardous environment are allowed to do so. There are a number of different accountability systems in use in North America, but they all have the same purpose — to control movement into and out of a hazardous environment so that every entrant's location and status can be tracked as long as the person remains in the hazardous environment.

In a typical accountability system, a designated person (*persons* in the case of multiple entry points) verifies that each entrant's PASS device is turned on and records each entrant's name, company, SCBA pressure, assignment, and estimated safe working time in the hazardous environment. In some systems, the identification part of the record keeping is done automatically through the use of a name tag (sometimes called a *passport*) carried by each firefighter (**Figure 2.2**). Identification can also be done by the use of a bar code reader that scans each entrant's code as the person passes through the

Figure 2.2 Personnel accountability is a critical element of fireground safety.

checkpoint. The other items — SCBA pressure, assignment, etc. — must still be recorded manually. However, this process can also be expedited and simplified by using a notebook computer at each entry point.

Another critically important part of an accountability system is the *personnel accountability report* (PAR). A PAR is an organized on-scene roll call in which each supervisor reports the status of his crew when requested. PARs may be requested at specified intervals or because of some benchmark event occurring. Among these benchmarks are the following:

- Changing attack modes from offensive to defensive
- Unexpected or catastrophic events (flashover, backdraft, structural collapse, report of a missing firefighter, or PASS device activation)
- Fire control or extinguishment.

PARs may also be requested at the Incident Safety Officer's discretion.

Using an accountability system is required by both NFPA 1500, *Fire Department Occupational Safety and Health Program*, and 1561, *Emergency Services Incident Management System*. Using such a system in fireground support operations requires the following:

- Development of a departmental SOP describing the system to be used (including when and how)
- Training all personnel in the use of the designated system
- Strict enforcement of the SOP during emergency incidents

If these three things are made a part of the departmental culture, fireground command and control will be improved, firefighter safety/survival will be increased, and the chances of the department having to defend itself in court will be reduced.

Structural Collapse

As the case history (described in Chapter 1) involving the collapse of a parapet wall indicates, firefighters can be at risk even outside of a burning building. Therefore, important elements in firefighter safety/survival are the establishment of collapse zones at these incidents and an ongoing assessment of the building's collapse potential.

In many departments, the policy is to cordon off an area equal to one and one-half times the height of the structure (**Figure 2.3**). Obviously, if the structure is as tall or taller than the adjacent street is wide, the collapse zone would, in effect, close the street completely. However, many departments routinely close the street in front of a burning building to improve access for emergency vehicles and to prevent pedestrians from entering the hazard zone.

Once inside the building, firefighters must con-

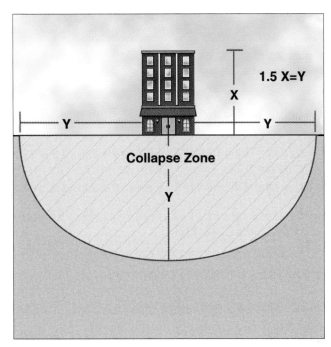

Figure 2.3 Establishing collapse zones can greatly enhance firefighter safety.

tinue to be vigilant for signs of impending structural collapse. The longer a fire burns inside a building, the more likely that fire-weakened structural members will suddenly and unexpectedly fail. To protect themselves in these situations, firefighters need to be aware of the impending collapse indicators. According to the National Fire Academy course entitled *Firefighter Safety and Survival*, these indicators are as follows:

- Heavy fire — no progress after 10-12 minutes in wood or ordinary construction
- Walls/floors bowing or sagging
- Distortion of doors/windows
- Beams pulling away from supports

- Little or no runoff while using heavy streams
- New cracks developing or moving
- Walls disassemble under stream impact

Other possible indicators can be added to this list. For example, if firefighters working inside or outside of the building hear creaking, cracking, or groaning sounds not normally associated with this type of fire, they should inform their supervisor immediately. If a team is working independently when it sees or hears any of these indicators, it should inform command of the situation and immediately withdraw until the integrity of the structure can be evaluated. In addition, if the building contains significant live loads (stock, furniture, boxes of water absorbent materials, etc.) or dead loads (heavy machinery, HVAC units, or fluid tanks), the added weight increases the collapse potential (**Figure 2.4**).

To help reduce the risk of firefighters being inside a burning building when it collapses, it is standard operating procedure in many departments to keep track of the elapsed time after the beginning of the initial attack. For example, in some departments the IC notifies dispatch when the initial attack begins, and dispatch announces the elapsed time at specified intervals — perhaps every 5 minutes. If significant progress toward control and extinguishment has not been achieved after 20 minutes, all interior crews are ordered out and the attack mode is changed from offensive to defensive.

The collapse of a burning auto parts store in Virginia, in which two firefighters were killed is ample reminder that burning buildings do collapse and, when they do, the results can be tragic (**Figure 2.5**). Departments need to be prepared to deal with this type of incident and that requires developing an SOP and training on its implementation. As have other major metropolitan departments, the Phoenix Fire Department has recognized this need and dealt with it. Its SOPs MP 202.03, *Lost/Trapped Firefighter Basic Survival*, and MP 201.04, *Rescue – Lost Firefighters Command Responsibilities*, are contained in Appendix A of this manual.

Figure 2.5 Burning buildings can and do collapse.

Rapid Intervention

As described in **Essentials**, a rapid intervention crew (RIC) is required by both NFPA 1500 and the OSHA regulations in 29 *CFR* 1910.134 whenever firefighters are in the hazard zone inside a burning building. The hazard zone as defined by OSHA is an IDLH environment whenever an interior fire is beyond the incipient (early growth) stage. At least two suitably equipped firefighters must be standing by outside of the hazard zone to rescue the interior crew, if necessary. The hazard zone is the portion of the building in which firefighters must

Figure 2.4 Heavy loads on or in the building increase the collapse potential.

use their SCBA to breathe smoke-free air. As with any other regulation, the two-in/two-out rule is subject to interpretation. How this rule is to be interpreted and implemented is beyond the scope and purpose of this manual. However, firefighter safety/survival may depend on rapid intervention following the collapse of a burning building.

Emergency Egress

Being lost or trapped in a burning building is a very stressful experience — for those in trouble as well as those trying to come to their aid. However, if firefighters in this situation have been trained in emergency escape techniques (sometimes called by the misnomer *self-rescue*) and they apply them calmly but quickly, their chances of survival are greatly enhanced.

Firefighter Trapped

When a firefighter is trapped in a burning building, his most important duty is to survive. To do that he must try to stay calm because panic can decrease his ability to think clearly and increase his rate of respiration which will deplete the SCBA air supply sooner. He may be able to make his air supply last longer if he practices *skip breathing* as described in **Essentials**. Given that he is trapped, he should move to the safest area available to him and transmit a Mayday signal to alert command of his situation and approximate location — provided that he has a radio. If he does not have a radio, he should activate his PASS device, shine a flashlight toward the ceiling, and wait for rescuers to arrive.

Knowing that a firefighter trapped in a burning building is almost certainly using his SCBA in order to breathe, rescuers should take spare SCBA cylinders with them as they search.

> According to NIOSH, so-called "buddy breathing" techniques are unreliable and are more likely to produce two victims instead of one. NIOSH recommends providing respiratory assistance and quickly removing the victim to a clear atmosphere.

If the firefighter is trapped under or entangled in debris, it may not be possible to immediately extricate him. If his SCBA is equipped with an Emergency Escape Breathing Support System (EEBSS) — a fitting designed to allow the cylinder to be refilled in the harness instead of being replaced — his cylinder can be filled from one brought in by the rescue team (**Figure 2.6**). In this situation, his air supply can be maintained by using as many spare cylinders as necessary until he can be freed from entrapment.

Figure 2.6 Trapped firefighters should be supplied with breathing air through the EEBSS connection on their SCBA.

WARNING!
Never remove your facepiece or in any way compromise the proper operation of your SCBA to share your air supply with anyone — not even another firefighter.

Firefighter Lost

Assuming that he does not have a disabling injury, if a firefighter is not trapped in a burning building but merely separated from fellow firefighters and lost or disoriented, there are a number of things that he can do to find his way out. First, he should listen for sounds of activity by other firefighters and try to retrace the steps that got him where he is. However, the route taken into the location may now be blocked by fire or debris. If the lost firefighter cannot hear other firefighters and has no way of contacting them, he should attempt to use the emergency egress techniques described in **Essentials**. Because of their potential importance to firefighter safety/survival, those techniques are repeated here:

- Locate a hoseline and follow it out (male coupling is closest to the exit, female is closest to the fire*).
- Crawl in a straight line (hands on floor, move knee to hand).
- Crawl in one direction (all left turns or all right turns) once in contact with a wall.
- Call out or make noise that other firefighters might hear.

*NOTE: If a 2½-inch (65 mm) or larger attack line was laid in reverse, the couplings may be opposite to the direction previously described.

The foregoing are all proven techniques that have worked in actual fireground situations. But if the situation makes them ineffective in getting the firefighter out of the building, he should use the escape techniques described in the following sections.

Locating Windows and Doors

When a firefighter is lost or disoriented in a pitch dark and/or smoke-filled part of a building, he should act on his decision to exit the building as quickly as possible. The first thing to do is to quickly locate a window or door that might provide an exit route. To do so he should move to the nearest wall. Staying low to avoid the heat in the upper part of the room, he should crawl along the wall "wiping" it with one gloved hand from the floor to as high as he can reach without standing up **(Figure 2.7)**. This technique should help him quickly locate any window that is within 4 feet (1.2 m) of the floor. If no windows are found, he will inevitably find a door.

Window Egress

Once a window has been located, the firefighter can push out the window and frame by any means necessary and available. The point is to quickly make the window opening large enough for him to pass through without having to remove his SCBA or any other part of his protective ensemble, so it is best to remove the entire window and frame. Even though there is some risk of injury to other firefighters who may be working directly below the window, the sounds of the window frame and glass hitting the

Figure 2.7 To find a window through which to escape, firefighters should "wipe" the wall as they crawl along a wall.

ground may draw someone's attention to the window. Once the window has been removed, the firefighter can crawl out of the window — provided that it is close to the ground. Even in some second-story windows, the firefighter may be able to lower himself out of the window opening and hang by his hands before pushing away from the wall and dropping to the ground **(Figure 2.8)**.

> ## WARNING!
> Jumping or dropping from any height while wearing SCBA may pull you over backwards and lead to serious injury. If possible, remove the SCBA unit first.

In the case of a window from which it is too high to jump or drop, the firefighter should straddle the windowsill and attempt to get the attention of

Figure 2.8 When escaping from a second-story window, firefighters can reduce the drop distance by hanging from the windowsill.

Figure 2.9 When escaping from windows above the second floor, firefighters should straddle the windowsill and attract attention.

someone on the ground (**Figure 2.9**). He can activate his PASS device, yell, and/or shine a flashlight to alert those on the ground of his situation. However, he should *not* drop his helmet or any other part of his protective ensemble in an attempt to get someone's attention.

If heat escaping from the window opening makes it impossible for him to continue sitting there, he may hook one leg over the windowsill and let his body hang below the opening. Obviously, this technique can only be done for a very short time while a ladder is being placed to allow him to climb down.

When a ladder is in place, he should swing himself onto the ladder and climb down in the normal way. Techniques that require a firefighter to dive onto the ladder head first and then swing his legs around and slide down the ladder beams have proven to be very dangerous. At least one firefighter has been killed, and several have been seriously in-

jured practicing these techniques. In a life-or-death situation, a firefighter must do whatever is necessary to save himself, but these high-risk techniques are *not* recommended.

Door Egress

When a lost or disoriented firefighter has crawled along a wall and found a door, he should check it for heat before opening it. If the door is cool to the touch, he should attempt to open it. Once open, he should feel around inside the room to try to identify its contents. This may tell him whether the room is a closet, storeroom, or some other type of space. In a residential occupancy, if the room contains shoes, clothing, etc., it is not likely to be the best way out. If it is another type of room, he should enter the room, close the door behind him, and begin to crawl along a wall as in the first room. This exploration should lead him either to a window or another door. If it is a window, he should follow the foregoing instructions. If it is another door, he should again check it for heat, and proceed as with the first one. This should eventually lead him to a window or door that will provide an exit path. However, if he is in a room without windows, and the only door he can find is hot to the touch, then he must consider breaching a wall to escape.

Wall Breach

Just as with opening a door, before a firefighter attempts to breach a wall to escape, he should feel it for heat. If the wall is cool to the touch, he can begin to create an opening large enough for him to pass through without having to remove his SCBA or any other part of his protective ensemble. Interior walls of either gypsum wallboard or lath and plaster over wood or metal studs are relatively easy to breach. This can be done with almost any forcible entry tool, a piece of furniture, or if necessary, a size 12 boot **(Figure 2.10)**. Removing the wall between any two adjacent studs will only create an opening approximately 14 inches (40 cm) wide. Therefore, it may be necessary to remove the wall sections on both sides of a stud and remove the stud also.

Figure 2.10 When all else fails, a firefighter may be able to break through a wall to escape.

Breaching interior walls with heavy wooden paneling or exterior walls of almost any material can be more difficult than breaching interior walls with wallboard or lath and plaster. However, given the incentive involved in this situation, it is certainly worth the effort. In this situation, the trapped firefighter may have to use whatever forcible entry tool he may have with him and/or whatever else he can find in the room that might help him breach the wall. It may require every bit of his ingenuity and skill to break or pry wooden siding away from wall studs or to chip the mortar from between bricks in a wall.

If he is lucky, someone outside will hear the activity taking place inside and realize what the situation is. Firefighters outside can then begin to help breach the wall. Given that they have a wide variety of tools at their disposal, if they can reach the point that needs to be breached, firefighters outside are likely to be able to breach the wall in short order.

Summary

Firefighters are often required to work inside of burning buildings — a hostile and sometimes lethal environment. If they are to avoid being injured or killed by any of several contingencies common to these fires, they must learn to recognize the signs of these phenomena before they develop. They must learn to recognize the dangers inherent in so-called "routine" fires and fires that have "self-vented." They must also learn to recognize the signs of imminent flashover, backdraft, and structural collapse — as well as how to avoid them. Finally, if they become lost or trapped in a burning building, they must know how to escape or initiate a Mayday call.

Chapter 3
Access to Structures

Chapter 3
Access to Structures

Before firefighters can force doors or take other steps to gain access into a burning building, they must be able to reach that building. This is not always easy to do. There are a variety of obstacles that can prevent or delay firefighters from reaching the building. Some of these obstacles are related to the topography of the building site. Others are because of steps that building owners have taken to protect their property and privacy.

This chapter discusses a variety of exterior obstructions and how to overcome them. It begins with a discussion of natural exterior obstacles such as topography and landscaping. Man-made exterior obstacles such as fences, walls, and gates are also discussed. Finally, security measures that can delay access to a building, and how to deal with them, are discussed.

Topography and Landscaping

How some buildings are situated on the property can have a significant effect on access to their exteriors. Many older mill buildings were built on the banks of rivers or streams because the water flow provided energy to operate machinery. Also, prior to the establishment of the EPA, these waterways were used to get rid of industrial wastes. Because many of these buildings were built on the very edge of the bank, approaching the rear of the building is difficult if not impossible (**Figure 3.1**).

Likewise, some other buildings are situated on mesas and other natural promontories to take advantage of breathtaking scenic vistas. Very large and expensive homes sometimes occupy the only flat area on the promontory and may even be cantilevered over the edge (**Figure 3.2**). Once again, access may be available to only the fronts of these buildings.

Figure 3.1 Some buildings are not accessible from all sides. *Courtesy of Mark Pare.*

Figure 3.2 Cantilevered buildings make fire department access difficult. *Courtesy of Wes Kitchel.*

To take advantage of lower land values and natural scenic beauty, office buildings and even manufacturing facilities are sometimes situated in relatively pristine rural areas (**Figure 3.3**). The sites chosen are often on ridge tops or other locations that provide a commanding view of the area. The sometimes steep slopes of these sites and the natural vegetation that covers them can severely limit access to all but the front of such buildings.

Even buildings that are located on relatively flat sites are often difficult to reach. Buildings located in office or industrial parks are often surrounded by man-made lakes or ponds or stone or brick walls that are part of the park's landscaping. Many have large flower beds that will not safely support a ground ladder and certainly not the weight of an aerial device. Many buildings also are set back a considerable distance from the street and can only be reached by narrow, meandering walkways that cannot be negotiated in an emergency vehicle. Even the lawn areas may be so well irrigated that they will not support the weight of fire apparatus (**Figure 3.4**).

After terrorist attacks on U.S. military buildings in the Middle East and the bombing of the federal building in Oklahoma City, many government agencies installed antiterrorism barricades outside of their facilities. These barricades may be massive concrete bollards, or they may be similar to the type of barricades used to separate opposing traffic lanes on streets and highways (**Figure 3.5**). Regardless of the type of barricade used, they are intended to keep vehicles from approaching the buildings. Unfortunately, this includes emergency vehicles.

Overcoming Site Obstacles

As mentioned earlier, just getting to the exterior of a burning building may be a challenge. However, firefighters must size up the situation and act accordingly. They must take advantage of whatever the situation allows them. Very often, the majority of such obstacles can be identified during pre-incident planning inspections. Once the obstacles have been identified, plans can be devised and resources obtained to allow these obstacles to be overcome.

During the plans review and approval process, it may be possible to require all-weather access to all sides of a planned building as a condition of approv-

Figure 3.3 Some commercial buildings are in locations with limited access.

Figure 3.4 Well-irrigated lawns will not support the weight of fire apparatus.

Figure 3.5 Many buildings have barricades designed to keep vehicles at a distance.

ing the building permit (**Figure 3.6**). Likewise, it may be possible and more practical to require the building owner to provide whatever is necessary to allow access to all sides of the building. Allowing access may involve clearing and maintaining a specified area free of vegetation or the construction of access roads that will support the weight of an aerial device or an engine. Or, if providing such access is impractical or too expensive, it may be possible to require a full sprinkler system to make the need for access less likely.

However, when a building is on fire and firefighters need to access the outside of the build-

ing, they may have to be very innovative in their approach. For example, if a building is inaccessible because it is situated atop a steeply sloped promontory, it may be necessary to position an aerial device on an adjacent driveway, street, or access road close enough to allow the building's exterior to be reached (**Figure 3.7**). Or, it may be necessary to lay a number of ground ladders on the slopes at strategic points around the building. The ladders on the ground can be used as a base for other ground ladders that are placed against the outside of the building (**Figure 3.8**). In some cases, it may be necessary to anchor the base ladders by driving metal stakes, ram bars, or similar tools into the ground under their bottom rungs (**Figure 3.9**).

Figure 3.6 Access for emergency vehicles may have to be negotiated during the planning for new construction.

Figure 3.8 One ladder is positioned on the slope and another ladder is extended from it to reach the building.

Figure 3.7 Access to some buildings may require the use of aerial devices set up on adjacent property.

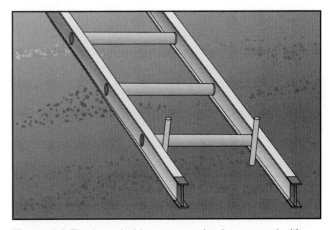

Figure 3.9 The base ladder may need to be secured with foundation stakes, rebar, or tools such as ram bars.

Gates

Obviously, the quickest way through a fence is by using a gate made for that purpose. However, for security reasons or simply for convenience, a growing number of gates are fully automated. Having the means to operate an automated gate or the knowledge of how to disable the mechanism and allow it to be opened manually can be extremely important during emergencies when time is critical. The time spent trying to get through an automated gate may mean the difference between a rescue and a body recovery. However, not all gates are automated. Many are simply manually operated gates that are locked with a padlock. Again, it is critically important that firefighters be familiar with the gates in their response district and know how to open them.

Manually Operated Gates

The majority of manually operated gates are either wooden, aluminum, or steel farm gates or steel gates in chain-link fences (**Figure 3.10**). Most manually operated gates have a simple latching mechanism, and its operation is usually obvious. Many are locked with a padlock or a padlock and chain. If a gate is locked with a padlock only, it may be possible to cut the shackle of the lock with bolt cutters. However, some locks have a case hardened shackle that is virtually impossible to cut with bolt cutters — and may even damage them. In that case, it may be possible to cut the staple on the hasp. On locks that do not have a hardened shackle, the shackle should be cut at the very top of the arc so that it can be welded back together and reused. If the gate is locked with a padlock and chain, the chain link closest to the lock should be cut so that the property owner can use the chain and lock again after the fire (**Figure 3.11**). If, for any reason, a padlock cannot be opened or cut, then removing the hinges or hinge pins should be attempted. If this is also unsuccessful, breaching the fence as described in the section on fences is another option.

In some cases, a padlock used to secure a gate will be protected by a sturdy metal shell, often a short length of steel pipe with the ends welded shut (**Figure 3.12**). There is usually only a small hole cut in the bottom of the shell to allow a key to be inserted into the padlock inside. The shell often precludes cutting the padlock because the

Figure 3.10 One of many types of farm gates.

Figure 3.11 The chain should be cut close to the lock.

Figure 3.12 Some gate locks are protected inside steel tubes. *Courtesy of Wes Kitchel.*

bolt cutter will not fit through the opening. In that case, the shell may have to be cut away using a rotary saw or an oxyacetylene cutting torch.

Automated Gates

Automated gates can be found in many different styles; however, they all have certain things in common. For instance, all are electrically powered and all are electronically controlled. Some of the gate controls are actuated by a small radio transmitter similar to a garage door opener (**Figure 3.13**). Others require a card key to be inserted into a scanner or a series of numbers entered into a keypad (**Figure 3.14**). Some automated gates are designed to be opened with the emergency vehicle's traffic signal controller. But these gates also have differences. Some are swinging gates hinged at one or both sides (**Figure 3.15**). Other automated gates are designed to move horizontally on small wheels attached to the bottom edge of the movable section (**Figure 3.16**).

Figure 3.13 Some automatic gates can be opened remotely.

Figure 3.14 Some automatic gates require a series of numbers to be entered.

All automated gates can be opened without the required transmitter or card key, but it may take more time. Those that have a sensor wire imbedded in the pavement of the exit lane can sometimes be opened by tossing a metallic object — a pry bar, scoop shovel, or metal garbage can lid — onto the area where the wire is located (**Figure 3.17**). Some of these gates are designed to operate in the absence of electrical power, and they are equipped with a hand crank. When the crank is inserted into the

Figure 3.15 Some automated gates swing open.

Figure 3.16 Other types of automated gates move laterally on small wheels.

Figure 3.17 Metal objects will open some automated gates.

proper opening in the motor housing, it can be used to open or close the gate manually. Others have a drive chain release that allows the gate to be pushed open or closed by hand. In other cases, it may be necessary to disconnect or even cut the swing arm that normally opens and closes the gate. Ideally, the swing arm can be disconnected by removing a pin or bolt from the point of connection to the gate or the drive motor (**Figure 3.18**). Failing this, it may be necessary to use a rotary saw equipped with a metal-cutting blade to simply cut the arm.

Figure 3.18 Removing the pin from the swing arm allows the gate to be pushed open.

Lockboxes

The owners of many properties to which access is limited by automated gates have installed lockboxes near their gates (**Figure 3.19**). They have done so because they do not want to take the chance that their rather expensive gates will be damaged if firefighters need to enter quickly, and because some fire departments refuse to accept keys or gate controllers. Some of the lockboxes contain a gate controller.

Figure 3.19 Some gates have lockboxes for fire department use.

Figure 3.20 If livestock are inside, firefighters must be sure to close the gate.

Others may contain a key that operates the gate without the controller or a card key that opens the gate. Still others contain a slip of paper with the numeric keypad combination needed to open the gate. Some keypad gate controllers are designed with a lockbox key receptacle so that the gate can be opened or closed with the fire department's lockbox key. However, it is extremely important that emergency vehicles leave the protected property by the same entrance that they used to gain access and that they close the gate behind them (**Figure 3.20**).

Fences

If, for any reason, a gate cannot be used or if access is needed where no gate exists, firefighters may have to breach a fence or scale a wall to have access to a burning building. Just as with topography, landscaping, gates, and other site-related obstacles, the importance of identifying fences within the response district during pre-incident planning cannot be overemphasized. Identifying fences that could delay access to a building, developing the necessary plans for getting over or through them, and acquiring the needed resources before a fire starts is by far the best way to approach the problem.

Wire Fences

Most fences are constructed to either keep something or someone in or to keep something or someone out. Many rural and agricultural fences are designed to keep livestock in — that is, in a pasture or feedlot — or to keep them out of a crop field. Farm fences most often consist either of three strands of barbed wire or wire fabric (sometimes called *hog wire* or *field fence*) attached to wood or metal posts. Some are a combination of barbed wire and wire fabric (**Figure 3.21**). The gauge of the wire is sufficiently small that these fences are easily cut with bolt cutters or even electrical wire cutters. Some agricultural fences are electrified to keep cattle from damaging the fence and breaking out. These fences are easily recognized by the insulators that hold a bare conductor wire. If the power to the fence cannot be shut off, only insulated wire cutters should be used to cut the charged conductor wire.

Another way to get through an agricultural fence quickly is to push it over with the bumper of a vehicle. Assuming that the fence is on ground that is suitable for the vehicle to drive on and that the situation demands quick access, the front bumper of a relatively heavy emergency vehicle should be eased up to a fence post. Once contact with the post is made, the vehicle can then be driven slowly forward until the post breaks off or bends over at ground level. This does only cosmetic damage to the vehicle, if any, and allows quick access through the fence.

Chain-Link Fences

Almost as common as barbed wire fences are the chain-link fences that surround schools, playgrounds, parks, correctional facilities, military installations, commercial and industrial properties, and a growing number of single-family residences. Chain-link fences consist of heavy-gauge steel fence fabric attached to steel posts. Many, but not all, of these fences have a steel top rail to add strength to the fence (**Figure 3.22**). Depending upon where these fences are installed and what they are intended to do, some have brackets atop the posts that hold strands of barbed wire in place (**Figure 3.23**). Others, especially those around correctional facilities, have coils of razor ribbon attached to the top of the fence to discourage potential escapees (**Figure 3.24**). Such security measures also make it more difficult for firefighters to get through these fences without injury. (See Security Measures section.)

Figure 3.23 Some facilities use barbed wire on their fences to discourage intruders.

Figure 3.21 A typical farm fence.

Figure 3.22 Many chain-link fences have top rails that can impede access.

Figure 3.24 Correctional facilities place razor ribbon atop their fences to discourage escape attempts.

If a chain-link fence must be breached to allow access to a burning building, firefighters have a number of options. The chain-link fence fabric is attached to the posts and top rail (if any) with wire bands. These bands are usually of a smaller gauge than are the strands of fence fabric. Therefore, they are more readily cut than the fabric itself. The wire bands can be cut with a rotary saw, bolt cutters, or wire cutters (**Figure 3.25**). Simply cutting the wire bands

Figure 3.25 Wire bands that attach chain-link fence fabric to the poles are easily cut with wire cutters.

between three or four adjacent posts will allow enough slack in the fence fabric to lay it down on the ground. Firefighters can then walk under the top rail, if there is one. However, the fence fabric can be quickly cut using a rotary saw (**Figure 3.26**). Or, if

necessary and time allows, the fence fabric can be cut one strand at a time using bolt cutters. The fence fabric should be cut as close to a post as possible to facilitate repair after the emergency. If an emergency vehicle must pass through the fence, the fabric can be removed as just described, and the post pushed over as discussed in the previous section on wire fences.

Wooden Fences

Many homes, office buildings, and other commercial structures are surrounded to some extent by wooden fences (**Figure 3.27**). If a wooden fence prevents access to a burning building, the fence will have to be breached. While wooden fences are found in many heights and styles, the majority are simply individual boards nailed vertically to a wooden framework. In most cases, the fence can be quickly dismantled simply by cutting the framework with a chain saw. Wooden fences can also be breached by pulling the individual boards off the framework. If access for a vehicle is needed, the same technique described in the section on agricultural wire fences can be used.

Figure 3.26 Chain-link fence fabric can be cut quickly with a rotary saw.

Figure 3.27 Some wooden fences can be formidable barriers.

Vinyl Fences

A growing number of properties are enclosed with rail fencing made of vinyl plastic or similar materials (**Figure 3.28**). The posts and rails are filled with plastic foam to make them more rigid. If these mainly decorative fences cannot be quickly dismantled, they are easily cut with a rotary saw or chain saw.

Decorative Metal Fences

Some upscale homes and residential developments are surrounded by decorative wrought iron or steel fences (**Figure 3.29**). If time allows, the individual vertical members or the framework to which they are attached can be cut using a rotary saw equipped with a metal-cutting blade. If this type of fence must be cut, the fastest way is to cut the ends of the horizontal frame members and remove an entire section at once. A less destructive way to cross these fences is with two ground ladders, one placed on each side of the fence (**Figure 3.30**). The ladders should be lashed or otherwise secured together where they intersect at the top of the fence. Or, a combination ladder can be set up in an A-frame configuration over the fence (**Figure 3.31**).

Figure 3.28 Vinyl fencing is easily breached.

Figure 3.29 A typical wrought iron fence.

Figure 3.30 Ground ladders placed over the fence allow firefighters to cross over.

Figure 3.31 An A-frame ladder can also be used to cross fences.

Masonry Walls

Because of an increased concern over personal security, a growing number of upscale homes and even entire housing developments, called *gated communities,* are enclosed within masonry walls (**Figure 3.32**). While many of the individual homes have automated gates (as previously discussed), some of the gated communities have a security

Figure 3.32 Many residential neighborhoods are surrounded by walls.

Razor Ribbon

Also called *concertina wire*, razor ribbon represents an even greater threat to firefighters than does barbed wire. Razor ribbon is usually installed in flexible coils atop chain-link fences and sometimes on the ground adjacent to them (**Figure 3.34**). It may also be found along the tops of parapet walls on commercial buildings. However, razor ribbon may be found anywhere that property owners are serious about preventing trespassers from entering. Firefighters must handle this material very carefully if they are to avoid injury. The same tools and techniques described for barbed wire also apply to cutting and crossing razor ribbon.

Fence Spikes

Iron and steel fences often have vertical members (sometimes referred to as *spikes*) that are sharply pointed at the top end to make them look menac-

Figure 3.33 Barbed wire must be secured before it is cut.

guard at the gate to screen those wishing to enter. Most of the walls are about 6 feet (2 m) high and roughly 1 foot (30 cm) thick. The same equipment and techniques described in the foregoing section can be used to cross these walls.

Security Measures

Some security measures — automated gates, for instance — may slow firefighters down while attempting to gain access, and they can be a threat if the security measures are not neutralized so that the firefighters can exit the same way they entered. Security measures such as barbed wire, razor ribbon, spiked iron fences, and trained guard dogs also have the potential to seriously injure firefighters — and prevent them from completing their assignments.

Barbed Wire

Whether barbed wire is strung between wooden or metal posts as part of a farm fence or on brackets atop a chain-link fence, this common fencing material can be a serious hazard for firefighters. Barbed wire can snag protective clothing and equipment straps to slow firefighters down. And, if they are not careful, firefighters can be seriously cut by the steel barbs. Whenever barbed wire must be cut, it should be securely held with pliers or similar tools on both sides of the point to be cut (**Figure 3.33**). This prevents the wire ends from recoiling and hitting someone. If it is decided to cross the wire rather than cutting it, a partially unfolded salvage cover draped over the wire will protect firefighters enough to allow them to place ladders as described in the section on wire fences.

Figure 3.34 Some security fences have razor ribbon on the ground as well as on the top. *Courtesy of American Security Fence Corporation.*

Figure 3.35 Many wrought iron fences have sharp spikes along the top.

ing and thereby discourage trespassers (**Figure 3.35**). While these spikes are rarely sharp enough to injure a firefighter (except in a fall onto them), they can snag protective clothing or equipment straps and thereby slow the firefighter down. The best way to avoid these obstacles is to remove them as previously described. If that is not possible, draping a partially unfolded salvage cover across the top of the fence will allow firefighters to place ladders as previously described, or crawl over without interference from the spikes.

Wall Tops

Some masonry walls are constructed with security measures built in, and others have them added. It is not uncommon for the columns or posts to extend above the top of the wall with sections of iron or steel fencing installed between the columns (**Figure 3.36**). These can be handled as described in the foregoing section on iron or steel fences. Other masonry walls have broken glass embedded in the top surface of the wall. These, too, can be handled in the same way as are the iron or steel fences.

Guard Dogs

Some of the fences and walls previously described are not intended to keep trespassers out. They are merely intended to slow them down and cause them to make enough noise to alert the guard dog within. Guard dogs may be found in almost any type of occupancy — single-family residences, salvage yards, warehouses, and even on the roofs of commercial buildings (**Figure 3.37**). These highly trained, extremely agile, and totally focused animals can easily overpower a firefighter and inflict serious injuries on him. They are a force to be reckoned with.

If a guard dog is keeping firefighters from approaching a burning building, they should immediately inform their supervisor or command and be guided by the instructions they receive. Depending upon the circumstances, they may be told to wait outside the fence until an animal control officer arrives to tranquilize or otherwise restrain the dog. Or, a police officer may be sent to destroy the animal. Under some circumstances, firefighters may be able to lure or coax the dog into a confined area that can be closed behind it and thereby remove the threat. However, if a guard dog attacks or threatens to attack firefighters already within the fenced or walled area, they may be able to fend the animal off with a stream from a hoseline or with a pike pole or other tool.

Booby Traps

Some property owners set up elaborate booby traps on their property to discourage anyone from approaching. These traps may include camouflaged holes or pits in the ground into which an unwary

Figure 3.36 Some walls have wrought iron sections between the pillars.

Figure 3.37 Guard dogs can seriously impede firefighter access.

firefighter might fall. They may also include charged electrical wires strategically placed to protect doors and windows. Booby traps may even include loaded firearms set up inside of a building with trip wires across door and window openings. This sort of paranoia is often found in those who traffic in drugs or conduct some other form of illegal operation on their property.

Other property owners keep exotic animals for security purposes. Peacocks and geese are very effective at detecting the approach of strangers and making enough noise to alert the property owner. However, other property owners keep venomous snakes, alligators, and other potentially dangerous animals to discourage intruders (**Figure 3.38**).

Figure 3.38 Some occupants keep poisonous snakes and other exotic animals on their premises to keep people out.

The best way for firefighters to protect themselves from booby traps and dangerous animals is to know of their existence prior to the incident and have appropriate countermeasures immediately available.

Summary

Before firefighters can force any doors or take any other steps to gain access into a burning building, they must be able to reach the building. Because of topography, landscaping, fences, walls, and a variety of security measures, this may not be easy to do. Firefighters may have to employ some unconventional techniques to overcome these obstacles. However, if they are to perform search and rescue instead of a body recovery, they must be able to deal with these obstacles quickly. By far, the easiest way to deal with them is to know of their existence and have the proper tools and techniques ready to use when needed. This can only be done through pre-incident planning.

Chapter 4
Access Into Structures

Chapter 4
Access Into Structures

When a fire is burning inside a building, the IC has two basic choices: use the on-scene resources to protect any exposures and allow the building to burn, or as is most often the case, order a search of the building and an offensive interior attack on the fire. The first choice is certainly justified if the risk to firefighters is clearly greater than the possible benefit from ordering them inside. For instance, if the building is so heavily involved in fire that the chances of anyone inside surviving are virtually nil or if the building is an unoccupied and abandoned derelict, the risks to firefighters in an aggressive interior attack are far greater than any possible benefits. However, such incidents are a small minority of the structure fires to which firefighters respond in North America each year. In the vast majority of cases, firefighters are justifiably put at some risk by being ordered to enter the burning building to conduct a search for trapped occupants and to extinguish the fire.

Given the case histories discussed in the preceding chapters, it should be clear that accurately sizing up a structure fire is critically important to the success of the operation and to firefighter safety and survival. Accurate size-up is also critically important when deciding how and where to gain access into a burning building. If the building is showing signs of backdraft potential, entry should be delayed until that potential has been mitigated with an effective ventilation operation conducted from the exterior of the building. In addition, the doorways and other openings that firefighters need to use for access into the structure may be congested by the occupants fleeing the building.

Gaining access into a burning building may be as simple as walking into the open doorway through which the occupants fled the building. Or, it may be as involved as having to overcome a security system, force a door or window, or breach a wall. However, the best way to force entry into any burning building is to know in advance what tools and techniques will be needed and to bring those tools to the building initially.

There are several reasons why firefighters might need to gain access into a burning building. Unless informed by a credible person that all occupants — people, pets, or livestock — are out of the building, firefighters will need to enter to conduct a primary and secondary search of the building. They may also need to create openings through which other firefighters trapped inside the burning building can escape. Firefighters may also need to enter the building to ventilate it. And, unless it is a very small fire that can be handled with a portable extinguisher, they will need to take one or more hoselines inside to extinguish the fire. These operations are discussed in more detail in Chapter 5, Interior Operations.

According to a NIOSH report, in March 1998, units were dispatched to a reported fire in a one-story commercial building in California. The first-arriving firefighters saw light smoke coming from the building, and a ventilation crew proceeded to the roof and began opening up. Another crew began forcible entry into the front of the building through two metal security doors. According to the report, it took from 7½ to 9 minutes to get these doors open. While three fire attack crews waited for the doors to be opened, conditions inside the building changed dramatically, and fire started coming from the ventilation hole that had been cut in the roof.

Once the front doors were open, the crews advanced hoselines inside to look for the seat of the fire. Approximately 15 feet (5 m) inside the front door, they encountered heavy smoke and near zero visibility. The crews advanced their lines approximately 30 to 40 feet (10 to 12 m) inside the building, but they could not locate the fire. Because conditions inside were rapidly deteriorating, the company officers ordered their crews to exit the building. However, one of the officers became separated from his crew and remained inside. Approximately one minute later, a partial roof collapse blocked the front door, trapping the officer inside. A rapid intervention crew was sent inside, and it located the victim. CPR was started immediately and continued on the way to the hospital where the victim was pronounced dead. The medical examiner listed smoke inhalation and burns as the cause of death.

While there may be other lessons to be learned, this case history illustrates the importance of being able to force entry into a burning building quickly. Scientifically controlled fire tests conducted by NFPA indicate that the *time available for escape* (TAE) from a burning building can be as little as 11 minutes after ignition due to heat buildup in a confined space such as a bedroom. In the same tests, the TAE was even less when lethal smoke concentrations were considered. Even if a fire is detected quickly and reported promptly, it still takes time for the nearest fire department units to receive the call, respond to the scene, size up the situation, and begin taking action. Therefore, any significant delay in gaining access into a building increases the likelihood that a small fire will develop into one that is larger, more difficult to control, and more dangerous for the firefighters assigned to extinguish it. And, it may mean the difference between a rescue and a body recovery.

This chapter discusses the tools, equipment, and techniques that firefighters may need to use to force locked doors in order to enter a burning building. Various types of windows and how to force them are also discussed. Finally, the tools, equipment, and techniques used for breaching exterior walls and overcoming various types of security systems are discussed.

Forcible Entry Tools

Any of the forcible entry tools described in **Essentials** might be capable of performing the evolutions discussed in this chapter. However, the use of those tools may be different here because of unique situations and applications. To safely and effectively use those tools in the situations described in this chapter, firefighters must be fully proficient in their use.

While all the standard forcible entry tools are important, perhaps the most important and most versatile forcible entry tool is the rotary saw, sometimes referred to as a *rescue saw*. **Table 4.1** shows the various blades that are available for rotary saws and their applications.

Table 4.1 Rotary Saw Blades
Carbide Tipped   *Uses:*   ● Heavy tar roof covering   ● Light-gauge metal roof coverings   ● Composition roof coverings   ● Wooden shingle roof coverings   ● Wooden structural members   ● Metal clad wood
Composite Carbide   *Uses:*   ● Heavy roof coverings   ● Wooden roof coverings   ● Wooden structural members   ● Light-gauge metal roof coverings   ● Metal clad wooden components   ● Forcible entry
Composite Metal   *Uses:*   ● Metal roof coverings   ● Steel structural components   ● Heavy forcible entry
Composite Masonry (Dry Cut)   *Uses:*   ● Brick   ● Concrete block   ● Concrete   ● Tile   ● Stucco

When using the rotary saw for forcible entry, firefighters must be aware of the capabilities and limitations of this versatile tool. For example, when equipped with the correct blade for the material being cut, these saws are extremely fast and efficient cutting tools. However, attempting to cut wooden doors with a metal-cutting blade — or vice versa — will significantly reduce the cutting speed and efficiency, and the saw could be damaged in the process. Also, when cutting metal, these saws produce a tremendous amount of sparks that can ignite adjacent combustibles (**Figure 4.1**). Therefore, rotary saws should not be used to cut metal where there are flammable fuels in close proximity. If such cuts *must* be made, a charged hoseline (1½-inch [38 mm] minimum) should be available for immediate use. In some cases, the blade of a rotary saw can bind in the material being cut. To avoid damage to the saw and possible injury to the operator, the saw should be shut off until the blade can be freed from the bind.

Figure 4.1 When used for cutting metal, a rotary saw may be a source of ignition.

As with all other fire service tools, the rotary saw must be maintained properly if it is to perform safely and effectively. One of the most important ways of ensuring the saw's safety and effectiveness is by making sure that the saw blades are serviceable. While the manufacturer's recommendations and departmental SOPs must be followed, the FDNY SOP on rotary saw blades is an example of reasonable guidelines. Its SOP is as follows:

- Replace 12-tooth woodcutting blades when two or more teeth are damaged or worn down more than the other teeth or when the tips are worn down to the circumference of the blade.

- Replace 24-tooth woodcutting blades when eight or more teeth are damaged or worn excessively, or the tips are worn down to the circumference of the blade.

- Replace composite concrete- or metal-cutting blades when they have been worn down sufficiently for the blade to fit inside an 8-inch (200 mm) circle.

All other forcible entry tools should be maintained according to the manufacturer's recommendations, departmental SOPs, or as described in **Essentials**.

Doors

As stated in **Essentials**, before any door is forced, firefighters should attempt to open the door in the normal way. In other words — *try before you pry.* Having to explain to irate property owners why an unlocked door was damaged or destroyed by over-eager firefighters is not something that chief officers enjoy. However, in many cases, the exterior doors into burning buildings will be locked and may have to be forced open. To do this quickly and safely, firefighters must be familiar with a wide variety of doors and locks and how to force them open. But before spending time and effort forcing door locks, firefighters should take the time to quickly evaluate other alternatives that may provide faster access. For example, the building may have a lockbox with door keys inside, the door may have a glass pane, or there may be a window next to the door. In these cases, it will usually be faster to unlock the doors with the keys from the lockbox, or to break the glass and reach inside to unlock the door (**Figure 4.2**). Replacing a pane of glass is usually cheaper than repairing or replacing a damaged door, doorframe, or lock set.

As mentioned earlier, today's firefighters must be familiar with a wide variety of doors and locks. New products and new and improved versions of familiar products make it very difficult for firefighters to stay current on the types of doors and locks in their respective response districts. However, because lives may depend upon a firefighter's ability to open a locked door quickly, the study and practice involved are clearly justified.

To be most efficient and to get doors open as quickly as possible, the proper tools need to be brought to the door initially. Having to return to the apparatus for a particular tool or piece of equipment or having to call for it and wait until it is brought to the door wastes critical time. Pre-incident planning inspections can help firefighters determine what will be needed if a particular door needs to be forced quickly (**Figure 4.3**).

The following sections discuss some typical and some atypical types of doors and locks and how to open them quickly. For more detailed information about door construction, refer to the IFSTA **Building Construction Related to the Fire Service** manual.

Figure 4.2 Entry can be gained quickly if keys are available in a lockbox. *Courtesy of Wes Kitchel.*

Figure 4.3 Firefighters should be familiar with any forcible entry problems they may encounter.

Residential/Commercial Doors

Many residential and commercial buildings have similar exterior doors. Some are conventional hollow-core or solid-core wooden doors as described in **Essentials**. Others are tempered glass or solid-core metal doors. In smaller buildings and occupancies that have relatively low occupant loads, the exterior doors open inward so the hinges are on the inside (**Figure 4.4**). In occupancies with higher occupant loads, the exterior doors must swing outward in the direction of exit travel. In most cases, the hinges on outward-swinging doors are on the outside (**Figure 4.5**). However, the exterior doors in some commercial buildings are double-acting doors; that is, they swing both inward and outward on pivot pins top and bottom.

Some commercial buildings house public assembly occupancies such as theaters and auditoriums with fixed seating or large open banquet halls or ballrooms. These buildings are designed to handle large occupant loads, and they commonly have exterior exit doors with panic hardware on the inside and no exterior hardware other than hinges (**Figure 4.6**).

Figure 4.4 Many office and small business doors swing inward.

Figure 4.5 Outward-swinging exit doors have hinges on the outside.

Figure 4.6 Buildings with large occupant loads require exit doors with panic hardware.

Forcing Residential/Commercial Doors

As described in **Essentials**, ordinary residential and office doors can usually be forced open quickly using standard forcible entry tools and with little or no damage to the door or doorframe. However, some exterior doors in these occupancies are solid-core metal doors set in steel frames. These doors resist being forced open by using the tools and techniques described in **Essentials**. Therefore, other tools and techniques must be used if entry is to be gained quickly.

A rotary saw equipped with a metal-cutting blade is one of the best tools to use for forcing an inward-swinging metal door set in a metal frame. The blade can be plunged through the rabbet or doorstop to cut the lock bolt (**Figure 4.7**). Or, it can be used to

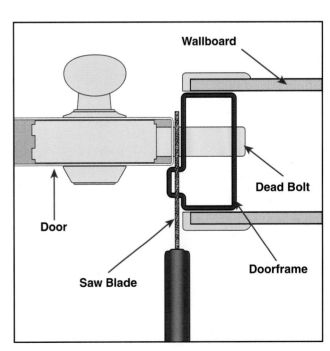

Figure 4.7 Cutting through the rabbet and dead bolt allows the door to be opened.

make two intersecting 45-degree cuts around the locking mechanism so that the door is free to open (**Figure 4.8**). On some of these doors, it may be necessary to make three perpendicular cuts around the locking mechanism (**Figure 4.9**).

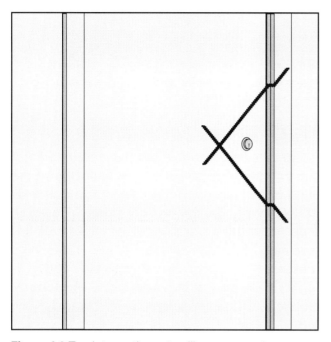

Figure 4.8 Two intersecting cuts will open some doors.

Figure 4.9 Some doors require three intersecting cuts to open them.

Once a cut has been made around a door lock, the door should open with little pressure from the outside. However, for a variety of reasons, some doors resist being opened even after cuts have been made around the locking mechanism. In these cases, considerable force may have to be applied to open the door. If pushing on the door with a gloved hand does not open it, additional force will have to be used. Striking the door with a shoulder is not recommended because it may cause injury to the shoulder and may allow the firefighter to fall through the doorway into a room that might be engulfed in flames. Likewise, standing in front of the doorway and kicking the door also leaves the firefighter exposed. A better technique is what some departments call a "mule kick." This technique is recommended because it uses the firefighter's strongest muscles to strike the door, and it affords the firefighter the protection of the wall if fire erupts from the doorway when the door opens (**Figure 4.10**).

Figure 4.10 If the door must still be forced open, a "mule kick" is the safest and most effective method.

On double doors, the rotary saw blade can be plunged through the weather strip and into the crack between the door leafs to cut the lock bolt (**Figure 4.11**). Once the locking leaf is open, the upper and lower latch pins of the other leaf can be opened in the usual manner.

If the door is an outward-swinging type and the hinges are exposed on the outside, it may be possible to drive the hinge pins out from the bottom so that the door can be removed (**Figure 4.12**). If the pins cannot be driven out, the hinges can be pulled with the fork of a Halligan or a claw tool or be cut off flush with the doorframe using a rotary saw (**Figure 4.13**). If available, an oxyacetylene torch or another exothermic cutting device can also be used,

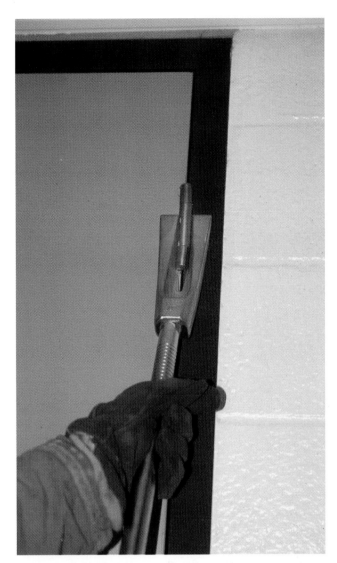

Figure 4.13 Exterior hinges can sometimes be broken off with a Halligan bar.

Figure 4.11 Cutting between the leaves of double doors will cut the dead bolt.

Figure 4.12 Pins in some exterior hinges can be driven out from the bottom.

but these techniques will probably take longer than using a rotary saw. Regardless of which tool is used, once the hinges have been cut off, the door can be pried out of the frame.

Finally, many residential and some commercial buildings have large single-piece slab doors that tilt up to open. These doors are most often used as garage doors in residential buildings and on loading docks of commercial buildings. Slab doors pivot on spring-assisted hardware mounted to the doorframe on each side (**Figure 4.14**). Some of these doors have a simple latch handle at one side that can be locked with a padlock. Others have a lock in the handle located on the centerline of the door, near the bottom. This type of latch is similar to that shown in **Essentials** and can be opened as described there.

Figure 4.14 A typical slab-type door and its hardware.

According to an NFPA report, in a 1995 incident firefighters advanced a charged hoseline through a residential garage to attack a fire in the interior of the house. Shortly thereafter, a sudden increase in fire intensity forced the crew to retreat back into the garage, but the heavy wooden garage door had closed spontaneously, cutting off their escape route and their water supply. Unable to open the garage door from the inside, the members of the trapped crew pounded on the door and yelled for help. Firefighters outside were eventually able to cut through the garage door and rescue those inside. Unfortunately, the officer in charge of the hose crew later died of smoke inhalation, and two of the firefighters suffered serious smoke inhalation and burn injuries. Nine of the firefighters involved in rescuing the trapped crew suffered a variety of injuries. One of the rescuers was injured seriously enough to require hospitalization.

This case history emphasizes the fact that forcibly opening doors into burning structures is not always for the purpose of *entering* the building.

Firefighters and others may be trapped inside and need an emergency escape route. And, it also shows that being able to open these doors quickly can save lives. Some departments force open *all* doors into a structure when there is significant fire involvement, provided that such action is consistent with the IAP.

In addition to the challenges involved in gaining access just discussed, many exterior doors also have some form of security system. These systems can be found in a variety of forms. Overcoming these impediments to forcible entry is discussed later in this chapter.

Industrial/Institutional Doors

In addition to the standard pedestrian doors at the office entrances to these occupancies, industrial/institutional buildings often have large tilt-slab, roll-up, or telescoping service doors. Service doors are found wherever large unobstructed wall openings are needed, such as at loading docks. Some roll-up doors are also used as fire doors in required separation walls. Many roll-up doors do not have an exterior latching mechanism.

One of the most common types of industrial/institutional service doors that firefighters may have to force open is the steel roll-up door (**Figure 4.15**). These doors are constructed of dozens of interlocking horizontal steel slats that ride up and down in tracks at both sides of the door opening. Unlike sectional doors (discussed next), the ends of the slats in roll-up doors do not have wheels or rollers attached to them, but the ends of every other slat have small metal guides that slide up and down in the

Figure 4.15 A typical steel roll-up door.

track. These doors are usually raised and lowered from inside the building using a manually operated or electrically driven chain hoist at one side of the door (**Figure 4.16**).

Other common industrial/institutional roll-up service doors consist of a number of horizontal panels connected by hinges (**Figure 4.17**). Sometimes called *sectional* doors, they are merely larger versions of some residential garage doors. These doors usually have small steel wheels attached to the ends of each panel or section that ride in steel tracks at each side of the doorway opening (**Figure 4.18**). This type of roll-up door is commonly opened and closed by an electrically driven chain mechanism attached at the center of the topmost panel of the door (**Figure 4.19**).

Another type of industrial/institutional service door is called a *sheet-curtain* door. These metal roll-up doors look exactly like conventional steel roll-up

Figure 4.17 A typical sectional door.

Figure 4.18 A sectional door is guided by steel wheels in tracks.

Figure 4.16 Once inside, a firefighter can use the lifting mechanism to raise the door.

Figure 4.19 A typical sectional door lifting mechanism.

doors so their existence in a particular occupancy must be identified during pre-incident planning inspections. Even though sheet-curtain doors look like conventional roll-up doors, they are quite different. Instead of dozens of individual interlocking slats, sheet-curtain doors are made up of a few interlocking flexible panels of relatively light-gauge metal (**Figure 4.20**). Each panel is embossed to give it the appearance of a conventional roll-up door. These doors function in the same way as conventional roll-up doors.

Regardless of the type of roll-up door, many of them have a conventional pedestrian doorway next to the service door (**Figure 4.21**). This doorway almost always has a metal-clad solid-core door or a solid metal door set in a metal frame.

A different type of industrial/institutional service door has recently become available. This new type of door is called a *Telescoping®* door (**Figure 4.22**). These doors consist of a number of interlocking, inverted U-shaped metal sections. When the door is open, the sections are nested together at the top of the doorway opening (**Figure 4.23**). As the name implies, the door sections telescope into position

Figure 4.21 Many roll-up doors have pedestrian doors beside them.

Figure 4.22 A typical telescoping door. *Courtesy of Jerry Shacklett.*

Figure 4.20 A typical sheet curtain door.

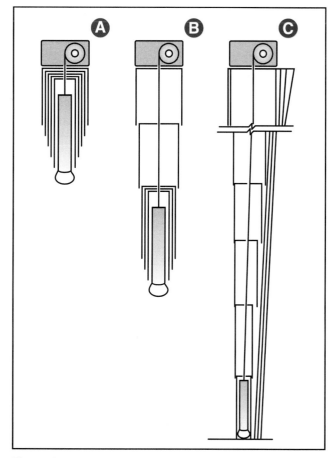

Figure 4.23 When telescoping doors are open, the sections are nested at the top of the doorway opening.

as the door is closed. When a telescoping door is closed, it forms a barrier of hollow interlocking sections, each with a rectangular cross-section (**Figure 4.24**). Like roll-up doors, telescoping doors are operated by chain-hoist mechanisms at one side of the doorway opening. These mechanisms can be operated manually or electrically, but unlike roll-up and sheet-curtain doors, telescoping doors are raised and lowered with internal cables and there are no springs or counterweights in the lifting mechanisms. However, like roll-up doors, many telescoping doors have conventional pedestrian doors beside them.

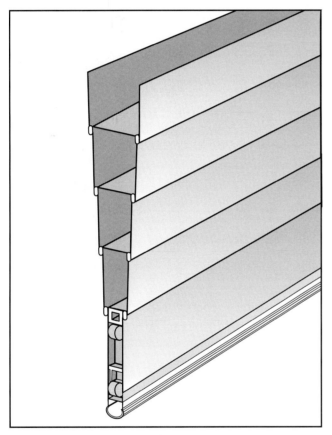

Figure 4.24 When telescoping doors are closed, each section interlocks with the one above and below it.

Forcing Industrial/Institutional Doors

In some cases, one of the quickest and most efficient ways to gain access through a roll-up, sheet-curtain, or telescoping service door is by forcing the pedestrian door beside it and then using the door-opening mechanism inside to raise the service door. Pre-incident planning inspections will confirm whether the pedestrian door provides access to the inside of the service door. The pedestrian door

can be forced as described in **Essentials** and in the preceding section on forcing residential/commercial doors. If there is no pedestrian door or if opening it does not provide access to the door-opening mechanism for the service door, another method will have to be used.

Historically, one of the most common methods of cutting through a roll-up or sheet-curtain door was to make a large triangular cut, sometimes called a *tepee cut*, in the center of the door. The purpose of the triangular cut is *not* to create an opening through which hoselines can be stretched, but only to provide an escape route for firefighters trapped inside or to allow access so that the door-opening mechanism can be used to open the door fully for interior access. Therefore, if this type of cut is used, the perimeter of the roll-up door must be protected from damage so that the door will not jam when the door-opening mechanism is used.

In a triangular cut, the base of the triangle is the bottom of the door, and the sides are formed by two 45-degree cuts. The apex of the triangle should be at least 6 feet (2 m) high in the middle of the door, but the higher the better. The cuts should not quite intersect at the apex (**Figure 4.25**). These cuts are most often made with a rotary saw equipped with a

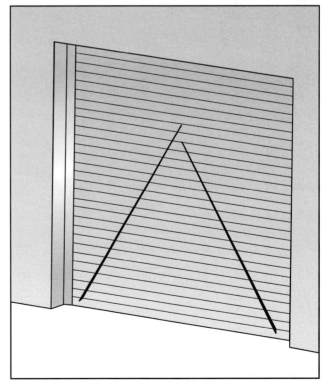

Figure 4.25 A typical triangular cut in a roll-up door.

metal-cutting blade. Once the triangular cut has been completed, the cut section of door can be flapped down in front of the door, or removed (**Figure 4.26**). Then, if fire conditions inside allow, firefighters can enter to raise the service door using the operating mechanism inside. If the door cannot be raised for any reason, the cut slats can be pulled from the sides to enlarge the unobstructed opening. The slats can sometimes be pulled by hand (wearing gloves), but pulling them with heavy-duty pliers is safer and more effective (**Figure 4.27**). The first slats or panels to be pulled should be those at chest height where most firefighters are strongest, and they should be pulled as close to parallel with the wall as possible.

Once the slats from the top of the cut are pulled, the top of the service door will usually roll up because of the spring tension in the operating mechanism if the mechanism is not locked. If it is locked, the lock should be cut off as described in **Essentials**.

Figure 4.27 Pliers should be used to pull slats. *Courtesy of Cedar Rapids (IA) Fire Department.*

WARNING!

Firefighters should not stand below older roll-up doors that are automatically retracting by the spring-operated mechanism because these doors may break loose from the wall and come crashing down.

However, the triangular cut takes a long time to create a relatively small opening. And, if the bottom of the service door is not at ground level, such as on some loading docks, the triangular cut is particularly ineffective. Triangular cuts are not recommended for telescoping doors.

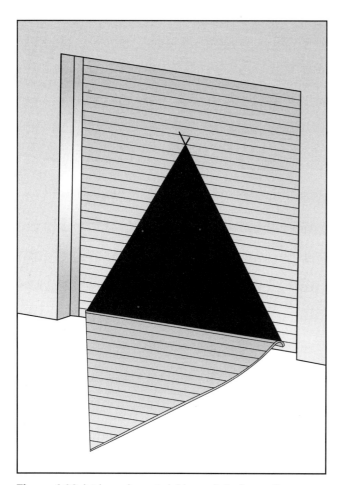

Figure 4.26 A triangular cut yields a relatively small opening.

Figure 4.28 A firefighter makes a single vertical cut in the center of the door. *Courtesy of Cedar Rapids (IA) Fire Department.*

Figure 4.29 A firefighter leans on one half of the cut door and removes slats from the other half. *Courtesy of Cedar Rapids (IA) Fire Department.*

Figure 4.30 Two firefighters remove slats from a roll-up door. *Courtesy of Cedar Rapids (IA) Fire Department.*

A much faster alternative to the triangular cut for opening roll-up or sheet-curtain doors is to make a single vertical cut down the middle of the door (**Figure 4.28**). As with the triangular cut, the higher that the vertical cut can be started, the better, as this creates the largest possible opening. If flames or excessive heat do not erupt from the vertical cut, a firefighter can lean against one half of the cut section and begin removing slats or panels from the opposite half of the door (**Figure 4.29**). If fire does show through the first cut, a firefighter can push on one half of the door with a long-handled tool while another firefighter pulls slats from the other half with pliers (**Figure 4.30**). Once the slats or panels are removed from both sides, the upper part of the door will roll up if the operating mechanism is not locked.

In some situations, roll-up or sheet-curtain doors are inset far enough that the slats or panels cannot be pulled out parallel to the wall in which the door is installed. In these cases, the cut slats can be pulled laterally as far as possible and then cut again in the middle to shorten their length (**Figure 4.31**). This allows the slats or panels below to fall and the upper part of the door to roll up.

If fire conditions inside an exterior roll-up or sheet-curtain door make a single cut in the center unsafe to use, an alternative is to make a horizontal cut across nearly the full width of the door, stopping about 1 foot (30 cm) from the doorframe on

Figure 4.31 In some cases, slats may have to be cut twice to allow them to clear the building. *Courtesy of Cedar Rapids (IA) Fire Department.*

each side. This horizontal cut should be about 6 feet (2 m) above the bottom of the door (**Figure 4.32**). A vertical cut (which does not quite intersect with the horizontal cut) is then made from each end of the horizontal cut down almost to the bottom of the door (**Figure 4.33**). Finally, when the vertical cuts and the horizontal cut are connected, the full section of door between the cuts will fall away creating a large access/egress opening (**Figure 4.34**).

When opening a telescoping door, the procedure just described should be used to cut the outer skin of the door sections. However, since these doors consist of hollow, box-like sections, once the outer skin is removed a second (slightly smaller) opening must be cut in the inner skin to finish the opening (**Figure 4.35**).

Some institutional buildings are designed to restrict the movement of those inside. Jails, prisons, and other correctional and detention facilities have

Figure 4.33 A vertical cut is made at each end of the horizontal cut. *Courtesy of Cedar Rapids (IA) Fire Department.*

Figure 4.34 This method creates the maximum possible opening. *Courtesy of Cedar Rapids (IA) Fire Department.*

Figure 4.32 A firefighter makes a single horizontal cut across a roll-up door. *Courtesy of Cedar Rapids (IA) Fire Department.*

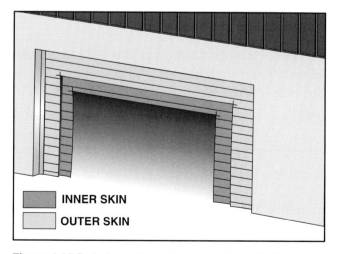

INNER SKIN
OUTER SKIN

Figure 4.35 Both the outer and inner surfaces of telescoping door sections must be cut.

a variety of very secure doors, gates, and other barriers. The quickest and most efficient means of gaining access into one of these facilities is to enlist the aid of a member of the institutional staff who can accompany the firefighters and unlock the doors, gates, and other barriers. If the fire inside such a facility is beyond the early growth stage, access inside will involve entering an IDLH atmosphere, so wearing SCBA will be required. Therefore, it may be necessary to enlist the aid of the institution's fire department or fire brigade. If the building is on fire and threatening the lives of those inside but the institution does not have fire-trained and equipped personnel — or if these personnel are unavailable — firefighters will have to use whatever means are at their disposal to gain access. Because the locks and latching mechanisms in these facilities are designed to resist being forced open, it may be quickest to simply cut around them as previously described in the section on forcing residential/commercial doors. However, because these interior doors and gates may be made of hardened steel, it may be necessary to use some form of exothermic cutting device to force them open.

Door Security Systems

Many exterior and some interior doors in a variety of different occupancies, including those just discussed, have security devices or systems designed to deny access except to those authorized to enter. Some of these devices are as simple as several dead bolts, a horizontally movable scissor gate, a horizontal security bar in saddles, or panic hardware on the inside of an exterior door. Others are electronic systems that require a series of numbers to be entered into a keypad to open them. Still others are electronic systems that require a card key to open them. Some even have sophisticated electronic fingerprint or iris recognition systems. Regardless of what type of device or system is installed, firefighters must be able to gain access into the building, or egress from it, quickly and efficiently when the building is on fire.

Overcoming Door Security Systems

The best way to overcome these door-controlling devices or systems is to identify them during pre-incident planning inspections and persuade the building occupant to install a lockbox. Whatever is needed to open the door — conventional key, card key, numeric code sequence, etc.— can then be placed inside for firefighters to use in an emergency. Using the means contained in the lockbox may be as fast or faster than forcing the door and is certainly less destructive.

In the absence of a lockbox, firefighters will have to cut the lock or force the door. The fact that there is not a lockbox on the building should be identified during pre-incident planning inspections. These inspections will allow firefighters to also determine the most efficient means of cutting the lock or forcing the door so that there is minimal delay in getting the necessary tools and equipment to the door when the building is on fire. Whatever method is chosen, it should be one that allows access into the building as quickly as possible. This may involve cutting off exposed locks or hinges, or it may involve cutting around the locking mechanism as described earlier. If a scissor gate is locked with a padlock, the lock can be cut off as described in **Essentials**, or the staple through which the lock shackle passes can be cut with a rotary saw. Scissor gates with built-in locks may be forced open with a manual or powered hydraulic spreader but using a rotary saw to cut the individual members around the lock will probably be faster **(Figure 4.36)**. If double doors have a horizontal security bar in saddles on the inside, the blade of a rotary saw can be inserted into

Figure 4.36 Scissor gates must be cut above and below the lock.

the crack between the door leafs to cut the bar. Or, the heads of the bolts holding the saddles can be cut off by plunging the blade of a rotary saw behind the bolt heads at a 45-degree angle to cut through the bolts (**Figure 4.37**). If firefighters know that a door has several dead bolts installed, they will also know to cut the door from top to bottom about one foot (30 cm) from the edge on the door handle side (**Figure 4.38**). If the doors are equipped with panic hardware, a chain saw can be plunged through the door a few inches (cm) above the panic bar. The bar of the saw can then be tilted down to operate the panic bar and open the door (**Figure 4.39**).

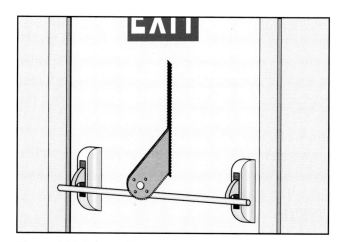

Figure 4.39 A door with panic hardware can be opened with a chain saw.

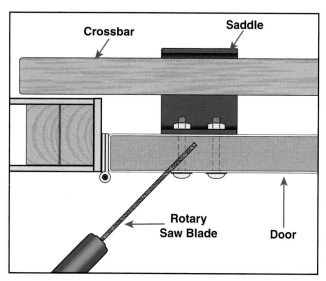

Figure 4.37 A rotary saw can be used to cut the blind bolts holding the security bar saddles.

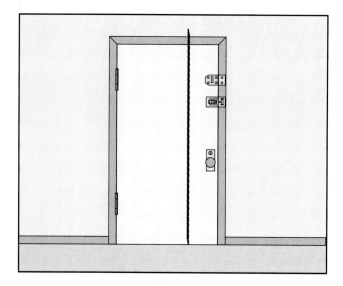

Figure 4.38 Knowing that a security door has numerous locks allows firefighters to save time by making a single vertical cut through the door.

Windows

There are perhaps as many different types of windows and window latches as there are doors and locks. Staying up to date on all the various types can be a daunting task for firefighters. However, just as with doors, the amount of time and effort that firefighters invest in learning about the different types of windows in their districts, and how to forcibly open them quickly and safely, can translate into lives and property saved. The following sections describe a variety of windows and how to open them.

For forcible entry purposes, windows are sometimes the quickest means of gaining access. Even when the windows cannot be opened, the panes may be broken out relatively easily and quickly. If the frame is undamaged, the cost of replacing the broken glass is usually, but not always, less than the cost of repairing damaged doors or walls. However, when window glass is removed to allow access into the building, it is often necessary to also remove the window frame. On the other hand, leaded glass windows, especially large, stained-glass windows in churches, temples, and fraternal buildings are sometimes priceless works of art that should be protected if at all possible (**Figure 4.40**).

Types of Windows

A wide variety of windows exist in both new and old buildings in most communities. Some of the more common types as described in **Essentials** are as follows:

● Fixed windows

● Double-hung (checkrail) windows

Figure 4.40 Some stained glass windows are works of art that should be protected if possible.

- Hinged (casement) windows
- Horizontal sliding windows
- Awning windows
- Jalousie windows
- Projected (factory) windows
- Hopper windows
- Energy-efficient windows

There are also a number of security windows discussed in the section on Overcoming Window Security Systems.

Breaking Windows

As always, *before breaking any window, try to open it first.* If it is necessary to break the window, the frame may have to be removed also. As described in **Essentials**, the entire pane should be broken out and the frame cleared of broken shards by scraping the frame with the breaking tool. The firefighter

breaking the glass should be in full protective clothing — including hand and eye protection — and upwind of the window. If using an axe to break the window, the firefighter should strike the window with the flat side of the blade. Regardless of which tool is used, the handle should be held higher than the blade to prevent glass from sliding down the handle. When working aboveground, windows should be broken inward whenever possible to avoid the "flying guillotine" hazard that may injure anyone working below, and may cut hoselines.

> ## CAUTION
> **Using the tip of a ground ladder to break a second-story window is dangerous and *not* recommended.**

There are other specialized windows designed for very specific applications. Regardless of the design or application, windows that resist being opened from the outside usually can and should be broken out when access is needed. However, many newer windows are glazed with or constructed entirely of extremely resilient plastics that are very difficult to break. In these situations, removing the entire frame with the window intact may be quicker and more efficient for entry purposes (**Figure 4.41**).

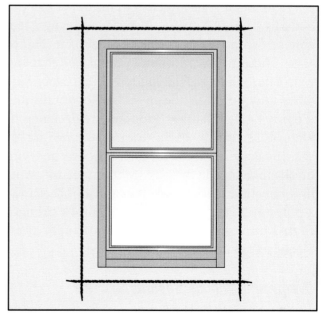

Figure 4.41 Windows with thermoplastic panes may have to be removed entirely.

Residential/Commercial Windows

Most residential/commercial windows can be forced open using the tools and techniques described in **Essentials**. However, there are some windows that require special knowledge and/or special tools and techniques to open them quickly. For example, those that have security bars, heavy screens, or sheet curtains over them can be a challenge if they have not been identified during pre-incident planning. If they have been identified (and they should have been), the necessary tools and techniques can be planned in advance and the personnel trained in their use so that there is little or no delay when needed during an emergency.

Industrial/Institutional Windows

As described in **Essentials**, the more common types of industrial/institutional windows can often be opened easily and quickly by simply breaking a pane of glass and reaching inside to release the latch. However, other types of windows in these occupancies present a more formidable challenge. Many have some form of security glass — either wired glass or break-resistant plastic. The tools and techniques needed to force entry through these windows are discussed in the following section on window security systems.

Window Security Systems

The most common type of window security system is a rigid metal grille attached to the outside of the building. The grille may consist of heavy-gauge steel wire screen or wrought iron or steel bars (**Figure 4.42**). These grilles are normally blind-bolted to the wall of the building or the window frame. Other windows may be protected by metal sheet curtains (**Figure 4.43**). Still other windows are designed to increase security by having a windowpane that resists breakage. Historically, such windows had wire mesh embedded in the glass. Modern security windows are more likely to have panes made of Lexan®, a polycarbonate plastic that is 250 times stronger than safety glass and 30 times stronger than Plexiglas® of the same thickness.

Overcoming Window Security Systems

To remove security screens or bars from windows, the fastest way is to cut the points of attachment

Figure 4.42 Typical security bars on a window.

Figure 4.43 Some windows are protected with sheet curtains.

with a rotary saw. If bolt heads are exposed, they can be cut off with a rotary saw (**Figure 4.44**). If the saw blade cannot reach the bolt heads, they can sometimes be removed by driving the fork of a Halligan or a claw tool under them (**Figure 4.45**). Otherwise, the points of attachment can be cut using an oxyacetylene torch or other exothermic cutting device. If the points of attachment cannot be cut, both ends of the upper horizontal bar should be cut as this will often allow the vertical bars to hinge on the lower horizontal bar and swing downward out of the way (**Figure 4.46**). If that does not create the necessary access, both ends of the lower horizontal bar should be cut also and the entire unit removed from the window. Windows protected by metal sheet curtains can be forced using the tools and techniques described earlier in the section on overcoming door security systems.

Figure 4.44 A rotary saw can be used to cut the points of attachment.

Figure 4.45 Bolt heads holding security bars can sometimes be popped off with a Halligan bar.

Figure 4.46 Cutting the upper points of attachment may allow window bars to swing down out of the way.

In addition to exterior security bars or screens, many buildings in high-crime areas have windows that are also designed to resist breakage. The tools and techniques needed to break these security windows are as follows:

Thermoplastic windows. Plexiglas® acrylic, Lexan® polycarbonate, and other thermoplastic windows may have to be opened to gain access into a burning building. A rotary saw with a medium (40 tooth) carbide-tipped blade is most effective when entry must be made through all types of plastic windows (**Figure 4.47**). As always, eye protection is critically important whenever a rotary saw is used. However, a rotary saw is the *only* fire service tool that will cut Lexan polycarbonate. The following technique described for cutting Plexiglas will *not* work with Lexan windows.

In the absence of a rotary saw, Plexiglas windows can be shattered. This is done by scoring an "X" on the pane and then striking the intersection of the

Figure 4.47 Plastic windowpanes can be cut with a rotary saw.

"X" with the point of a pick-head axe (**Figure 4.48**). The pane will usually break along the "X," and if so, the pieces can be pulled or bent out. Another method is to strike the pane in the center with a sledgehammer (**Figure 4.49**). Usually this will not break the pane, but it may bow it enough to allow it to slip out of its frame.

Laminated windows. Many security windows are glazed with laminated glass similar to that in automobile windshields. A sheet of plastic is sandwiched between two sheets of plate glass. When broken, the glass shards cling to the plastic laminate. Firefighters can take advantage of this characteristic and simply cut out the panes of glass with an axe, hatchet, or a glass saw such as those used in vehicle extrication.

Figure 4.48 Scored plastic windowpanes can be broken with the point of an axe.

Figure 4.49 Scored plastic windowpanes can be broken with a sledgehammer.

Wired-glass windows. Another common form of security window uses wire mesh imbedded in the glass panes. Like laminated glass, the pieces of broken glass cling to the wire mesh and therefore can be cut out in one piece. The same tools used to cut laminated glass can be used to cut wired glass.

Film-coated glass. The windows of many buildings, especially the windows on the south and west walls, have a reflective film applied to the inside of the glass to reduce glare from the sun. When broken, film-coated windows will sometimes behave in a manner similar to laminated windows. That is, the glass shards may cling to the film, and the window can fall out in one large piece. When breaking these windows, firefighters must be careful to not allow the glass to fall on them.

Walls

The types of walls that firefighters may have to breach for interior access are many and varied. They range from the ordinary wood-frame walls of single-family dwellings to reinforced concrete walls of commercial or industrial buildings – and the many types between these two extremes. As with all other fireground support operations, the key is to be able to breach any type of wall as safely and as quickly as possible. One of the most important aspects of this capability is a thorough knowledge of the building gained through pre-incident planning inspections. This allows firefighters to know in advance what tools and techniques are needed to breach the exterior walls of a particular building. With this knowledge they can bring the proper tools with them initially and not have to lose time going back to the apparatus to get them. The tools most commonly used to breach exterior walls are the rotary saw, chain saw, circular saw, battering ram, sledgehammer, concrete breaker (jackhammer), and the air chisel.

Whenever an exterior wall must be breached, eye protection is a critical part of the firefighters' protective ensemble. In such situations, NFPA 1500 requires that firefighters use *both* their helmet faceshields *and* goggles or safety glasses. In situations where a concrete or masonry wall must be breached, considerable dust can be produced so respiratory protection should also be used. In some cases, filter masks may be sufficient. However, because the firefighters should be wearing their SCBA, the facepieces may provide both respiratory and eye protection (**Figure 4.50**).

Another important aspect of breaching an exterior wall for access into a structure is locating where to cut. Just as in cutting ventilation openings, when cutting through an exterior wall it is usually better to cut one large opening instead of several smaller ones. Both time and effort will be saved if the job is done right the first time. Knowledge of the structural design of the particular building, gained through pre-incident planning inspections, will often help firefighters decide where openings should be made — and where they should not. For example, choosing a section of wall at random (without knowing the structural design) may result in opening the exterior wall where an interior wall intersects. A good deal of time and effort could therefore be wasted because the interior wall would have to be removed before the opening would be usable, or an entirely new opening might have to be made. In the absence of detailed knowledge of a particular building, and sometimes with it, one of the fastest ways to make a usable opening in an exterior wall is to make two vertical cuts down from the bottom corners of a window opening to the

Figure 4.50 When cutting masonry walls, firefighters should wear SCBA.

floor. The window and the section of wall below it can then be removed and a relatively large opening is created with less time and effort being expended than by cutting the same size opening in a blank wall (**Figure 4.51**). Obviously, if there are no window openings in a wall that must be breached, knowledge of the building is critical to locating where to cut.

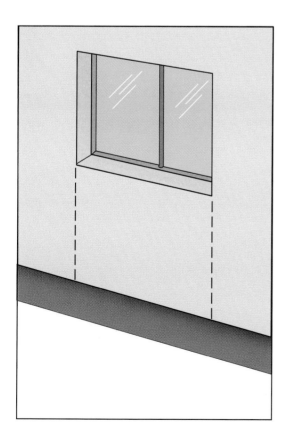

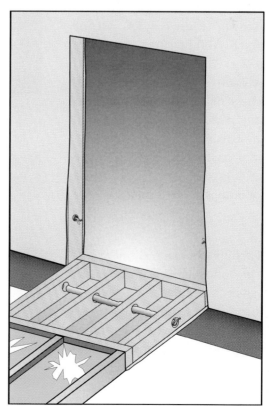

Figure 4.51 An exterior wall can be breached quickly by using existing window openings.

Types of Exterior Walls

There are many types of exterior walls that firefighters may have to breach to gain entry into a building. The most common types of exterior walls are as follows:

- Wood-frame
- Masonry
- Concrete
- Metal

Wood-Frame Walls

Gaining access into ordinary wood-frame buildings sometimes involves breaching an exterior wall. Wood-frame walls are often covered by some form of wooden siding such as plywood panels, vertical or horizontal planking, or wooden shingles (**Figure 4.52**). Some wood-frame walls are covered with vinyl or aluminum siding (**Figure 4.53**). Other wood-frame walls are covered by stucco over wire mesh, which is often backed by gypsum wallboard nailed to the studs (**Figure 4.54**). However, some older stucco walls consist of the finish layer of plaster over wire and tar paper covering diagonal wooden planking. Some wood-frame walls are covered by a veneer of brick or stone (**Figure 4.55**). The exterior walls of some older residences, warehouses, and former military buildings are covered with large asbestos shingles over plywood or planking (**Figure 4.56**).

In many cases, breaching exterior walls of wood-frame structures can be done relatively quickly with a rotary saw, chain saw, or a circular saw. However, firefighters cutting through these materials – especially the asbestos shingles – must wear respiratory and eye protection as part of their protective ensemble. Because of the possibility of plumbing or electrical wiring inside the walls, the building's utilities should be shut down before cutting begins.

Figure 4.52 Plywood wall coverings come in many different styles and finishes.

Figure 4.53 This vinyl siding shows the effects of heat from a fire next door.

Figure 4.54 The texture of a typical stucco wall.

Figure 4.55 A typical wood-frame wall (covered by a veneer of brick) after a fire.

Figure 4.56 Many older structures are covered with asbestos shingles.

Figure 4.57 The header course confirms that this is an unreinforced masonry wall.

In some cases, URM walls can be breached with a rotary saw equipped with a masonry blade. It may also be possible to break out a section of wall using a battering ram or a sledgehammer. However, all these tools and techniques tend to be slower than using electric or pneumatic concrete breakers. Obviously, eye protection is extremely important when using these tools to breach a masonry wall. In addition, the decibels produced by these tools make hearing protection critical also.

Concrete Walls

Some exterior walls may be reinforced or unreinforced poured concrete. Depending upon the age, quality, and thickness of the concrete, these walls can be some of the most difficult and time consuming to breach. Therefore, breaching poured concrete walls is usually considered too difficult and time consuming to be a reasonable option except in some structural collapse situations. All poured concrete walls are much more difficult to breach than other types of walls. But if deemed necessary, it can be done.

Manual breaching tools, such as battering rams and sledgehammers, are rarely effective on poured concrete walls. A variety of power tools can be used to breach walls that have *knockout* panels built into them. Sometimes called *blowout panels*, knockout panels are large sections of poured concrete walls that are designed to be removable so that large tanks or other large objects can be brought into or re-

Masonry Walls

As mentioned in the previous section, masonry walls are often just a veneer over wooden or metal structural members. In those cases, the tools and techniques discussed earlier are the ones to use. However, in some buildings the exterior masonry walls are full-thickness assemblies that are made entirely of mineral material. For example, they may be cement-filled concrete blocks or a double-course brick wall. Double-course brick walls (also called unreinforced masonry [URM]) can usually be identified by certain bricks or courses being laid perpendicular to the other courses. In this *header course*, which may be every fifth, sixth, or seventh course, the ends of the bricks are visible (**Figure 4.57**). Other masonry walls may simply be curtain walls of brick or stone veneer over concrete blocks or a metal framework.

moved from the building (**Figure 4.58**). In buildings with these panels, a rotary saw equipped with a masonry blade can be used successfully. A diamond chain saw will also work. As mentioned earlier, an electric or pneumatic concrete breaker may be most efficient.

In many older concrete and masonry buildings, window and doorway openings that are no longer used have been bricked up (**Figure 4.59**). These bricked-up areas are often easier to breach than the surrounding wall areas. The brickwork can often be knocked out with a sledgehammer or battering ram.

Breaching reinforced concrete walls is so time consuming that it is rarely done until after a fire is extinguished. However, if these walls must be breached, the reinforcing steel (rebar) will have to be cut to create a large enough opening for access by firefighters. The rebar can be cut with hydraulic cutters, such as those used to cut brake pedals in vehicle extrication, or with a rotary saw equipped with a metal-cutting blade (**Figure 4.60**). Rebar can also be cut with an oxyacetylene cutting torch or other exothermic device if it is available on scene.

Figure 4.58 Concrete walls with blowout panels may lend themselves to being breached. *Courtesy of John Hinton.*

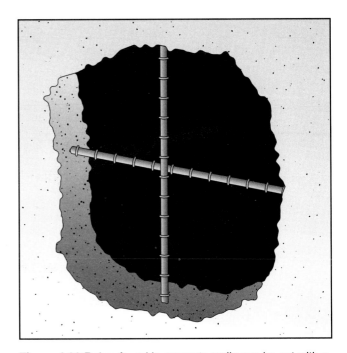

Figure 4.60 Rebar found in concrete walls can be cut with a hydraulic tool.

Metal Walls

Lightweight metal walls are common on a wide variety of building types. The metal siding panels are usually attached to wooden or steel framing with screws but removing the screws to create an access opening may be too slow to be practical. In most cases, the gauge of the metal panels is such that, if necessary, it can be cut with an axe. Metal walls also lend themselves to being cut with an air chisel such as is used in vehicle extrication (**Figure 4.61**). However, the tool of choice is often the rotary saw because it is almost always readily available and it is very effective. Because of the amount of sparks produced by these saws when cutting metal, they should only be used where flammable materials are a safe distance away or a charged hoseline is close at hand.

Figure 4.59 Window openings that have been bricked in lend themselves to being breached.

Figure 4.61 Light gauge metal walls can be breached using an air chisel.

Summary

Once firefighters have reached the outside of a burning building, they must use information gathered during pre-incident planning inspections and information gathered during size-up to decide what are the best ways of gaining access into the building. Forcing doors and windows is usually the safest and fastest way to get inside. However, the doors and windows may be protected with security systems that must be overcome before these openings can be used. In some situations, it may be advantageous for firefighters to breach an exterior wall to gain access into the building. One of the most important things that contributes to entry being made quickly and safely is pre-incident planning. Such planning allows firefighters to know what tools and techniques will be needed to force entry into any particular building. Armed with this knowledge, they can approach a burning building with the correct tools to do the job right the first time.

Chapter 5
Interior Operations

Chapter 5
Interior Operations

Once firefighters have reached a burning building and have gained access into it, they are in a position to perform some of their most important work. The actions they take inside a burning building often deal directly with saving lives and reducing property loss. In addition, working inside allows firefighters to directly observe conditions within the building and to report those conditions to the IC. Because conditions inside may vary significantly from how they appear outside, these direct observations may provide critical information to a vent crew on the roof and will provide the IC with essential information that may validate the Incident Action Plan (IAP), warrant a change in the attack mode, or alter the IAP in some other way.

The IC should implement the agency's SOP on personnel accountability whenever firefighters enter the hazard zone within a burning building. In addition, when an interior structure fire is beyond the incipient phase(early development stage), OSHA defines it as an IDLH atmosphere and that triggers the two-in/two-out rule. These procedures are intended to save firefighters' lives.

This chapter begins with a discussion of lifesaving techniques such as primary and secondary searches, thermal imagers, and sheltering in place. It continues with discussions of other interior operations such as heat removal and salvage. Finally, the chapter concludes with a discussion of those things that firefighters can do in support of interior fire suppression operations.

Search and Rescue

The interior operations that relate most directly to saving lives are *search* and *rescue*. As described in **Essentials**, almost all structure fires require both a

primary and a secondary search. However, the number and types of resources needed to conduct these search and rescue operations safely and effectively vary from one fire to another depending upon a number of variables in each situation. While there are other variables, the most common ones are the *type of building* that is burning, the *time period*, and the *fire situation*.

Type of Building

In this context, building "type" includes the construction type, occupancy type, and the age of the building. As previously discussed, some types of construction tend to contain a fire while others contribute to its spread. For example, fire can spread more rapidly in an open warehouse than in a highly compartmentalized office building. Some building types are more vulnerable than others to losing their structural integrity during a fire, making them more prone to early collapse. For example, buildings that have lightweight roofs supporting heavy dead loads may collapse sooner than those with other types of roof assemblies (**Figure 5.1**). Some buildings make

Figure 5.1 Heavy loads on roofs increase the chances of roof collapse.

forcible entry relatively easy; others make it much more of a challenge. For example, gaining entry into buildings with window bars, metal-clad exterior doors, and other security measures is more difficult than in buildings without such devices. All these variables can and should be identified during pre-incident planning inspections so that the problems can be anticipated and techniques and procedures developed to overcome them. For more information on pre-incident planning, see NFPA 1620, *Recommended Practice for Pre-Incident Planning*. For a typical pre-incident planning form, see Appendix B of this manual.

Obviously, some types of buildings have a greater life safety hazard than others. For example, fully occupied places of public assembly and high-rise office buildings have a greater life safety hazard than many other building types (**Figure 5.2**). Also, residential type buildings — apartments, motels, hotels, and single-family dwellings — may have a greater

life safety hazard than some other types of buildings. However, the occupant load to be expected in these and other occupancies may vary significantly with the time period involved.

Time Period

In this context, "time period" refers to both the time of day and the day of the week when a fire is burning. In most residential occupancies, the highest occupant loads are to be expected during the night and early morning hours when people are likely to be asleep. Elementary and secondary schools are likely to be most heavily occupied during the daytime hours on weekdays (**Figure 5.3**). Post-secondary schools may also be occupied in the evening hours. Retail, commercial, and industrial occupancies are likely to have their highest occupant loads during the day and early evening. Bars, nightclubs, movie theaters, and other public assembly occupancies are most likely to have their heaviest occupancy between noon and about 2:00 a.m. However, the occupant loads in other buildings — hospitals, nursing homes, and residential care homes — are not affected by the time of day or the day of the week (**Figure 5.4**). They have a relatively constant occupant load around the clock. Obviously, when search and rescue operations are necessary in heavily occupied residential or public assembly occupancies, large numbers of personnel will be needed — and needed immediately! While the time period involved can be a factor in the occupant loads of these occupancies, the other major variable affecting search and rescue operations is the fire situation.

Figure 5.2 When fully occupied, high-rise office buildings have a significant life safety hazard.

Figure 5.3 Elementary schools are occupied at specific times. *Courtesy of Donna Gill.*

Fire Situation

The volume of fire, its intensity, its rate and direction of spread, and what is being threatened by it are all variables related to the fire itself. Depending upon the type of construction, the fire load, the occupancy type, the occupant load, how large the fire is and how it is behaving, all relate to the need for search and rescue. Some of these variables will intensify the need for search and rescue; others will reduce it. For example, if a residential building is *heavily* involved when the first fire department unit arrives, the firefighters must quickly try to determine whether anyone is still inside the building. If the answer is yes — based on direct observation or information from a credible person — firefighters may be put at risk to conduct an immediate search for the occupants (**Figure 5.5**). Given that immediate action by the first-arriving crew may save a life, a rapid intervention crew (RIC) is not required for them to enter the hazard zone for search and rescue, but one should be established as soon as possible.

> The *immediate action* exception to the *two-in/two-out* rule _does not_ include a search to determine whether lives are in jeopardy. The exception applies only to situations where lives are *known* to be at risk.

If firefighters must conduct a search of the floor above the fire, they are in a very hazardous location because of the potential for the fire to extend upward onto that floor. Therefore, it is extremely important that charged hoselines be in place to protect their exit stairway and that a secondary means of egress be provided. This secondary means of egress can sometimes be provided by ground ladders placed at the windows on that floor. However, these ladders are vulnerable to fire issuing from a window below them (**Figure 5.6**). Also, if the firefighters

Figure 5.5 Information from a credible person may trigger an immediate search of a burning building.

Figure 5.4 Hospitals are occupied at all times.

Figure 5.6 Ladders placed over windows are vulnerable to damage by the fire.

Figure 5.7 Some fires preclude an effective search of the interior.

are on a floor that is above the reach of the available ground ladders, then an aerial device may be needed.

On the other hand, if the building is *fully* involved — regardless of the other variables — interior search and rescue would be precluded by the fire situation (**Figure 5.7**). In this case, protecting any exposures and mounting a defensive exterior fire attack are probably all that can be done until the fire is knocked down. After the fire has been knocked down, a slow and methodical search for bodies can be conducted. However, since this is no longer an emergency situation, firefighters should not be put in serious jeopardy during the secondary search.

As discussed in **Essentials**, when the risk/benefit analysis suggests that a search and rescue operation is indicated, the involved building should be searched twice. For obvious reasons, these are designated as *primary* and *secondary* searches.

Primary Search

In the absence of credible information that a life could be saved by immediate action, OSHA regulations require that a RIC be established before firefighters are allowed to enter the hazard zone. The RIC must be maintained as long as any firefighters remain in the zone or until the hazard has been mitigated. The primary search of a burning building is conducted as soon as a sufficient number of personnel are on scene to form a search team of at least two members and a RIC of at least two members. While in the hazard zone, the search team members must remain in visual or voice (not radio)

contact with each other. They must also remain in contact with the RIC, but this contact may be by radio. In addition to full PPE, SCBA, and a radio, search team members should also take forcible entry tools, rope bags, and flashlights inside with them. These items will help locate and access any victims and may help the firefighters escape if necessary.

The purpose of the primary search is to determine whether everyone has left the burning building or if there are one or more occupants who must be rescued. The techniques for conducting a safe and effective search are as described in **Essentials**. However, a growing number of fire departments are using electronic devices that assist in finding victims in heavy smoke. These devices are called *thermal imagers* or *thermal imaging cameras* (TIC) (**Figure 5.8**).

Figure 5.8 Thermal imaging cameras can greatly improve search effectiveness. *Courtesy of Bullard.*

Thermal Imagers

Several different types of thermal imagers are available to fire/rescue agencies. Most imagers use one of two technologies — microbolometer technology or BST (barium, strontium, titanium) technology. A thermal imager functions by detecting the heat

Figure 5.9 Some thermal imagers have pistol grips. *Courtesy of Scott Technologies, Inc.*

Figure 5.10 Thermal imagers may operate hands-free because they are attached to the helmet. *Courtesy of Scott Technologies, Inc.*

signature (minute amounts of thermal radiation) produced by fires and some living organisms. Handheld units are available — some with pistol grip handles and some without (**Figure 5.9**). Others are designed to be mounted on a helmet (**Figure 5.10**). Some units are capable of remote transmis-

sion so that the image can be seen on a monitor at the command post or some other location. Some imagers are designed primarily for locating the seat of a fire by being calibrated to respond to temperatures in excess of 900°F (465°C). Others are capable of differentiating between body temperature and that of surrounding materials. Regardless of the type of imager used, the heat of a fire or other exothermic reaction may be detected through windows and some interior walls. This may help to pinpoint the seat of a fire when it is obscured by heavy smoke. Thermal imagers can also be used on the roof of a burning building to help identify the seat of the fire, and to locate roof supports. For more information on this application, see Chapter 8, Vertical Ventilation.

All imagers have certain limitations. For example, even though they are designed for use on the fireground, many are relatively fragile and dropping one may put it out of service until it can be recalibrated. Imagers can also be put out of service, at least temporarily, by becoming overheated or by a condition known as a "whiteout." A whiteout occurs when the imager is overwhelmed by the heat signature produced by a very intense fire and the screen suddenly goes white. While thermal imagers will detect the heat signature produced by a fire or a live person, in some cases the signature can be blocked by walls and other solid objects.

Another possible disadvantage to using thermal imagers is that only the team member operating the camera sees what the device is detecting. The other team members must depend upon the camera operator to keep them informed of any possible dangers or changes in fire behavior. If the operator fails to do so, the other team members could be in jeopardy.

The two major advantages of using a thermal imager during primary search are speed and effectiveness. If an entire room can be scanned from the doorway, or just inside it, the time-consuming and sometimes difficult task of physically searching the room becomes unnecessary. This can save a considerable amount of time. Victims overcome by oxygen deprivation sometimes collapse in areas that cause them to be missed during a physical search. The sensitivity of a thermal imager can greatly reduce the likelihood of this happening and thereby increase the effectiveness of the search.

Another major benefit of using thermal imagers is a reduced likelihood of firefighters becoming lost or trapped. This is especially true if every team operating inside a burning building is equipped with a thermal imager.

Pre-incident planning is critically important to identifying occupancies that have a greater than normal life hazard and/or are configured in a way that would make a physical search both labor-intensive and time-consuming. Considering the resource demands involved in conducting an effective primary search in these occupancies, the expense of purchasing one or more thermal imagers and training department personnel in their use may be justified.

Rescue

When occupants are found during the primary search, their condition and their overall situation must be assessed. This assessment is necessary to determine whether they merely need assistance in escaping from the building or whether they are incapable of escaping because of impairments, injuries, or entrapment. It is critical that command be informed of the situation and of any additional resource needs.

Some building occupants, especially the very young and the very old or those under the influence of drugs or alcohol, may be frightened, confused, and disoriented by the sounds of a smoke detector, fire alarm bell, and/or the sirens and air horns of arriving fire and rescue vehicles. They may be physically capable of escaping without assistance but are mentally incapable of doing so; therefore, they remain in the familiarity of their rooms where they feel safe. If the atmosphere outside their rooms is clear enough for them to breathe and they would not otherwise be in danger from the fire, they can be escorted out of the building. If conditions outside their rooms will not allow them to be escorted out, they may have to be rescued through an exterior window. The equipment and techniques described in **Essentials** can be used to rescue these victims.

If occupants are injured or they are trapped because the fire has cut off their normal means of escape, their medical condition and their situation will have to be assessed and appropriate action

taken. These actions *will* include keeping command informed of the situation and *may* include stabilizing the victims before any rescue attempt is made. However, if their location is immediately threatened by the fire or imminent structural collapse, it may be necessary to rescue the victims before medically stabilizing them. It is a choice of risking further injury during the rescue or risking death from the fire. In some situations, it may be possible to protect trapped and/or injured victims without immediately rescuing them. This technique is known as *sheltering in place*.

Sheltering In Place

It may be impractical to evacuate the entire population of a heavily occupied burning building — not to mention *rescuing* them. For example, in fully occupied high-rise office or residential buildings it is often not practical — and not necessary — to attempt to evacuate or rescue every building occupant. Instead, those not in immediate danger from the fire — primarily those located below the fire floor — may be better protected by being allowed to remain in the building and perhaps in their own rooms. Even occupants above the fire floor may be out of danger if the fire is well contained and the occupants are several floors above it. Obviously, the fire situation must be continually monitored and any change that might put occupants at risk would trigger an immediate change in the plan.

Some residential and commercial buildings are designed with sheltering in place as part of their life safety plan. Their design includes what are called *areas of refuge*. According to NFPA 101, *Life Safety Code®*, an area of refuge is "a space that is part of the normal means of egress but that is protected from fire by an approved sprinkler system or by means of separation from other spaces within the same building by smokeproof walls or by virtue of being located in an adjacent building." While the Americans with Disabilities Act (ADA) uses the term *area of rescue assistance*, the practical meaning is the same as for area of refuge, provided that the area meets all other requirements for wheelchair access, etc. Both areas of refuge and areas of rescue assistance are equipped with emergency communications systems.

If the burning building is equipped with a common communications system that allows all occupants to hear an announcement at the same time, and the system is still operational, it can be used to notify occupants about which floors or areas of the building need to be evacuated and which are safe for them to continue to occupy. If there is no such system available, electronic bullhorns or other public address systems may be used for this purpose (**Figure 5.11**).

Figure 5.11 If a building is without an intercom system, firefighters may have to use alternate means of instructing occupants.

Secondary Search

As described in **Essentials**, a secondary search is conducted after the primary search has been done and the initial fire suppression and ventilation operations have been completed. A secondary search should be conducted as soon after the primary search as resources and the fire situation allow. However, the secondary search should be conducted in the same manner as a body recovery operation — slowly and methodically and without putting firefighters at unnecessary risk.

As mentioned in **Essentials**, the secondary search should be performed by personnel who were not involved in the primary search. This reduces the likelihood of any area being overlooked. Also, if there are large amounts of debris from the fire, especially if all or a portion of the building collapsed after the primary search was completed, it may be advisable to use thermal imagers during the secondary search. As always, the results of the secondary search are reported through channels to command.

Heat Removal

Another important function that firefighters can perform once they are inside a burning building is that of heat removal. However, in this context, heat removal is *not* the same as ventilation that is used as part of a coordinated fire attack. Ventilation as part of a coordinated fire attack is discussed in the next three chapters of this manual. Heat removal, on the other hand, is removing heat from the areas where interior crews are working by channeling it to another portion of the building or to the outside.

Removing the heat from the interior of the structure as soon as possible can have several positive effects. It allows heat to escape to the outside and thereby makes the interior temperature more tenable for anyone inside the building — both firefighters and any remaining occupants. Along with the heat, residual smoke can also be removed, which makes the atmosphere inside the building more breathable. It can also reduce the amount of heat and smoke damage to the building and its contents.

During an interior fire attack, fireground support personnel working in close coordination with the attack crew(s) and the vent crew on the roof can dramatically reduce the amount of heat and smoke to which the attack personnel are exposed. This is done by the support personnel opening large holes in the ceiling to allow the heat and smoke to vent into the attic and out through a vent hole in the roof. Obviously, close coordination is necessary to prevent fire spread from the fire floor into the attic — the vent hole must be made as soon as the ceiling is pulled, if not prior to it.

Once a fire has been knocked down, firefighters inside the building sometimes remove heat by placing smoke ejectors in open windows and doors or by discharging hose streams through open windows. These techniques also are discussed in greater detail in the ventilation chapters. The other way that heat is removed from the interior of a building is by firefighters opening exterior windows and doors. This technique is sometimes called *vent as you go*.

Vent As You Go

When a fire has burned for some time inside a building, especially a fire that has smoldered for hours, parts of the building well away from the seat of the fire may become charged with heat and smoke. As heat and smoke are forced up open stairwells and down connecting hallways, any offices or other rooms to which the doors were left open will fill with heat and smoke. The heat and smoke from a smoldering fire may also be spread throughout the building by the HVAC system. In that case, virtually every room in the building may be charged with heat and smoke. Clearing these smoke and heat-filled spaces is when the vent-as-you-go technique is most appropriate.

> # CAUTION
> **Indiscriminately opening windows throughout a building can compromise positive pressure ventilation operations.**

Indiscriminately opening windows can also draw the fire to these openings and possibly cut off egress routes. Therefore, firefighters should use this technique only when it is coordinated with other fireground operations. Firefighters should not employ vent-as-you-go unless ordered to do so.

When a room filled with heat and smoke must be searched, any exterior windows in that room can be opened to allow the heat and contaminants out. However, this should only be done after closing the door to the hallway and marking the door to indicate that firefighters are inside (**Figure 5.12**). This will facilitate the search of the room by allowing it to air out and will do so without compromising any positive-pressure ventilation that may be in progress. Once the room has been searched, the firefighters inside can exit the room leaving the windows open. They must close and mark the hallway door to indicate that the room has been searched (**Figure 5.13**).

Salvage

While *salvage* is but one part of *loss control*, it is nevertheless a very important function for firefighters working inside a burning building. Preventing or reducing non-fire loss is one of the three primary goals of every emergency response agency on every call — life safety, incident stabilization, and property conservation.

As with every other aspect of fireground support operations, the salvage part of loss control begins with pre-incident planning. Such planning allows firefighters to become familiar with the buildings and occupancies within their response districts and to thereby anticipate where potential problems exist and devise ways to mitigate those problems. Knowing what problems exist, and where, allows firefighters to train on the necessary techniques and to bring the necessary tools and equipment to the building when a call is received. In most cases, the tools, equipment, and techniques needed to perform safe and effective salvage operations are as described in **Essentials**. While any interior structure fire may contain elements that will challenge the skills of the firefighters assigned to suppress it, some of the most challenging from a salvage standpoint are *attic fires*.

Attic Fires

Dealing safely and effectively with attic fires starts with an accurate size-up. As discussed earlier, the size-up actually starts with pre-incident planning before the fire call is received. If the firefighters involved are familiar with the building and its construction — particularly the construction of the roof assembly — they have a distinct advantage compared to fighting a fire in a building with which they are unfamiliar.

While knowledge of general building construction is valuable, a familiarity with the particular attic involved allows the firefighters to anticipate how a fire is likely to behave in that attic and how that may affect the structural integrity of the roof assembly. For example, if they are familiar with this particular

Figure 5.12 When firefighters begin the search of a room, they should mark the door with a slash.

Figure 5.13 When firefighters complete the room search, they should change the slash mark into an X.

building they know whether the attic has one or more smoke/fire barriers and whether those barriers are intact or have been penetrated. Intact smoke barriers can help contain an attic fire to a portion of the attic, and their absence may enable the fire to spread throughout the entire attic. Local codes may require 1-hour walls between units that extend through the attic and the roof. Unfortunately, portions of these partitions are often damaged, penetrated for access, or removed, rendering them ineffective as fire stops. It is also important to know about any storage in attic spaces because attic storage can add significantly to the building's fuel load and can contribute to structural failure. Firefighters familiar with the building will also know whether the roof assembly was built on-site (also called *stick-built framing)* or contains prefabricated roof trusses. If trusses were used, they will know whether the gang nails (steel gusset plates) were corner-nailed. If not, the trusses are likely to fail much

sooner in a fire. They will also know whether the ceiling is suspended from open-web trusses. If so, the entire assembly may suddenly collapse into the interior of the building when exposed to intense flame impingement. For more information on roof assemblies, refer to Chapter 8, Vertical Ventilation.

One of the most critical elements in the rapid and efficient extinguishment of an attic fire by suppression crews is for them to have access to the fire in order to attack it. In many cases, an intact ceiling separates suppression crews from a fire in the attic, so the decision is made to pull the ceiling with pike poles or ceiling hooks. In some attics, the insulation has been sealed under a sheet of plastic. This additional layer of material can make the job of pulling ceilings and opening the attic much more difficult. When ceilings are pulled, large amounts of insulation and other debris — some of which may be on fire — can drop down onto the contents of the room below. Therefore, firefighters should delay pulling the ceiling until they have protected the contents of the room below with salvage covers. The tools, equipment, and techniques described in **Essentials** should be used to cover the contents of the room immediately below the attic fire (**Figure 5.14**).

Another tactic that is quick and effective in reducing the intensity of an attic fire is to penetrate the intact ceiling with one or more piercing nozzles (**Figure 5.15**). If piercing nozzles are not available, a small hole can be made in the ceiling and a nozzle set on a wide fog pattern can be pushed up a short distance into the attic. Regardless of which type of nozzle is used, this form of indirect attack is most effective when done close to the seat of the fire. This technique allows the fire to be attacked without having to wait for the contents of the room to be protected with salvage covers. The two operations can be conducted simultaneously.

Once knockdown has been achieved, the hole in the ceiling can be enlarged for further extinguishment — but not until the contents of the room have been fully protected with salvage covers. When all rooms under the area of fire involvement have been protected, the rest of the ceiling may be pulled down as necessary until the attic fire is completely extinguished and overhaul is completed.

However, in many cases, pulling the ceilings to expose the attic from below is still frequently performed. It allows suppression crews to attack the fire directly, and in most cases, this results in rapid extinguishment. While this tactic is effective, it is not without its risks. As mentioned earlier, if the ceiling is suspended from open-web trusses that have been weakened by the fire, the entire roof assembly may suddenly collapse. Once again, if these roof assemblies and the deadloads they support are identified during pre-incident planning inspections, firefighters will be able to make a more informed assessment of the risk/benefits of pulling ceilings in these buildings.

Water Removal

Water used to extinguish an interior structure fire, whether from automatic sprinklers, master stream appliances, or handline nozzles, can add a tremendous amount of weight for the structure to support. If that water is not drained away through floor drains and scuppers or is not channeled down stair-

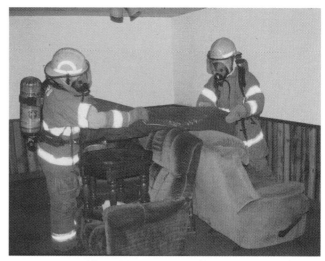

Figure 5.14 Especially when there is fire in an attic, the contents of the room immediately below should be covered if they cannot be removed.

Figure 5.15 Piercing nozzles can be very effective in attacking attic fires.

ways, it can add enough weight to the building to threaten its structural integrity. Therefore, another important salvage-related function of fireground support personnel inside a burning building is to remove the accumulated water as quickly and as efficiently as possible. There are a number of proven techniques for this purpose.

Assuming that no more water is being added, water that has accumulated on the floor of a burning building can sometimes be removed by simply using brooms or squeegees to push the water toward open floor drains or open stairways (**Figure 5.16**). In other cases, it may be necessary to remove toilets from the floor to allow water to drain down the sewer lines. If these techniques are not successful, it may be necessary to build a chute on the floor below and drill a large hole in the floor to drain the water into the chute and out an exterior window.

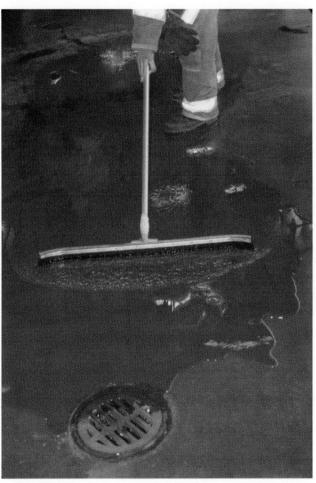

Figure 5.16 To reduce collapse potential and to help reduce fire loss, water should be removed as soon as possible.

A situation in which an accumulation of water may not threaten the structural integrity of the building, but is no less intolerable, is when a basement or other subsurface area has been flooded. These situations can render a building uninhabitable by shorting out electrical service to the entire building, by extinguishing pilot lights in central heating units, or by becoming contaminated with untreated sewage. As long as the water accumulation has not become contaminated with sewage, ignitable liquids, or other hazardous materials, fireground support personnel may be assigned to remove the accumulation. The usual means of removing this water is by using a portable auxiliary pump to direct the water into the nearest storm drain. For more information on salvage, refer to Chapter 12, Loss Control.

Summary

Most fireground activities are "support" operations. Support operations can and do occur prior to, during, and after the "fire attack." The success or failure of the support operations greatly contribute to the success or failure of the fire attack. Once inside a burning building, fireground support personnel can perform some of their most important duties. They can assess conditions within the building that may not be obvious from the outside. They may perform search and rescue. They may remove heat and smoke from inside the building to make it more tenable for firefighters and occupants alike. They may perform salvage work that is essential to meeting the objective of conserving property. Finally, companies assigned to fireground support operations may be split up to perform other operations in support of the overall fire suppression effort. When such reassignments are made, the need for effective communications and personnel accountability is increased.

Chapter 6
Ventilation Size-Up

Chapter 6
Ventilation Size-Up

In 1978, a California fire department responded to a report of a structure fire. First-arriving units found a working garage fire in a two-story, wood-frame residence. Firefighters could see that the fire was extending from the garage into the attic. The truck company was assigned to conduct a primary search of the interior and to check for fire extension. It took several minutes for truck company personnel to find the attic access at the top of the stairs. By the time the decision was made to pull the second-floor ceiling, the attic was heavily involved. Sudden and complete failure of the roof assembly soon followed, resulting in severe injuries to seven firefighters.

The foregoing incident underscores the importance of early and aggressive ventilation of interior structure fires — especially attic fires. Had the truck company been assigned to vertical ventilation instead of checking for fire extension from the interior, the results might have been quite different.

This chapter reviews basic fire behavior and smoke behavior as they affect ventilation size-up. Also discussed is how building construction may affect ventilation size-up. Finally, the coordination of ventilation efforts with rescue and fire suppression operations is discussed along with other ventilation size-up considerations.

Ventilation Overview

As described briefly in **Essentials**, one of the most effective tactics available to firefighters is *ventilation*. However, as in the foregoing case history, fire departments tend to ventilate too little rather than too much — and often too late. It sometimes appears that a legitimate concern for property conservation — doing the absolute minimum of property damage in the ventilation process — is allowed to dictate the type and amount of ventilation that is done. For example:

- Time is lost trying to force open a window rather than breaking it out.
- A ventilation opening is not cut in a roof, and the attic fire below is allowed to spread.
- A ventilation opening is made, but it is too small to adequately vent the heat, smoke, and gases being produced so the fire in the building spreads as if there were no ventilation opening.

Even when an adequate ventilation opening is made, ventilation is often done as an afterthought — that is, after the fire inside the building is already knocked down. As with any other aspect of emergency service, if actions are not taken with appropriate aggressiveness, the problem often continues to escalate and the property that was not sacrificed during ventilation is ultimately lost to the fire — along with a great deal more. Properly done, ventilation can contribute significantly to the achievement of all three of the major goals on every incident: life safety, incident stabilization, and property conservation.

Early and effective ventilation of a structure fire draws heat, smoke, and toxic fire gases away from trapped occupants and firefighters alike. Ventilation increases the chances that trapped victims will survive. Ventilation also decreases the chances of a rollover, flashover, or backdraft, and that reduces the likelihood of firefighters being injured. In addition, ventilation reduces the amount of punishment that the firefighters working inside the building will have to endure during search, rescue, and fire suppression operations.

When firefighters are not subject to accelerated fatigue because of extreme temperatures within the building and are not in danger of heat-related conditions such as heat exhaustion or even heat stroke, they can attack the fire more aggressively. This aggressiveness allows them to achieve earlier knockdown, which contributes to incident stabilization.

A properly placed ventilation opening of adequate size will provide the shortest possible path by which the fire and its products can exit the building. It also channels heat and smoke away from uninvolved portions of the building. Both of these effects contribute to a reduction in property lost to the fire —property conservation.

Ventilation efforts should always be in concert with existing atmospheric conditions, taking advantage of natural ventilation whenever possible. However, in some situations, natural ventilation may be inadequate and may have to be supplemented or replaced with forced ventilation to provide a tenable atmosphere and to facilitate rescue and suppression operations. *Forced ventilation* involves the use of fans, blowers, nozzles, and other mechanical devices to create or redirect the flow of air within an involved compartment to facilitate operations within the compartment.

Some terms are commonly used (and misused) by many firefighters when discussing forced ventilation theory and methods. For example, the term *positive pressure* is redundant because pressure is always positive. The term *negative pressure* is a misnomer because an *absence* of pressure is a vacuum. Using the term *venturi effect* is not technically accurate to describe the *entrainment* of air being expelled from a confined space. However, because all of these terms are in such widespread use in the fire service, they will also be used that way in this manual. For purposes of clarity, *positive pressure* will refer to *blowing* air from outside a confined space into the space, *negative pressure* will refer to *expelling* (ejecting) air from within a confined space to the outside, and *venturi effect* will be used to describe air being drawn into the stream of air being mechanically expelled from a space. In this context, "outside" may include an area within a building but outside of the space to be ventilated, as well as outside of the building.

One of the most important elements in the size-up of a structure fire is that relating to ventilation. Before orders are given to ventilate a burning structure, the IC must consider the effects that ventilation will have on the intensity of the fire. Before actually opening the building, consideration must be given to the readiness of attack crews to advance hoselines to facilitate search and rescue operations, for fire attack, and for exposure protection. To be both safe and effective, ventilation operations must be coordinated with fire attack.

The IC must first determine *whether* ventilation is necessary and, if so, when, where, and in what form it should be initiated. Ventilation is a tactical operation. Its purpose is to direct the movement of the products of combustion and to remove them from the building to facilitate rescue and fire attack. Some situations may simply require locating and extinguishing the fire and then ventilating afterward to clear residual smoke from the structure. Others will require early and aggressive ventilation to allow search/rescue and fire suppression personnel to enter and work inside the building.

For ventilation to be most effective, it must be done sooner rather than later — sometimes even before the fire attack has begun — provided that it is performed as part of a coordinated strategic effort. The type of ventilation used (vertical vs. horizontal or natural vs. forced) must also be the most appropriate for the situation. Ventilation must be *adequate* — capable of handling the volume of heat, smoke, and toxic gases being produced by the fire — and it must be done with appropriate aggressiveness.

However, in their zeal to do the best possible job, firefighters assigned to ventilate a burning building may develop tunnel vision and fail to recognize elements in the situation that could threaten their safety or that of others at the scene. Therefore, firefighters must be trained to quickly but thoroughly size up the situation, weigh the risks and benefits of the tactical options available, and base their actions on what is safe and of the greatest benefit to the overall operation. Some agencies use the simple mnemonic — what have we got, what are we going to do, what do we need? To effectively size-up a ventilation situation, firefighters must have at least a basic understanding of how fire, smoke, and gases behave under various conditions and what effect ventilation will have on the fire.

Fire Behavior

As described in **Essentials**, unless interrupted by some outside intervention (fire attack or automatic fire suppression system activation), a compartment fire starts with the ignition stage and progresses through four additional stages:

- Growth
- Flashover
- Fully developed
- Decay.

A fire may start inside a building at any time of the day or night if the right conditions exist. If the fire occurs when the area is occupied, it is likely to be discovered and controlled in the ignition stage or early in the growth stage. But if it occurs when the building is closed and deserted or when the occupants are asleep, the fire may go undetected until it has gained major proportions. For ventilation to be performed safely and effectively, it is critically important that firefighters be able to recognize the stage of development of the fire that is burning inside the building.

Firefighters may be confronted by any of the latter four stages of fire, and the ventilation tactics used will vary depending on the stage in which the fire is found. Firefighters must also be aware of the potentially hazardous conditions — rollover, flashover, and backdraft — that may occur as a fire progresses through the four stages. Even though discussed in **Essentials**, their importance to firefighter safety justifies a review of these stages here.

Growth Stage

The growth stage is that which follows the actual ignition. Early in the growth stage, the fire is limited to the materials first ignited. In this stage, the oxygen content in the air has not been significantly reduced; therefore, the fire is producing water vapor (H_2O), carbon dioxide (CO_2), sulfur dioxide (SO_2), carbon monoxide (CO), and trace amounts of other gases. Some heat is being generated and the temperature will increase with the progress of the fire. The fire may be producing a flame tempera-

ture well above 1,000°F (537°C), yet the temperature in the room at this stage may be only slightly above normal. If the fire is extinguished at this point, simply opening a window and removing the screen (natural horizontal ventilation) may be all that is required to adequately ventilate the compartment (**Figure 6.1**). At other times in the growth stage, mechanical or forced horizontal ventilation may be required (**Figure 6.2**).

Figure 6.1 Opening windows may be all that is necessary to ventilate a building.

Figure 6.2 PPV is often the most effective ventilation method.

Early in the growth stage, oxygen-rich air is drawn into the flame as convection (the rise of heated gases) carries the heat to the uppermost regions of the compartment. The heated gases spread laterally at the top and then downward, forcing the cooler air to lower levels and eventually igniting all the combustible material in the upper levels of the room. This early portion of the growth stage is sometimes called the *flame-spread* phase. At this point, the temperature in the upper portions of the compartment can exceed 1,300°F (700°C). The presence of this heated air is one of the reasons that firefighters must stay low and use SCBA. One breath of this superheated air can cause serious lung damage.

Rollover

Sometimes called *flameover*, a rollover occurs when unburned combustible gases released during the ignition and early growth stages of the fire accumulate at the ceiling level. These superheated gases mix with oxygen as they spread, under pressure, away from the fire and into uninvolved areas. When their flammable range is reached, they ignite. A fire front develops, expanding very rapidly as it rolls across the ceiling (**Figure 6.3**). This is another reason why firefighters must stay low when conducting interior operations.

Rollover differs from flashover (discussed in the following section) in that during a rollover only the gases at the upper levels burn — not the entire contents of the room. The rollover continues until the fire stops producing the flammable gases that

are feeding the rollover. Extinguishing the main body of the fire is the most direct way of eliminating these gases.

> Even though a hoseline is operating, rollover can occur if a sufficient volume of superheated gases are spreading across the ceiling. Effective ventilation on the side of the fire opposite the fire attack reduces the chances of a rollover.

Flashover Stage

Flashover occurs when there is simultaneous ignition over the entire surface of a room and its contents. Originally, it was believed that combustible gases released during the early stages of a fire caused flashover. It was thought that these gases collected at the ceiling level and mixed with air until they reached their flammable range and then suddenly ignited causing flashover. It is now believed that while rollover may occur, it precedes flashover.

The actual cause of flashover is attributed to the buildup of heat from the fire itself. As the fire continues to burn, heat radiates down from the ceiling and all the contents in the fire area are gradually heated to their ignition temperatures. When they reach this point, simultaneous ignition occurs, and the compartment becomes fully involved in fire. The actual ignition is almost instantaneous and can be quite dramatic. A flashover can usually be avoided by directing a stream of water toward both the ceiling level and

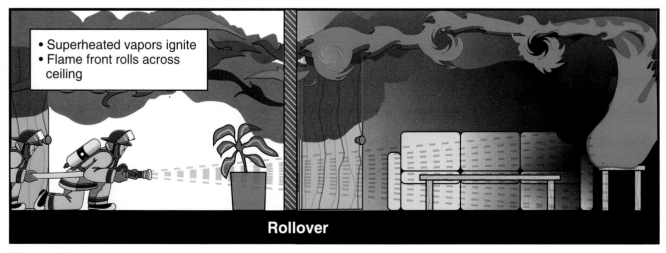

- Superheated vapors ignite
- Flame front rolls across ceiling

Rollover

Figure 6.3 To protect themselves, firefighters must stay low during a rollover.

the contents of the room to cool them below their ignition temperature and by early and aggressive ventilation.

Fully Developed Stage

Following flashover, a compartment fire continues to burn intensely. During this stage, sometimes called the *free-burning* phase, the fire continues to burn. In a closed compartment it will burn until there is insufficient oxygen to react with the fuel. In this situation, the fire is gradually reduced to the decay stage and needs only a new supply of oxygen to burn rapidly or explode. Effective ventilation at this point allows the hot gases to be channeled harmlessly to the outside, allows hoselines to be advanced into the involved areas, and permits the remaining products of combustion to be forced out ahead of the hoselines.

Decay Stage

In the decay stage, flame may diminish completely if the compartment is sufficiently airtight. In this instance, burning is reduced to glowing embers. The room becomes completely filled with dense smoke and superheated gases. Smoke is forced under pressure from cracks and other tiny openings. As the fire continues to smolder, the gases in the compartment may reach a temperature of well over 1,000°F (537°C). The intense heat continues to vaporize the lighter fuel fractions, such as hydrogen and methane, from the combustible material in the room. Because there is little available oxygen, the CO produced cannot combine with oxygen to form CO_2 as it did in the earlier stages. These fuel gases add to those produced earlier and further increase the hazard to firefighters because of the possibility of a backdraft (discussed in the following section). It is critical that this potentially lethal condition be handled properly.

Backdraft

Firefighters confronted with a confined fire that is late in the fully developed (free-burning) stage or in the decay stage risk initiating a backdraft if they fail to recognize the conditions and open the structure improperly. A *backdraft* is the rapid, almost instantaneous combustion of flammable gases, carbon particles, and tar balloons produced by materials that are burning under conditions of insufficient oxygen.

Except under carefully controlled conditions, combustion is rarely complete. Some of the fuel elements of the burning materials are not consumed but are released into the surrounding atmosphere in the form of unburned combustible gases. It is not necessary that a material be aflame to emit these gases. Many combustibles begin to smoke and liberate combustible gases (pyrolysis) before they actually burst into flame. In such cases, either there is not enough available oxygen to support fire or the ignition temperature of the material has not been reached. Nevertheless, the gases and carbon particles being produced are highly flammable. Effective ventilation (usually vertical) releases smoke and hot, unburned gases from the upper areas of the compartment and allows them to escape harmlessly into the atmosphere (**Figure 6.4**). Improper ventilation at this time, such as opening a door or window, supplies the missing link — oxygen. As soon as the needed oxygen rushes in, the combustion process resumes with devastating speed and a backdraft occurs — truly qualifying as an explosion.

While *oxidation* is the chemical union of oxygen with other elements and *combustion* is merely rapid oxidation, a backdraft is *extremely* rapid oxidation — on the order of an explosion. Carbon is a naturally abundant element present in wood, plastics, petroleum products, and all other organic materials. When these materials burn in the presence of abundant oxygen, the CO produced combines with the available oxygen to form CO_2.

Figure 6.4 Vertical ventilation can reduce backdraft potential.

However, if the available oxygen is limited, some of the carbon monoxide has no oxygen with which to unite. Under these conditions, massive amounts of carbon monoxide may be present in the smoke. Therefore, one warning sign of a potential backdraft is this dense, black, carbon-filled smoke in a confined space. If oxygen is reintroduced into the space, it combines with the carbon and the smoke becomes less black, turning yellow or grayish yellow instead. As described in **Essentials** and in Chapter 1 of this manual, the following characteristics may indicate a potential backdraft condition:

- Pressurized smoke exiting small openings
- Confinement and excessive heat
- Little or no visible flame
- Smoke leaving the building in puffs or at intervals (appearance of breathing)
- Smoke-stained windows
- Black smoke turning dense, grayish yellow

Upon arrival at a structure fire, firefighters must exercise extreme caution if the siding or other outside wall coverings are hot, or even noticeably warm, and little or no fire is evident. This may indicate that a hot, smoldering fire has been burning in the building for some time, giving off large quantities of superheated gases that are still within the building. This assumes that the building is still tightly closed and that the surface heat is not caused by fire inside the wall where the heat is detected. Using a thermal imager at this point can also help identify the fire conditions inside the building (**Figure 6.5**).

Figure 6.5 A thermal imaging camera can help locate the seat of a fire.

If visibility through the windows is practically zero because of smoke or carbonaceous tar coating the windows and little or no fire can be seen inside (or perhaps only a faint orange glow visible through the smoke), it is reasonable to assume that the fire has been smoldering for some time. This is an extremely dangerous condition.

> # WARNING!
> When backdraft conditions exist, horizontal ventilation should *not* be attempted if any other options are available.

If these conditions are seen upon arrival, all on-scene and responding units should be informed of the conditions and vertical ventilation initiated as soon as possible. While vertical ventilation is usually the best way of safely mitigating backdraft conditions, it may not always be possible. For example, if the fire is located on an intermediate floor of a multistory building and there are no vertical shafts, it may not be possible to vent the fire vertically. If the fire appears to be well contained, such as in a concrete utility vault, it may only be necessary to monitor the compartment until the smoldering fire goes out because of a lack of oxygen or fuel. This allows the gases within the compartment to eventually cool below their ignition temperature and make it safe to open the space. However, this procedure could be very time consuming, and the fire may not remain fully contained; therefore, waiting for the gases to cool may not always be a practical solution. Another option may be the use of piercing nozzles to penetrate the space and accelerate the cooling process by initiating a form of indirect fire fighting (**Figure 6.6**).

When the signs of a potential backdraft have been recognized, firefighters should not stand directly in front of doors, windows, or other openings. The gaseous products of the backdraft expand as they exit the opening because the atmospheric pressure outside the building is lower than the pressure inside. Therefore, it is especially important that they not stand within the V-shaped force pattern that would emanate from such openings.

Figure 6.6 Using a piercing nozzle can absorb enough heat to reduce backdraft potential.

Figure 6.7 All-metal buildings tend to limit fire spread.

Figure 6.8 Dehydrated wood increases the flammability of older structures.

Fire Spread

Fires inside buildings spread in different ways and at different rates. Because these fires are less affected by prevailing winds than are wildland fires, the principal variables are the ways in which heat is transferred. As described in **Essentials**, the three recognized ways by which heat is transferred are conduction, convection, and radiation. From the standpoint of fireground support operations, a structure fire is most affected by *radiation* (the primary mechanism of fire spread) and *convection* (the tendency of heat to rise).

However, other variables affect fire spread inside of buildings. One variable is the type of construction. The other variable is the avenues available for fire spread.

Construction

As discussed earlier in this manual, some construction materials — such as masonry and protected steel — tend to contain a fire (**Figure 6.7**). Other materials, such as unprotected wood (especially very old and very dry wood) and many new synthetic materials, add fuel to the fire and contribute to its spread (**Figure 6.8**). The presence or absence of a functional automatic sprinkler system can also greatly affect fire spread within a building. The presence or absence of elevator shafts and other vertical openings can also affect fire spread. Common attics such as those in strip malls also promote fire spread.

Avenues of Spread

The physical layout of a building can either contribute to fire spread or retard it. Fire can spread rapidly through a building with large, uninterrupted spaces — such as warehouses or large offices with cubicles separated only by half-walls. On the other hand, a fire on a floor comprised of individual offices is more likely to remain localized to the room or area of

Figure 6.9 Fire spread can be limited by self-closing fire doors.

origin. However, if the individual compartments face a long, uninterrupted central hallway, they are more likely to become involved than if the hallway were interrupted at intervals by automatic fire doors or other fire-rated assemblies (**Figure 6.9**).

A single-story building, regardless of how large, is far less prone to fire spread than a multistory building of equal size. In a multistory building, convection causes heat, smoke, and other fire gases to spread upward through open stairwells, elevator shafts, and pipe races.

From the standpoint of size-up, if firefighters have familiarized themselves with the physical layout and construction of the burning building and if their knowledge of the building is current, they can more accurately assess its fire spread potential. They can anticipate whether the fire is likely to remain localized or spread throughout the building. They can also determine where ventilation techniques can be applied most effectively to limit the spread of the fire (**Figure 6.10**).

Figure 6.10 Selective ventilation can greatly affect fire spread.

Smoke Behavior

One of the most reliable indicators of the fire conditions within a burning building is the behavior of the visible smoke. For their own safety, firefighters should remember that smoke contains a host of different toxic substances, perhaps even airborne asbestos particles (a known carcinogen). Therefore, firefighters should follow the safety behaviors listed in Chapter 2, Firefighter Survival, including the one that says — *never* breathe smoke. Also for their own safety and for the effectiveness of the fireground operations, firefighters must be able to accurately assess smoke behavior. The variables in smoke behavior that firefighters should look for when sizing up a working structure fire are the smoke's volume, color, density, and pressure.

Volume

There are differences in the volume of smoke produced by various materials when they burn and by the conditions in which they burn, but the volume

of smoke is still a good general indicator of the fire situation. In general, the greater the volume of smoke is, the bigger and more intense the fire will be. While it is possible for a large fire to produce little smoke, these conditions rarely exist outside of the laboratory or in certain industrial processes. It is far more likely that a small fire will produce a large volume of smoke, depending upon what is burning and under what conditions. Some petroleum products produce huge volumes of smoke from relatively small fires. However, in most structure fires, firefighters should assume, until proven otherwise, that a lot of smoke equals a lot of fire (**Figure 6.11**).

Figure 6.11 In general, the amount of smoke indicates the amount of fire.

Color

In some ways, the color of the smoke being produced by a fire is a more reliable indicator of fire conditions than the volume of smoke being produced. For example, whitish-gray smoke generally indicates that cellulose-based materials (wood, paper, etc.) are burning in an atmosphere with abundant oxygen. On the other hand, dense black smoke is generally produced by hydrocarbons such as petroleum and petroleum-based materials. But, as discussed earlier, this dense black smoke may also be the result of virtually any material burning in an atmosphere where the oxygen supply is limited — such as in a developing backdraft condition. To make these distinctions, firefighters must consider the overall situation and not just the color of the smoke.

Regardless of the oxygen supply, certain other materials produce smoke of distinctive and identifiable colors when they burn. For example, materials containing sulfur produce thick yellow smoke. Pyroxylin plastics, such as those used in ordinary T-squares and other drafting tools, produce a brown-to copper-colored smoke when they burn — a sign of deadly oxides of nitrogen (**Figure 6.12**).

Figure 6.12 Brownish, copper-colored smoke indicates deadly oxides of nitrogen.

Few structure fires involve only one type of fuel. They represent a mixture of burning materials — some primarily hydrocarbons and some primarily cellulose. Because many of these burning materials produce smoke that is extremely toxic — sometimes lethal in even minute concentrations — firefighters must assume that any smoke, regardless of color, is toxic. Therefore, they should always follow the safety behavior previously mentioned — *never* breathe smoke.

Density

Another smoke-related variable that firefighters must consider when sizing up a structure fire is the smoke's *density*. As with smoke volume and color, its density is a good general indicator of fire conditions within the building. Small fires of low intensity usually produce light, hazy smoke. Conversely, dense heavy smoke usually indicates a large and relatively intense fire. But there are exceptions to both of these generalities. For example, when an attic fire is confined to the area above the ceiling, there is often only a light haze on the floor below the fire. On the other hand, a relatively small fire that smolders for a long period of time can fill an entire building with heat and very dense smoke.

Smoke density can also be an indicator of a fire's stage of development. In the earlier stages of a fire in a confined space, there is abundant oxygen and the fire burns relatively clean. It may produce relatively little smoke, and the smoke is not particularly dense. However, by the time the fire has burned into its decay stage, the available oxygen has been largely consumed. The longer the fire burns, the less oxygen is available to support combustion. As the oxygen is depleted, the smoke becomes progressively more dense.

Pressure

As the fire heats the smoke and other gases within a structure, the gases expand and create pressure. As the fire gets bigger and more intense, more pressure is created. Pressure causes the smoke to move. The greater the pressure is, the greater the movement will be. When the entire space within a compartment has been filled with smoke, the smoke will be forced out through every available opening.

Figure 6.13 Smoke under pressure indicates an intensely burning fire within.

When firefighters see a large volume of very dense smoke billowing out under great pressure, there can be little doubt that a large and intense fire is burning within the building (**Figure 6.13**). However, as described in the preceding scenario, if firefighters see light smoke moving lazily on the top floor of a building, it does not always mean that there is not a fire burning very intensely above them. Once again, the firefighters must not base their entire size-up on a single observation. Each observation must be considered in relation to the overall situation.

Building Construction

In addition to sizing up the location and extent of the fire, the IC must also consider the building age, type, design, and occupancy when making fireground ventilation decisions. Type and design features that have a bearing on these decisions include the types of materials of which the building is constructed, the number and size of roof vents and wall openings, the number of stories, and the availability of roof access (**Figure 6.14**). Also to be considered are security devices on window and door openings, as well as the direction in which the openings face in relation to exposures and the prevailing wind. Building construction features are discussed in greater detail in Chapter 8, Vertical Ventilation, and Chapter 9, Special Ventilation Operations.

For purposes of ventilation size-up, the following four critical building construction factors should be considered:

Figure 6.14 The age, type, and size of a building can affect ventilation decisions.

- Age and type of building
- Construction features that help fireground operations
- Construction features that hinder fireground operations
- Construction features that are peculiar to the particular occupancy of the building

Age and Type of Building

Knowing approximately when a particular building was constructed can provide firefighters with information that may be critical to their fighting a fire in that building safely and effectively. Older buildings, newer buildings, and all those in between have certain advantages and disadvantages with regard to their fire resistance, fire spread characteristics, and susceptibility to structural collapse.

The type of building involved can also affect the ventilation size-up process. Single- or multi-family residences, commercial buildings, industrial buildings, and high-rises all have characteristics in common as well as those that are unique.

Older Buildings

While "older" is obviously a relative term, for purposes of this manual it refers to buildings constructed before the end of World War II in 1945 (**Figure 6.15**). Before World War II, many jurisdictions had no building codes. During the war, many buildings were constructed by or for the military. These buildings were often intended as temporary structures and were of substandard construction. In the years immediately following the war, many local jurisdictions adopted building codes for the first time because of the building boom expected as part of the transition from a wartime economy to a peacetime economy.

Even though many older buildings are unique, many others share common characteristics. Many older buildings were constructed with walls of unreinforced masonry (URM), primarily brick, giving them the capacity to contain the heat of a fire longer than many buildings of other materials (**Figure 6.16**). While this can reduce fire spread to other structures, it can also increase the chances of backdraft conditions developing. URM structures are also prone to structural collapse.

Older wood-frame buildings were most often built from full dimension lumber. When damaged by fire, full dimension lumber retains its strength longer than the lumber used in newer buildings. However, because the lumber is so old, it is more

likely to be dehydrated and therefore more susceptible to ignition than newer lumber. Older buildings are more likely to have balloon-frame construction that allows fire to spread inside the walls from the basement to the attic or even from top to bottom. Unless they have been remodeled, and many of them have, older buildings may have knob-and-tube wiring with substandard insulation on the wiring (**Figure 6.17**). The number of circuits and outlets may be inadequate to handle the many elec-

Figure 6.16 URM buildings contain fire well, but they have relatively high collapse potential.

Figure 6.15 Many older buildings were constructed before building codes were adopted.

Figure 6.17 Very old buildings may have substandard knob-and-tube wiring.

trical appliances commonly used today. This makes these buildings more susceptible to electrical fires. Many older buildings used lamella roof systems or bowstring truss assemblies (**Figure 6.18**). These roof assemblies have a history of sudden and total collapse in fire situations.

When they were remodeled, many older buildings had heavy HVAC units added to roof systems that were not designed to support that sort of dead load. This can increase the roof assembly's collapse potential significantly. Some older buildings have had a second roof assembly added above the first one. Discussed more in Chapter 8, Vertical Ventilation, these so-called *rain roofs* can make ventilation difficult and more dangerous. Many older buildings had false ceilings installed, and this created concealed spaces where fire could burn undetected. The original wooden window frames in many older buildings were replaced with aluminum or plastic ones. A large number of older buildings have had new siding added — many with asbestos shingles (**Figure 6.19**). Others added aluminum or vinyl sid-

ing. Still others added massive metal grilles to give their exteriors a more modern look (**Figure 6.20**). These grilles add another layer of material that must be breached when gaining access through exterior windows for rescue or horizontal ventilation. The exteriors of many older buildings have been extensively changed with the addition of decorative fascia, awnings, marquees, and cornices. These modifications often added heavy overhead structures that increase the danger to firefighters from structural collapse. The exteriors of other older buildings have been refurbished using polystyrene foam covered with a weatherproof coating of a granular plastic material such as Dryvit®, USG®, and others (**Figure 6.21**). Although the polystyrene foam is flammable, these materials are extremely lightweight and represent little collapse threat to firefighters.

The net result of these modifications is that many older buildings are not as they appear from the outside. They may appear to be modern but are really

Figure 6.18 Many buildings have potentially dangerous arched roofs.

Figure 6.19 Older buildings often have asbestos shingle siding.

Figure 6.20 Many commercial buildings have installed metal grills over their exterior windows.

Figure 6.21 The exterior of many older buildings have been refurbished using polystyrene foam structures that look like masonry.

a modern shell over an older, pre-code building that may have significant fire spread and/or collapse potential. Numerous modifications may have replaced original features with newer ones made of synthetic materials, increasing the potential for highly toxic smoke being produced when these buildings burn.

For firefighters to increase the accuracy of their ventilation size-ups, they need to be aware of the modifications that have been made to older buildings in their response districts. This awareness is usually gained through a conscientiously applied, ongoing program of pre-incident planning inspections.

Newer Buildings

Even though many postwar buildings were constructed according to a building code, they may not necessarily meet current code standards. For example, some newer buildings were constructed during the Vietnam War when the majority of the available copper was reserved for the military. Therefore, many of those buildings had aluminum wiring installed, which has been identified as the probable cause of numerous structure fires.

Newer buildings also contain a greater percentage of synthetic materials than older buildings. These materials may be found in carpeting, interior doors, window frames, furniture, and interior finishes. As mentioned earlier, these materials add to the fuel load and significantly increase the amount of toxic gases produced during an interior structure fire.

Newer buildings, especially residences, are also more likely than older ones to incorporate lightweight construction materials, methods, and systems. Many newer buildings use parallel chord trusses or wooden I-beams to support floor and roof assemblies (**Figure 6.22**). Other newer buildings incorporate panelized roof systems. Many incorporate factory-assembled lightweight wooden roof trusses. These relatively new construction methods and materials generally reduce the cost of construction, but the long spans and enclosed voids increase the likelihood of early structural collapse under fire conditions.

WARNING!

Because lightweight construction can fail suddenly and unexpectedly during a fire, the IC should be notified whenever these materials are found during ventilation operations.

Figure 6.22 Floor/roof support structure typical of many newer buildings.

Features That Help

A number of building construction features are of some help to firefighters on the fireground. Generally, these features tend to resist the effects of the fire, reduce fire spread, and reduce the likelihood of structural collapse. During the size-up of a structure fire, firefighters should look for these features and factor them into their assessment of the building. Features that help firefighters are those that resist the effects of fire, reduce the likelihood of structural collapse, and those that reduce the spread of fire.

Features That Resist the Effects of Fire

Light-gauge steel framing members. Buildings that incorporate light-gauge steel framing members are far less likely to contribute to fire spread than those with traditional wooden framing (**Figure 6.23**).

Features That Reduce the Likelihood of Structural Collapse

Steel framing that is protected by drywall panels is virtually impervious to fire, and this contributes to structural integrity being maintained. Buildings that incorporate structural insulated panels (polystyrene foam sandwiched between sheets of OSB) also resist the effects of fire, and they slow the fire's spread (**Figure 6.24**). As long as these panels are intact, they help the building maintain its structural integrity.

Features That Reduce Fire Spread

Self-closing fire doors. Among the most helpful building construction features are self-closing fire doors (**Figure 6.25**). Whether activated by fusible links or by fire/smoke detection systems, these doors limit the spread of fire on any particular floor by compartmentalizing it. As long as these doors are not blocked open or otherwise prevented from operating as designed, they can be of tremendous benefit to firefighters.

Automatic sprinkler systems. Another helpful building feature is an automatic sprinkler system. When functioning properly, these systems generally keep fires in check long enough that firefighters need only do final extinguishment, salvage, and overhaul. However, automatic sprinklers can be overwhelmed by rapidly accelerating fires in certain fuels. These systems can also be rendered ineffective by anything that prevents the water from the sprinklers reaching the fire. If firefighters encounter a major fire in a fully sprinklered building, they must assume that either the system is nonfunctional or that an extremely intense fire has overwhelmed the system.

Built-in fire suppression systems. Other built-in fire suppression systems are also of help to firefighters. Flooding systems that discharge CO_2, Halon, or dry chemical agents all have generally the same capabilities as automatic sprinkler systems — but on a more limited scale (**Figure 6.26**).

Figure 6.24 Some newer structures are built with structural insulating panels.

Figure 6.23 Steel framing tends to limit fire spread, but it may fail quickly with direct flame impingement.

Figure 6.25 Self-closing fire doors are designed to limit fire spread.

These systems are usually designed to protect a single compartment within a building and not the entire building as in an automatic sprinkler system. However, the same size-up conclusions apply to compartments with built-in systems as those that have automatic sprinkler systems.

Elevator shafts. One construction feature that is common to most multistory buildings is one or more elevator shafts. Elevator shafts can be both a hindrance and help during interior fires. They can be a hindrance when they provide an avenue for fire and smoke spread from one floor to the next. On the other hand, they can also allow vertical ventilation of a fire below the top floor by providing an avenue by which smoke and hot gases can be vented through the roof without having to pass through intervening floors.

Automatic smoke vents. From a ventilation standpoint, perhaps the most helpful feature a building can have is automatic smoke vents (**Figure 6.27**). Some of these vents open when a fusible link within the vent hood releases. Others are opened automatically by smoke detectors inside the building. Still others are designed with plastic panels that melt from the heat of a fire and fall out. Ideally, buildings with panelized roof systems, or any other system that is prone to early collapse during a fire, will have automatic smoke vents. Having these vents prevents firefighters from having to walk on these sometimes unstable roof structures to perform vertical ventilation.

Features That Hinder

To effectively manage construction features that can hinder fireground operations, and which sometimes place firefighters in mortal danger, firefighters need to arm themselves with knowledge of the buildings within their districts before a fire call is received. Frequently traveling the streets and thoroughfares within the district and observing what is being done to modify buildings is time well invested for firefighters. As new construction or major modifications to existing structures are being done, firefighters should visit the sites as often as possible to identify what materials and methods are being used in these buildings. The knowledge gained could save their lives and the lives of others (**Figure 6.28**).

Figure 6.26 Flooding systems are designed to extinguish a fire or keep it in check until firefighters arrive.

Figure 6.27 A typical automatic smoke vent. *Courtesy of The Bilco Company.*

Figure 6.28 To increase their fire fighting effectiveness, firefighters need to be very familiar with their districts.

As mentioned in the preceding section, some of the construction features that help firefighters can also be a hindrance to them. Construction features that can hinder firefighters include those that don't resist effects of fire, increase fire spread, increase likelihood for structural collapse, and make firefighter entry more difficult.

Features That Increase Fire Spread

Elevator shafts. As mentioned earlier, elevator shafts can be used to vertically ventilate a building. However, they can also make fire spread from floor to floor more likely (**Figure 6.29**).

Synthetic materials. As previously mentioned, many newer buildings, and older buildings that have been extensively remodeled, contain large quantities of synthetic materials. These materials may be in structural components, trim pieces, finishes, or furnishings — or all of these (**Figure 6.30**). Regardless of how these materials are incorporated into the building, they tend to increase the rate of

fire spread and significantly increase the amount of smoke and the toxicity of the combustion products when these materials burn. For those fighting fires in these occupancies, wearing SCBA is not an option, it is an absolute necessity.

Features That Make Entry More Difficult

Planters and other landscape features. Whether installed for esthetic reasons or as antiterrorist barriers, masonry planters and similar features can keep fire apparatus some distance from a burning building (**Figure 6.31**). This can force firefighters to carry all their equipment a considerable distance from the apparatus to the building, as well as making it much more difficult for them to place ground ladders at strategic positions around the exterior of the building.

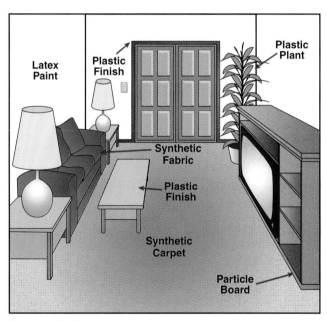

Figure 6.30 Modern buildings contain vast amounts of synthetic materials.

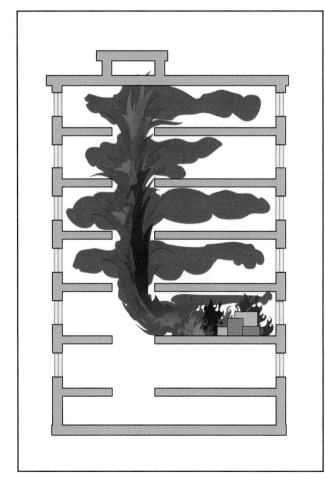

Figure 6.29 Elevator shafts can allow fire to spread from floor to floor.

Figure 6.31 Access to many public buildings is restricted by physical barriers.

Figure 6.32 Exterior metal grilles can hinder efforts to gain access during a fire.

Security doors. These features help deny access to vandals or burglars, who often start fires to destroy evidence of their crimes. Security doors also make entry by firefighters more difficult and time consuming.

Exterior metal grilles. The often elaborate installations may be decorative or installed for security reasons (**Figure 6.32**). Regardless of why they were installed, these features may hinder firefighters by making their entry more difficult and time consuming.

Features That Increase the Likelihood of Structural Collapse

Liquid tanks. A water tank added to the roof of a building to supply an automatic sprinkler system also adds considerable weight when full (**Figure 6.33**). The extra weight can greatly increase the chances of structural collapse.

Automatic sprinklers. These systems that are designed to keep small fires in check until firefighters arrive. However, they can also threaten the structural integrity of a building by adding the weight of thousands of gallons of water to the floors of the building if there is inadequate drainage.

Heavy construction features. Many buildings have masonry parapet walls, cornices, and other decorative features along the roofline. These features can greatly increase the structural collapse hazard for firefighters performing forcible entry or setting up ventilation equipment at the base of these exterior walls (**Figure 6.34**).

Figure 6.33 Water tanks and other heavy dead loads increase collapse potential.

Figure 6.34 Unsupported parapet walls have a high collapse potential.

Remodeled buildings. Buildings such as the Chinese food warehouse in Washington state that have been remodeled numerous times over the years may include structural changes that weaken floor systems, roof systems, etc. As mentioned earlier, buildings to which heavy HVAC equipment has been added to the roof may be more prone to roof collapse than before the installation.

Lightweight roof assemblies. Roof assemblies supported by unprotected steel posts can fail quickly when exposed to direct flame impingement (**Figure 6.35**).

Open- web trusses. Floor and/or roof systems that incorporate these trusses can have large open floor areas uninterrupted by posts or other vertical supports because of the strength of the trusses. However, under intense fire conditions these trusses can suddenly fail and allow the entire assembly to collapse.

Metal gusset plates (gang nails). Used to hold wooden truss components together, these light-gauge metal plates can warp under the heat of a fire and thereby lose their ability to hold the assembly together (**Figure 6.36**). This can lead to sudden and catastrophic failure of these assemblies. Therefore, some jurisdictions require that the gusset plates of factory-engineered and fabricated wooden truss roof assemblies be corner nailed or an automatic sprinkler system be installed in the attic.

Figure 6.36 Metal gusset plates can warp and fail during a fire.

Weathered buildings. Firefighters must beware of buildings that have been abandoned and exposed to the weather for an extended period. Weathering seriously diminishes the structural integrity of exposed building components.

Features Related to the Occupancy

In many cases, construction features that can either help or hinder fireground operations are directly related to the occupancy or use of the building. For example, buildings used for the manufacture of microelectronic components often contain high-voltage electrical wiring and equipment. They often store highly toxic gases in vaults, and these gases are piped through the walls to various locations within the building (**Figure 6.37**). If firefighters are unaware of these potential hazards or are unfamiliar with how to recognize them, they can inadvertently cut into the wiring or piping with catastrophic results. In addition, older industrial

Figure 6.35 Unprotected steel posts can fail early in a fire.

Figure 6.37 Some occupancies contain highly hazardous materials.

buildings may still have electrical transformers filled with polychlorinated biphenyls (PCB), a known carcinogen.

Buildings related to the electroplating industry also contain some potentially lethal features. These buildings house acid baths used to strip old finishes from metal components (**Figure 6.38**). They also have high-voltage electrical equipment and considerable quantities of hydrogen cyanide used in the plating process. An awareness of these potential hazards, where they are located, and how to deal with them can be a matter of survival for firefighters.

Figure 6.38 Electroplating operations contain some extremely hazardous materials.

Grain elevators and other commercial or industrial buildings have open pits, shafts, and chutes necessary for the type of operation normally conducted there. Some of these occupancies use huge augers to feed raw materials into crushers, choppers, or other potentially hazardous devices. While OSHA has made great strides in reducing the dangers associated with such features by requiring the installation of guardrails, lock-out/tag-out requirements, and similar safety devices, firefighters may have to enter these facilities when vision is totally obscured by heavy smoke. Firefighter survival may depend upon an awareness of the potential hazards, knowledge of the hazards' location, and how to mitigate or avoid them.

Coordination With Rescue and Fire Attack

A very important part of sizing up a ventilation situation involves coordinating the ventilation operations with other fireground operations — particularly with the rescue and fire attack operations. The ventilation operation must be coordinated with rescue and fire attack because the fire often increases in intensity when ventilation is initiated. This happens because of the inrush of oxygen-rich air replacing smoke and other fire gases that exit through ventilation openings. In most cases, charged hoselines should be in place to cover both internal exposures (uninvolved areas within the fire building) and external exposures (adjacent buildings or other combustibles) before the building is ventilated. Visibility improves as smoke and gases are expelled; therefore, rescue and suppression crews should be ready to immediately move into the building to complete their respective assignments.

Because large quantities of smoke and fire will often erupt from ventilation openings — and firefighters are trained to extinguish fire — a natural impulse for inexperienced firefighters is to use hoselines to attack the flames. However, doing so can be devastating to rescue and fire attack crews inside. Directing a hose stream into a building through a ventilation exit opening obstructs the natural flow of smoke, steam, and other gases out of the building and keeps them inside, defeating the purpose of ventilation. Visibility, which should be improving, suddenly degenerates as the natural convection currents are upset. The steam that is generated can burn the firefighters inside (even through their protective clothing). Heat again becomes trapped within the structure, and the atmosphere quickly deteriorates from tenable to untenable.

CAUTION
Never **direct hose streams into ventilation exit openings.**

Establishing and maintaining the required level of coordination demands that everyone on the fireground know and understand the incident action plan (IAP) and how the plan affects their particular part of the operation. In other words, the required coordination demands a high level of communication and cooperation. Coordinating the ventilation operation with rescue and fire attack generally involves three components: timing, location, and method.

Timing

The timing of ventilation operations can be one of the most critical aspects of the operation, both in its effectiveness and in its safety. Regardless of where ventilation openings are made, or what type of ventilation is used, if the operation is started too soon or too late, it can seriously disrupt the rescue and fire attack operations. For example, if a large ventilation opening is made before rescue and attack crews are ready to enter the building, the fire can grow and spread faster that it otherwise would because of the increased oxygen available to it. On the other hand, if creating a ventilation opening is not started until after rescue and attack crews have entered the building, they may have to endure unnecessary punishment from the heat and smoke inside until the opening is made. Therefore, the ventilation crew must get into position and be ready to make the ventilation opening as soon as forcible entry is completed and rescue and attack crews are ready to enter.

Location

Deciding where to locate the ventilation opening is often dictated by where the fire is located in the building and the extent of the fire's development. In general, the ventilation opening should be made as close to the seat of the fire as safely possible. This provides the greatest effect for the amount of resources invested. However, the most important consideration is that the ventilation opening draw the fire, heat, and smoke away from any trapped occupants. Since suppression crews should be attacking the fire from the unburned side, channeling the fire away from any occupants should also draw it away from the firefighters inside. Some of the factors that have a bearing on where to ventilate include the following:

- Location of the fire
- Location of occupants
- Interior and exterior exposures
- Type of construction
- Purpose or use of occupancy
- Extent to which the fire has progressed
- Condition of the building and its contents
- Existing openings (skylights, ventilators, monitors, etc.)
- Direction and velocity of the wind
- Available personnel and equipment

However, locating the seat of the fire may not always be easy to do. When the smoke is not readily visible, such as at night, other indicators must be used. One of the other indicators that can be used is heat. As a structure fire develops, progressively higher temperatures are produced. Unless the fire vents itself by breaking a window or burning through to the outside, these high temperatures continue to build well into the fully developed stage. Firefighters can get some indication of the intensity of the fire by feeling walls, doors, or windows for heat; by looking for discolored or blistered paint; or by using thermal imagers (**Figure 6.39**). Hot spots may indicate the location of the seat of the fire. For example, a basement fire may sometimes be located by a hot spot on the floor above it, or an attic fire may be revealed by an area of melted snow on the roof. Where an involved building is one of a connected series in a commercial block or strip mall, checking the interior walls or exterior windows of adjoining occupancies may disclose the fire's location. If interior crews find an exceptionally hot area, this can then be transmitted to the ventilation crew to help them decide where to ventilate. Knowing the exact location and severity of the fire is critical to making sound ventilation decisions.

If the fire is found to be in the attic, the ventilation opening should be made over the area of heaviest fire involvement (**Figure 6.40**). If this area is unsafe, the opening should be made between the fire and the uninvolved portion of the building in a location where firefighters will not be in jeopardy. If neither of these options is possible, a defensive tactic (such as trench/strip ventilation discussed in Chapter 8) may have to be considered.

Figure 6.39 Thermal imaging cameras can help firefighters assess fire conditions.

Figure 6.40 Vertical ventilation is often the most effective.

If the fire is one or more floors below the top floor of a multistory building, vertical ventilation may not be the best option, unless an elevator shaft or other vertical channel is available. Without an adequate vertical channel, horizontal ventilation may be indicated.

Method

Deciding on the most appropriate method of ventilation must take into consideration where to ventilate (based on the demands of the situation) and the results to be obtained from the various ventilation options. The major considerations are whether to ventilate horizontally or vertically and whether to use natural or forced ventilation. While some aspects of vertical ventilation may also apply to horizontal ventilation, ventilating a room, a floor, a cockloft, an attic, or a basement will each require somewhat different techniques. A more complete discussion of horizontal ventilation is presented in Chapter 7, and vertical ventilation is discussed in Chapter 8.

Horizontal Versus Vertical Ventilation

As described in **Essentials**, horizontal ventilation is accomplished by opening windows or doors to allow smoke to escape and fresh air to enter. Structures in which horizontal ventilation may be appropriate include the following:

- Buildings in which the fire is not large enough to necessitate opening the roof
- Buildings with windows or doors close to the seat of the fire
- Buildings in which the seat of the fire is below the top floor
- Buildings in which fire has not entered structural voids or concealed spaces

Vertical ventilation is accomplished by opening a structure at the highest point by cutting holes in roofs or by opening doors, scuttles, or skylights to allow the heat and smoke to travel upward and out of the structure. Structures in which vertical ventilation may be appropriate include the following:

- Buildings with fire in the attic, cockloft, or the top floor
- Windowless buildings with few exterior doors
- Buildings with large vertical shafts (light wells, elevators, hoistways, etc.)
- Buildings in which fire has entered structural voids or concealed spaces

Natural vs. Forced Ventilation

Ventilation efforts should be in concert with existing atmospheric conditions, taking advantage of natural ventilation whenever possible. If conditions are favorable, natural ventilation is fast and efficient because it requires no additional personnel or equipment to set up and maintain. However, in some situations natural ventilation may be inadequate and may have to be supplemented or replaced by forced ventilation to provide a tenable atmosphere for rescue and suppression operations. Forced or mechanical ventilation involves the use of fans, blowers, nozzles, or other mechanical devices to create or redirect the flow of air inside an involved space.

Using forced ventilation eliminates or reduces the effect of unstable and erratic winds on ventilation efforts. Having a reliable and controllable airflow allows for greater control of the movement of heat and smoke. Forced ventilation can channel the airborne products of combustion out of a building by the most efficient and least destructive path and allow fresh air to be reintroduced into the space. When the fire situation permits, using forced ventilation in conjunction with natural ventilation allows a tenable atmosphere to be restored faster and more efficiently than with natural ventilation alone.

Situations Requiring Forced Ventilation

Whenever natural ventilation is inadequate or inappropriate, or if other elements in the situation limit or preclude natural ventilation, forced ventilation is needed (**Figure 6.41**). Otherwise, there are no definite rules governing when forced ventilation should or should not be employed. In general, forced ventilation is indicated in the following situations:

- When the location and extent of fire has been determined

- When the type of construction is not conducive to natural ventilation

- When natural ventilation slows, becomes ineffective, and needs support

- When fire is burning below grade in structures

- When the contaminated area within a confined space is so large that natural ventilation is impractical or inefficient

Figure 6.41 When natural ventilation is inadequate, PPV may be needed.

Other Ventilation Size-Up Considerations

Other items that need to be considered in sizing up a ventilation situation are exposures, both internal and external, and the weather. Ventilation operations can be seriously affected by wind, humidity, and temperature.

Exposures

Because horizontal ventilation does not normally release heat and smoke directly above the fire, some routing of the smoke and fire gases to an exterior opening may be necessary. Firefighters must consider the threat to internal exposures that this can create. The routes by which the smoke and heated gases travel to reach the exterior openings may be the same corridors and passageways that occupants may need for egress. In horizontal ventilation, fire and heated gases are released through window openings or doorways. Consequently, there is the constant danger that they will ignite the structure above the point where they escape or that they may be drawn into windows above the ventilation opening (*lapping* or *autoexposure*) (**Figure 6.42**). There is also the danger of the vented fire and gases igniting adjacent structures or other combustibles.

Firefighters must also consider the possible threat to external exposures from ventilation efforts. Horizontal ventilation can threaten exposed buildings through radiation and/or direct flame contact. Smoke may also be drawn into adjacent buildings by their HVAC units. Vertical ventilation may also threaten nearby structures if hot brands or embers that are carried aloft by convection fall onto combustible roofs or into dry vegetation or if adjacent structures are taller than the fire building.

Weather

By their very nature, buildings are designed to resist the effects of weather. However, any opening in the building, whether man-made or caused by the fire, allows the surrounding atmosphere to affect what is happening inside the building. The most important weather-related influences on ventilation are *wind*, *humidity*, and *temperature*.

Wind

Wind conditions are always a factor in determining the proper ventilation procedure. Because of the dangers of wind blowing fire toward an external exposure, feeding oxygen to the fire, or blowing the fire into uninvolved areas of the building, problems may be encountered when using horizontal ventilation. Likewise, a strong enough wind can overpower the natural convective effect of a fire and drive the fire, smoke, and hot gases back onto those inside the building. Once again, ventilation efforts should be in concert with the prevailing wind, not against it.

Humidity

High relative humidity tends to keep the products of combustion from rising into the atmosphere, thus keeping these products at or near ground level.

Under these conditions, vertical ventilation will be more difficult, more dangerous to firefighters, more time consuming, and will almost certainly require the use of forced ventilation.

Temperature

While the atmospheric temperature usually has little direct effect on the behavior of fire within a structure, on a hot summer day it can have a profound effect on some ventilation operations. As discussed in Chapter 9, Special Ventilation Operations, atmospheric temperature can affect the neutral pressure plane in high-rise buildings. The temperature on the flat roof of a commercial building — often black or dark gray and surrounded by a parapet wall — can be significantly higher than the temperature at street level. The effects of the elevated temperature on ventilation crews, in full PPE and doing very strenuous work, must be considered. The crews are at risk of heat exhaustion or even heatstroke, and their productivity will be reduced because of fatigue and dehydration. Fatigue and dehydration can delay the completion of the firefighters' assignments and will require earlier and more frequent rest breaks and/or crew reliefs (**Figure 6.43**).

Cold atmospheric temperatures, and the conditions they produce, may also affect ventilation operations. In winter, snow and ice accumulations on the roofs of buildings can increase live loads, conceal potential hazards, and delay the completion of vertical ventilation operations. The

Figure 6.42 Horizontal ventilation above the fire floor may allow fire to enter that floor.

Figure 6.43 In very hot weather, firefighters may need earlier and more frequent relief.

Figure 6.44 Snow or ice on a roof greatly increases the slip hazard for firefighters. *Courtesy of Peter Sells.*

dangers to firefighters may also be increased due to poor footing on wet or icy roofs (**Figure 6.44**).

Summary

For firefighters to effectively size up a ventilation situation in a burning building, they must have at least a basic understanding of how fire, smoke, and fire gases behave under a variety of fire and environmental conditions. They must understand how the construction of the burning building may affect the ventilation process. Finally, they must understand the effects that ventilation may have on the fire situation and know how to coordinate the ventilation efforts with rescue and fire attack operations.

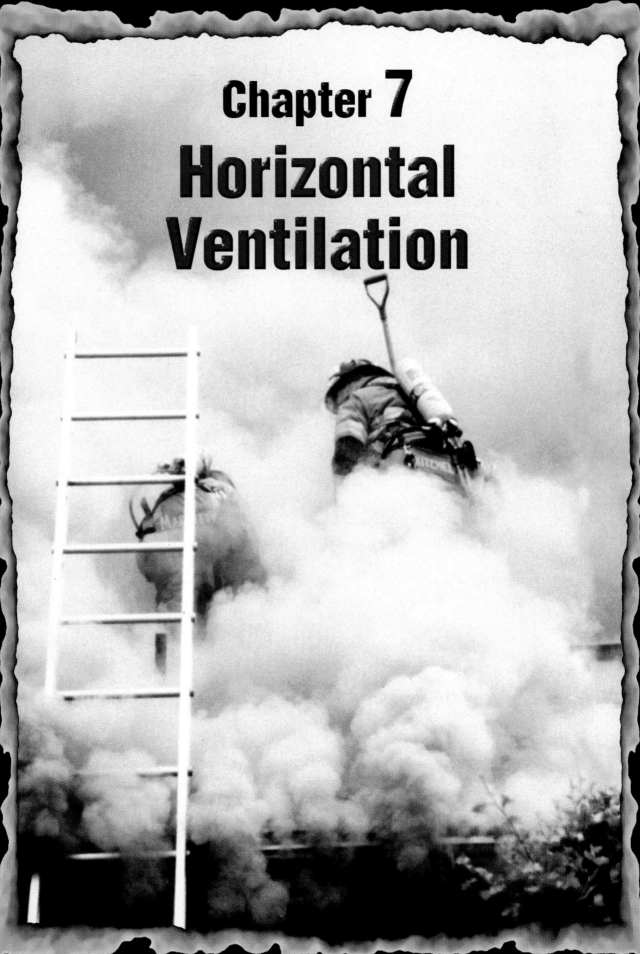

Chapter 7
Horizontal Ventilation

Chapter 7
Horizontal Ventilation

Horizontal ventilation is the most frequently used form of ventilation because most fires in buildings are small nuisance fires that do little damage and produce more smoke than fire. These situations may only require that the windows and doors of the affected occupancy be opened to allow the residual smoke to be ventilated. Also, firefighters entering a building for search and rescue or fire attack start a form of horizontal ventilation by opening doors or windows to make entry. Other fire situations, such as working fires below the top floor of multistory buildings, may also lend themselves to horizontal ventilation.

However, just as horizontal ventilation can help reduce fire loss, it can also increase it by helping to spread the fire. Windows that are opened to allow heat and smoke out of a burning building can also allow the fire to spread to adjacent buildings, or the open windows may allow the fire to lap upward into uninvolved floors of the building of origin. Fire issuing from an open window can also spread into the attic through vents under the eaves of the building.

This chapter reviews the tools and equipment needed to initiate horizontal ventilation, as well as the construction of walls and horizontal openings. The importance of establishing and supporting horizontal ventilation and the techniques involved in natural and forced horizontal ventilation are also discussed.

Horizontal Ventilation Tools and Equipment

Under the right conditions, practically every forcible entry tool described in **Essentials** can be applied to horizontal ventilation. In the removal or opening of doors, windows, or other barriers, axes and more specialized prying and cutting tools may be required.

Ventilation Tools

Bolt cutters or rotary saws may be needed for removing locks and security bars. Pike poles, ceiling hooks, and other tools may be used for breaking windows. As described in Chapter 4, Access Into Structures, openings in metal walls can be cut with axes, rotary saws, or air chisels. Openings in roll-up doors are most often made with rotary saws.

It is important that firefighters know the limitations of the available ventilation tools as well as how to use and maintain them for maximum safety and efficiency. Using a tool for something other than its intended purpose can needlessly endanger firefighters and damage the tool. Regular preventive maintenance of ventilation tools improves their performance and maximizes their safety.

Ventilation Equipment

The mechanical devices necessary to supplement or alter the natural airflow in a structure or other confined space can take several different forms. Some of this equipment, such as smoke ejectors and blowers, are very familiar to most firefighters. Other devices, such as HVAC systems, may be less familiar and will require further investigation and study. These devices and systems have led to greater efficiency and versatility, enabling firefighters to accomplish ventilation operations more rapidly than ever before. In addition, accessories, such as flexible ducts, stacking and hanging devices, and other support systems allow for flexibility in the placement of smoke ejectors.

The development of blowers has added another major option to ventilation equipment and techniques. Set up just outside the building to create a slight positive pressure within, these units can make a significant contribution to a fire department's horizontal ventilation capabilities.

NOTE: For purposes of clarity, in this manual the term *ejector* refers to any device positioned within the space or in the exit opening to *expel* contaminated air from the space (**Figure 7.1**). The term *blower* refers to any device positioned outside of a space to blow in fresh air to create a slight positive pressure within (**Figure 7.2**). The term *fan* will be used interchangeably with blower and ejector.

Figure 7.2 A typical smoke blower.

Fans

Fans can be driven by electric motors, gasoline-powered engines, or water (hydraulic) pressure (**Figure 7.3**). Each type has advantages and disadvantages. For example, those driven by electric motors are quieter than those driven by gasoline engines, and they do not contaminate the air with exhaust smoke. However, those driven by gasoline engines may move a greater volume of air than do electric fans. Those driven by hydraulic pressure can add water damage to the loss if they leak.

Flexible Ducts

The flexible ducting that some departments use for ventilation is similar to but larger than that used by utility workers when they are required to work in confined spaces, especially in spaces that are below grade. The ducting consists of a treated fabric tube (usually yellow in color) over a continuous steel

Figure 7.1 A typical electric smoke ejector. *Courtesy of Super Vac.*

Figure 7.3 A water-driven smoke blower. *Courtesy of Ramfan Corp.*

coil that provides support and keeps the duct open throughout its length (**Figure 7.4**). Because it is supported by the steel coil, this ducting can be used in either PPV or NPV operations (**Figure 7.5**). This type of ducting is available in a variety of sizes.

Other departments use flexible ducting that is up to 24 inches (10 cm) in diameter, and is made of smooth, translucent plastic (**Figure 7.6**). This ducting has no steel reinforcement and is kept open by the pressure of the air being forced through it. To expel smoke from a compartment an electrically driven blower must be positioned inside the com-

Figure 7.6 An exhaust bracket keeps smoothbore ducting open during operation. *Courtesy of Tempest Technology.*

partment (**Figure 7.7**). If an electric blower is not available, the blower must be positioned outside of the building or compartment and the duct deployed to in the innermost portion of the compartment (**Figure 7.8**). However, because this ducting is larger and has a smooth inner surface, there is less friction loss that with conventional ducting. With less friction loss to overcome, a considerably larger volume of air or smoke can be blown through this ducting.

Because of the amount of time involved in setting up flexible duct ventilation systems, this technique is usually not appropriate as part of an

Figure 7.4 Ducting can be used to ventilate a confined space.

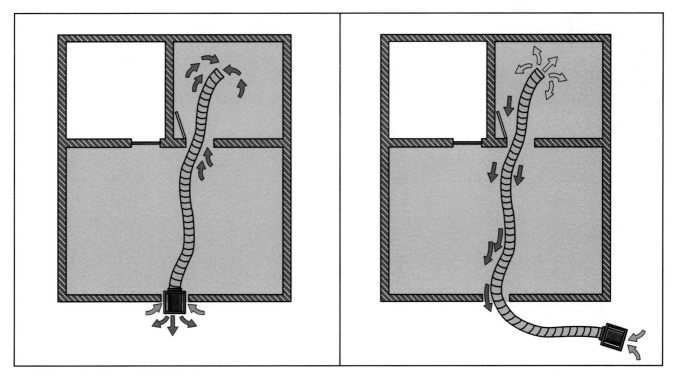

Figure 7.5 Flexible ducting can be used in both NPV and PPV operations.

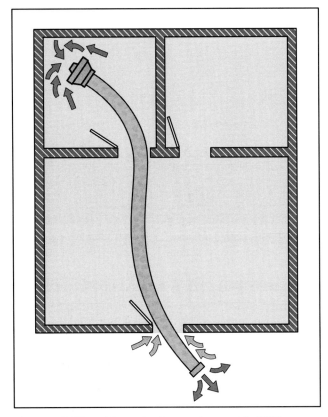

Figure 7.7 Smoothbore ducting can be used in NPV operations.

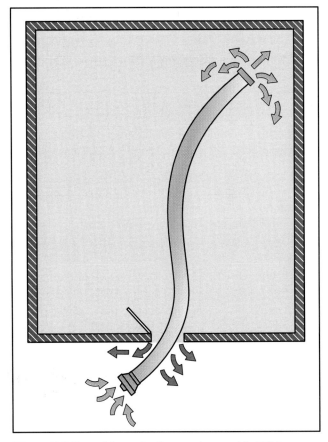

Figure 7.8 Smoothbore ducting can be used in PPV operations.

initial fire attack. However, after a fire has been knocked down, using these devices to move cold smoke and/or other airborne contaminants to the outside can be very effective. Using flexible ducts in this way allows smoke and gases to be channeled through a building without contaminating it. For example, with a fan and flexible duct combination, an exhaust line can channel smoke down a hallway, through a room, or through an entire building without causing smoke damage or contamination (**Figure 7.9**). Being able to channel smoke or gases through a flexible duct to the outside without contaminating other areas is particularly useful in shopping malls where there are many unrelated occupancies and in hospitals, schools, or office buildings.

Using flexible ducting, two or more smoke ejectors can be coupled together to ventilate smoke from basements, attics, suspended ceilings, and other confined spaces. Also, ducting can provide fresh air for rescue crews involved in long-term confined space operations such as in utility vaults, sanitary sewers, silos, and other hostile environments.

When using negative-pressure ventilation, it is important to remember that replacement air must be brought into the area from which contaminants

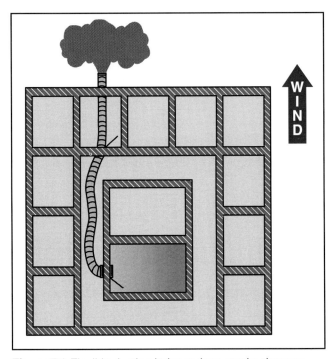

Figure 7.9 Flexible ducting helps reduce smoke damage.

are being expelled. This can be difficult when ventilating areas that have only one relatively small opening for exhaust and replacement air. However, by providing the replacement air (positively) via a flexible duct to the most distant part of the compartment, it is possible to exhaust the contaminants and bring replacement air through the same doorway or access opening (**Figure 7.10**).

Using the ejector/flexible duct combination is also an excellent method of ventilating areas below grade. It works well for removing heavier-than-air gases that settle near the floor and in low areas. A smoke ejector can be positioned at ground level or above, with the flexible duct running through a window or down a stairway or elevator shaft into the basement (**Figure 7.11**). Replacement air can be channeled through the same opening in which the fan is located or through other available openings. Because of the hazards associated with heavier-than-air gases and/or oxygen deficiency, it is important to remember that even with replacement air being supplied, personnel working below grade should be constantly monitored.

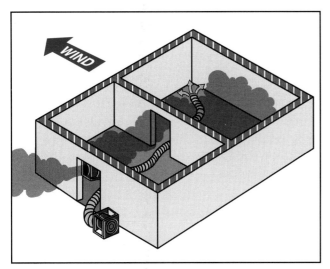

Figure 7.10 Using PPV to provide replacement air during an NPV ventilation operation.

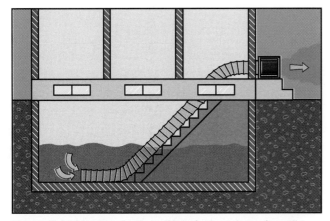

Figure 7.11 Flexible ducting allows for a variety of ventilation operations.

Building Construction Related to Horizontal Ventilation

As discussed in earlier chapters, having a working knowledge of standard construction methods and materials will help firefighters to create ventilation openings for horizontal ventilation safely and efficiently. The construction practices described in this section are those in general use across North America but may not be typical of those used in some local areas. Firefighters should use pre-incident planning inspections to become familiar with the construction practices used in their particular areas.

The following sections discuss the most common construction features that firefighters may have to breach during horizontal ventilation. These construction features are walls, windows, and doors.

Walls

To create horizontal ventilation openings in walls safely and efficiently, firefighters need to be familiar with the types of walls present in their response districts, and with the types of walls in specific target hazards. This familiarity can only be obtained through an ongoing program of pre-incident planning inspections. The following section discusses some of the most common types of walls that firefighters may have to breach for horizontal ventilation—stem walls, interior firewalls, and exterior walls.

Stem Walls

Many modern buildings have continuous foundations of concrete, although older structures may have brick or stone foundations. The stem wall, located between the foundation and the first floor, may extend well above the ground if the building occupies a sloping site (**Figure 7.12**). A high stem wall may make it necessary for firefighters to work from ladders when creating openings in walls for horizontal ventilation.

Figure 7.12 A typical stem wall.

Interior Fire Walls

Fire walls are rated assemblies designed to reduce the likelihood of horizontal fire spread by compartmentalizing a building with fire-resistive separations. Fire walls are constructed of masonry or of a specified thickness of gypsum board (drywall) over a wood or metal frame. They must extend the entire width of the building and, in most cases, extend up to and above combustible roofs (**Figure 7.13**). If these walls have been penetrated with unprotected openings, fire may pass through these openings, requiring ventilation to be performed on both sides of the wall.

The potential for flammable fire gases to accumulate on the uninvolved side of a fire wall in an attic or cockloft emphasizes the need for early and effective ventilation of these areas. Otherwise, these gases may accumulate, unknown to the firefighter, until they reach a source of ignition. Depending on the availability of oxygen within the space, the ignition of these gases may result in a fire with explosive force.

Figure 7.13 A typical exterior fire wall.

Generally, fire walls should not be breached for ventilation purposes. Holes in fire walls can provide additional oxygen to the fire and/or provide a path of travel for heat, smoke, and fire gases. Drafts created by the holes may also draw the fire toward the openings because of the availability of oxygen at the openings and on the other side of the wall.

Exterior Walls

As described in earlier chapters, to protect a building from the elements and to support its roof structure, most buildings have substantial exterior walls. Exterior walls may be masonry, masonry or other veneer over frame, or metal.

Masonry and Concrete Walls. Exterior masonry walls usually range from 8 to 12 inches (20 cm to 30 cm) or more in thickness, depending upon the material used. The walls may be of reinforced concrete (poured in place, tilt-up, or precast panel), concrete block, or unreinforced masonry of brick, or stone (**Figure 7.14**). Windowless masonry/concrete walls, regardless of the specific material, are formidable barriers that are so difficult and time consuming to penetrate that they are rarely breached for ventilation purposes. If they must be breached, for

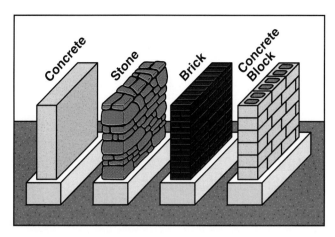

Figure 7.14 The various types of masonry walls.

whatever purpose, heavy-duty power equipment such as electric or pneumatic jackhammers should be used.

Veneer-Over-Frame Walls. These walls are essentially frame walls in which the 2- × 4-inch or 2- × 6-inch (50 mm by 100 mm or 50 mm by 150 mm) wood or metal studs are covered with a layer of plywood or oriented strand board (OSB) for shear strength. One layer of brick or stone (real or imitation) is added to the exterior and/or interior surface to give the appearance of a solid brick or stone wall (**Figure 7.15**). A veneer of stucco may be applied over a gypsum board base or over chicken wire and tar paper directly over the studs. In some areas, exterior plywood siding is nailed directly to the studs because this provides the required shear strength and the exterior finish in one layer (**Figure 7.16**). As described in Chapter 6, Ventilation Size-Up, some buildings have a veneer of polystyrene plastic foam applied to the outside for aesthetic purposes. This foam veneer may be blocks or sheets as much as a foot (30 cm) thick. After the foam is applied to the wall, it is sealed against the weather with a granular finish, giving the appearance of a solid masonry wall (**Figure 7.17**). These walls can be recognized by the hollow sound they make when tapped with a tool.

Unlike solid masonry walls, veneer-over-frame walls are much easier to breach with conventional forcible entry tools. Many of the same techniques used to strip roof coverings from a roof can be applied to the veneer covering of exterior walls. For example, if a windowless building with a stucco or plywood veneer must be breached for horizontal ventilation, the wall can be sounded with a tool to

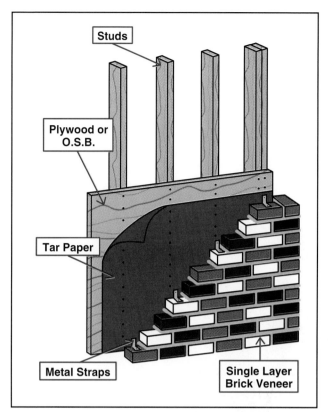

Figure 7.15 The most typical way that masonry veneer is used in building construction.

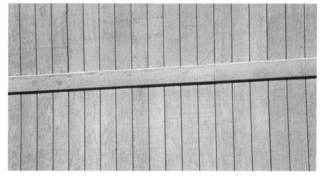

Figure 7.16 Typical plywood siding on a building.

Figure 7.17 Some buildings have a veneer of polystyrene foam that looks like masonry.

locate the studs, the perimeter of the opening cut with an axe or power saw, and the veneer stripped away with axes or rubbish hooks. Likewise, a rotary saw equipped with a masonry blade can quickly cut through a brick or imitation stone veneer to allow the veneer to be stripped away (**Figure 7.18**). Masonry veneer can also be breached with sledgehammers or battering rams, although this is a slow process.

Figure 7.18 Masonry walls can be cut with a rotary saw.

CAUTION
Breaching walls that are covered by brick or stone veneer may expose gas lines or electrical wiring inside the walls.

Tall masonry veneer walls can present a substantial collapse potential because of the way some of them are attached to the studs. Some veneers, such as brick or stone (real or imitation), are attached to the studs with thin, corrugated sheet-metal straps (**Figure 7.19**). On a concrete block wall, one end of the strip is embedded in the mortar joint between the blocks and the other end in the mortar joints between the bricks or stones. On a wood frame wall, one end of each strap is nailed or screwed to a stud, and the other end is embedded in the mortar joint between the bricks or stones. Under fire conditions, these straps can fail because they pull out or because they snap when weakened by the heat of the fire. Firefighters should keep this potential collapse hazard in mind during breaching operations.

Figure 7.19 Thin metal straps hold the veneer to the wall.

Metal Walls. The exterior walls of metal buildings are usually of light-gauge sheet metal formed into rectangular panels that are applied vertically over a wood or metal frame. They may be nailed to wooden members or attached to a metal frame with screws. Some metal walls are merely *curtain walls* attached to a rigid structural steel frame. In this application, there usually are no studs in the exterior wall, only lightweight horizontal members between the heavy steel pillars (**Figure 7.20**). These walls are easily cut with conventional hand or power tools, and they lend themselves to being cut open as are some metal roll-up doors. In some cases, the panels can be removed quickly using an electric screwdriver.

Figure 7.20 A typical all-metal building.

Windows
For horizontal ventilation purposes, windows are some of the best means of creating the necessary exterior openings. Even when the windows cannot be opened, the panes may be broken out quickly and with relative ease. If the frame is undamaged, the cost of replacing the broken glass is usually, but not always, less than the cost of repairing damaged doors or walls. However, leaded glass windows, es-

pecially large, stained-glass church windows are sometimes priceless works of art that should be protected if at all possible.

A wide variety of windows exist in both new and old buildings in most communities. As described in Chapter 4, Access Into Structures, the most common types are fixed windows, single- and double-hung windows, casement windows, horizontal-sliding windows, awning windows, jalousie windows, projected windows, hopper windows, and energy-efficient windows. For photos or illustrations of these types of windows, refer to the IFSTA **Essentials of Fire Fighting** manual.

Fixed Windows

As the name implies, a fixed window does not open but has a permanently glazed pane(s) set in a wooden, vinyl, or metal frame. They range from small, sometimes irregularly shaped windows to large picture windows. Fixed windows are often flanked by double-hung or casement windows or are stacked with awning or hopper windows that can be opened.

Single- and Double-Hung Windows

Single-hung windows have one movable section and in double-hung windows, both halves are movable. In both cases, only half of the window area is available for ventilation unless the panes are broken out.

Casement Windows

These windows have one or two side-hinged, outward-swinging sashes, and the screens are on the inside. Double-casement windows may be separated by a fixed pane or simply by a vertical post called a *mullion*. The entire window area is available for ventilation when open.

Horizontal-Sliding Windows

These windows have two or more sashes, one of which is fixed and the other(s) movable. From the inside, the movable sash can often be lifted out of the frame without damaging the window. In most designs, half of the window area is available for ventilation without breaking the panes.

Awning Windows

These windows have one or more top-hinged, outward-swinging sashes. Single- awning windows are often combined with a fixed sash in a larger unit. All the openable area is available for ventilation.

Jalousie Windows

These windows consist of narrow horizontal panes of glass set in pivoting brackets at each end. The panes overlap in a shingle-like fashion. They are very difficult to open from the outside without breaking the panes. When open, they offer the entire area for ventilation.

Projected Windows

These windows, also known as *factory windows*, may be hinged at the top or bottom and may swing inward or outward. All the openable area is available for ventilation.

Hopper Windows

These windows have bottom-hinged, inward-swinging sashes. They are often just awning windows that have been installed upside down. Like awning windows, hopper windows offer all the openable area for ventilation.

Energy-Efficient Windows

Some energy-efficient windows are double- or triple-glazed. Regardless of how many panes are in each window, there is always a space between the panes (**Figure 7.21**). This space is usually filled with air, but may be filled with argon or some other inert gas. Although there are several brands of energy-efficient windows, they are commonly referred to

Figure 7.21 This cutaway shows the space between the panes of energy-efficient windows.

as *thermal* windows. While these windows offer some additional protection from an exposure fire, they also present some disadvantages for firefighters. Because of their superior insulating properties, thermal windows hold in more heat than conventional windows. This can delay the fire being seen by passersby, accelerate the development of flashover conditions, and increase the likelihood of backdraft conditions developing.

There are other specialized windows designed for very specific applications. Regardless of the design or application, windows that resist opening from the outside usually can and should be broken out when a horizontal ventilation opening is needed. However, many newer windows are glazed with or constructed entirely of Lexan® or other extremely resilient plastics. As also discussed in Chapter 4, these windows are very difficult to break. In these situations, removing the entire frame with the window intact may be quicker and more efficient for ventilation purposes (**Figure 7.22**).

One additional aspect of window construction must also be considered — security measures. Because a tool can be inserted between the bars of many security devices and still break the glass, these devices are more of a problem for forcible entry than for ventilation. However, windows covered with heavy-gauge screen may not even allow a tool to pass through, and the screen will have to be removed if that window is to be opened for horizontal ventilation.

Figure 7.22 In some cases it is faster to simply remove the entire window assembly.

Doors

Doors present the same sorts of problems for ventilation as for forcible entry, but they also provide opportunities to make horizontal ventilation very effective. Doorway openings are often larger than many window openings. So, for the same investment of time and effort, opening a door often results in a bigger and therefore, more effective ventilation opening.

Regardless of its design or location, a door opened for ventilation purposes should be blocked open or removed from the frame (**Figure 7.23**). Opening or removing the door from the frame prevents the door from being closed inadvertently during the ventilation operation, which could have serious consequences.

Figure 7.23 Penthouse (bulkhead) doors should be blocked open when used for ventilation.

In most cities and towns, the variety of windows in the community is rivaled only by the variety of doors. The most common types of exterior doors used for ventilation purposes are the swinging door, the sliding door, and several different types of roll-up doors. Also of importance to horizontal ventilation are the various types of interior fire doors. Described in the following sections are the construction features of the types of doors that are the most useful for horizontal ventilation. For a more complete discussion of doors and any other aspect of building construction, refer to the IFSTA **Building Construction Related to the Fire Service** manual.

Swinging Doors

In addition to the standard types of swinging doors described in **Essentials**, some residential occupancies, care facilities, and hospitals have self-closing, rated fire doors in the interior hallways (**Figure 7.24**). These doors may be held open by fusible links as described earlier for sliding fire doors, or they may be held open by electromagnets connected to the fire detection system. When the system is activated by either heat or smoke, the power to the electromagnets is interrupted and that releases the doors allowing them to close. Such systems are designed to compartmentalize a building and thereby confine a fire to its area of origin.

Figure 7.25 A typical commercial sliding door.

Figure 7.24 One of many types of self-closing fire doors.

Sliding Doors

From the standpoint of horizontal ventilation, the two most important types of sliding doors are exterior sliding doors and interior sliding fire doors. Exterior sliding doors are most common on storage, commercial, industrial, or agricultural buildings. They are generally suspended from a horizontal track on the exterior wall of the building (**Figure 7.25**). Most doors of this type are manually pushed open or closed. Because the track is level, these doors will usually remain in the position in which they were left, so blocking them open is usually not necessary. These doors are usually metal or metal clad. They have a variety of locking mechanisms but often just a hasp and padlock. Because these doors usually cover relatively large openings, they can be very advantageous for ventilation. The other common type of exterior sliding door is the framed-glass sliding door most often found in residential units (**Figure 7.26**).

Figure 7.26 A residential sliding glass door.

The sliding type of interior fire door is a metal-clad rated assembly that is suspended from a slanting track attached to the surface of a rated firewall (**Figure 7.27**). In high-traffic areas where it would be impractical to continually open and close a fire door, the door is held in the open position by a cable connected to a fusible link at the top of the doorway opening. When the heat of a fire passes through the doorway, the link fuses and separates to release the cable. Gravity then rolls the door into position, closing off the opening. Because the track is slanted, once the door rolls into the closed position it will remain closed unless manually opened. Before fire doors are reopened, firefighters must make sure that there is no longer any danger of fire spread through that doorway.

These doors may also represent a hazard to firefighters working within a building. The heat of a fire may cause the door to activate and close behind them, thereby cutting off one (and perhaps their only) escape route. The door may also close on a hoseline and restrict or stop its flow. Therefore, these doors should be blocked open with a pike pole or other suitable tool. Because they are intended to stay in place once activated, these doors tend to be quite heavy and may be very difficult to push back up the track, especially if obstructed by fallen debris.

Overhead-Type Doors

These doors also come in a variety of types and styles. They vary from wooden slab doors or lightweight wooden or metal sectional doors (typical of residential garage doors) to heavy-duty service doors used in commercial and industrial occupancies (**Figure 7.28**). Some of the heavy-duty doors are also rated fire doors, held in the open position by fusible links as described previously. The same safety precautions apply.

Roll-Up Doors

From a ventilation standpoint, roll-up doors are sometimes a problem because they can be difficult to force open. In addition to the time involved in forcing these doors, the door components may be bent in the process, and the door may not open

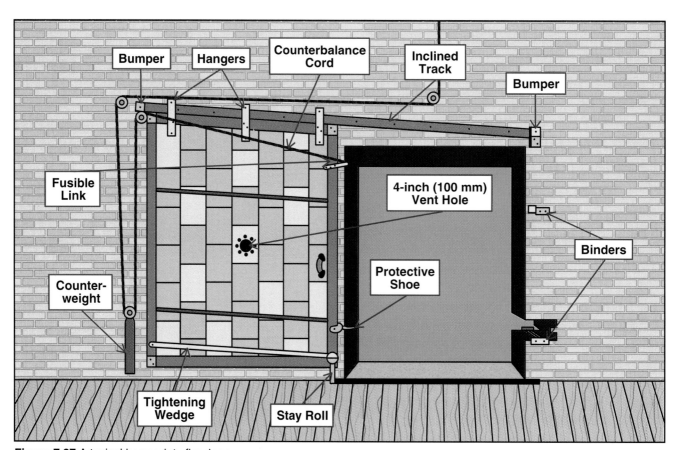

Figure 7.27 A typical heavy-duty fire door.

Figure 7.28 A typical commercial roll-up door.

fully because of the distorted metal. As described in Chapter 4, if a triangular or other type of cut is made in the door, which may be faster than forcing the door, the size of the opening will be smaller than the door being fully open (**Figure 7.29**). This smaller opening will obviously reduce the volume of airflow compared to that available with the fully open door, so this opening should be used to gain access to the interior where the regular door-opening mechanism can be used. As also mentioned in Chapter 4, roll-up doors often have a conventional pedestrian door adjacent to them. If so, it is sometimes easier to enter through this door and open the roll-up door from the inside.

Telescoping Doors

As discussed in Chapter 4, telescoping doors have characteristics in common with other large service doors, but they also have certain unique features. The most significant difference between telescoping doors and other types of service doors is that telescoping doors consist of two layers (skins) separated by at least two inches (5 cm) of air space. From the bottom of the door, the space between the inner and outer skins becomes progressively larger toward the top of the door (**Figure 7.30**). Depending upon the size of the door, the space between the inner and outer skin can be more than 13 inches (33 cm). The techniques described in Chapter 4 can be used to open telescoping doors for horizontal ventilation.

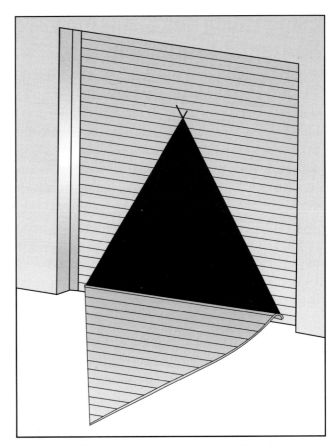

Figure 7.29 A triangular cut produces a relatively small opening.

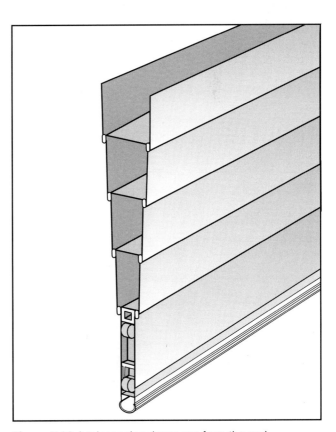

Figure 7.30 A telescoping door seen from the end.

Establishing and Supporting Horizontal Ventilation

A form of horizontal ventilation is often started when firefighters make entry into a building for search and rescue and/or fire fighting (**Figure 7.31**). Ideally, however, establishing horizontal ventilation will result from a more conscious decision and from a more deliberate act. While wind intensity and direction are always factors, the most important factors in deciding where to make the initial ventilation opening are that the exit opening be made as close to the seat of the fire as possible and that it be opposite the point from which attack lines will advance (**Figure 7.32**). If ventilation is attempted without knowledge of the location and extent of the fire and the arrangement of rooms and partitions in the building, uninvolved portions of the building (and any occupants) may be jeopardized.

Just as structure fires should be attacked from the unburned side to avoid spreading the fire into uninvolved areas, horizontal ventilation should also be initiated at a point that will limit fire spread.

Under ideal conditions, an exit opening should first be made on the leeward side of the building, immediately followed by an interior attack from the windward side. However, if the seat of the fire is on the windward side of the building, creating an opening on the windward side (closest to the seat of the fire) will tend to spread the fire throughout the building (**Figure 7.33**). Under these conditions, it may be possible to counteract the effects of an adverse prevailing wind by pressurizing the building from the leeward side before creating an exit opening on the windward side (**Figure 7.34**).

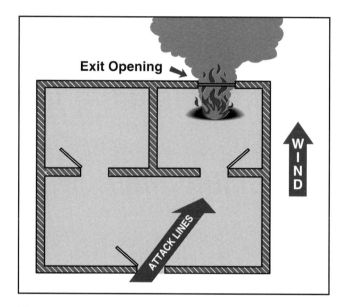

Figure 7.32 Whenever possible, the ventilation opening should be close to the seat of the fire.

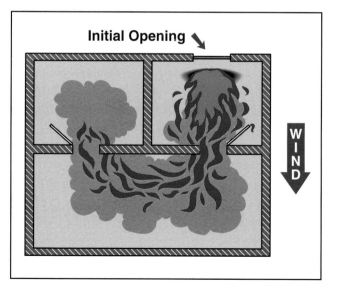

Figure 7.33 If the seat of the fire is at the windward end of the burning building, the wind may spread the fire throughout the structure.

Figure 7.31 Firefighters start horizontal ventilation when they enter a burning building.

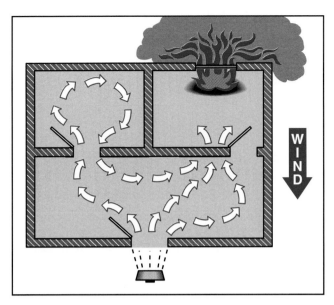

Figure 7.34 Aggressive PPV can sometimes overcome an adverse wind.

Precautions Against Upsetting Established Horizontal Ventilation

Firefighters should be careful not to block or close openings that channel fresh air into the area that is being ventilated. Established ventilation may also be upset if additional openings are made that redirect the air currents intended for ventilating the area. Some things that can upset established horizontal ventilation are as follows:

Improper Application of Ventilation
If ventilation is improperly applied, such as by starting the operation before attack lines are ready to be

taken into the building, the fire can be intensified and can spread to uninvolved areas of the building (**Figure 7.35**).

Inadequate Control of Exit Openings
Effective horizontal ventilation can be rendered ineffective by crews arbitrarily opening windows without being ordered to do so. To be effective, a proper balance between the volume of air being introduced and the size of the exit opening must be maintained (**Figure 7.36**).

Improperly Located Exit Opening
If the exit opening is improperly located so that heat and smoke are drawn into uninvolved portions of

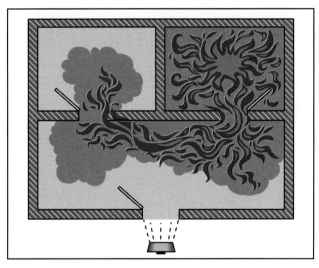

Figure 7.35 Ventilating too soon can spread the fire within the building.

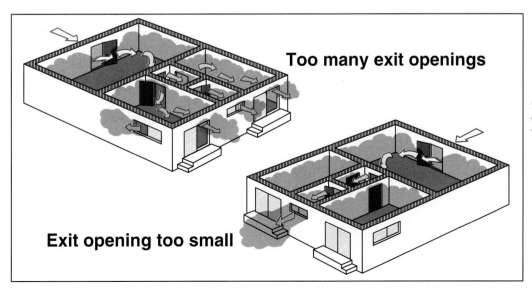

Too many exit openings

Exit opening too small

Figure 7.36 Exit openings must be controlled if ventilation is to be most effective.

the building, escape routes may be denied to occupants, attack crews may be subjected to unnecessary punishment, and fire damage may be increased (**Figure 7.37**).

Improperly Directed Fire Streams

If fire streams are directed into ventilation exit openings, whether horizontal or vertical, the results can be disastrous (**Figure 7.38**). Natural convection currents can be reversed, causing mushrooming within the structure. Also, the additional steam generated can injure and/or drive interior crews from the building.

Improper Placement of Salvaged Contents

If large piles of furniture or other contents are stacked in the wrong location during loss control operations, they can have a detrimental effect on ventilation efforts. Contents stacked in hallways or too near doorways or windows can impede the flow of air into and out of the structure. This can reduce the effectiveness of natural or forced ventilation, whether horizontal or vertical (**Figure 7.39**).

Obstructions to Horizontal Ventilation

Even when firefighters make good decisions about where, when, and how to ventilate a building, factors within the building can significantly reduce the effectiveness of the ventilation operation. Such things as the layout of the building and how the contents are arranged can create impediments to effective ventilation. Under adverse conditions, the wind can hinder the ventilation process as much as it can help it under more favorable conditions. Even firefighters standing in open doorways can affect airflow unfavorably.

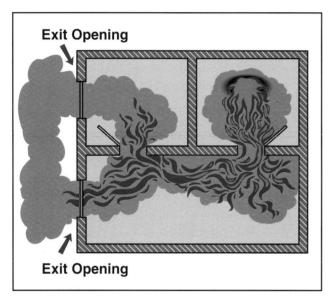

Figure 7.37 Improperly located exit openings can adversely affect ventilation efforts.

Figure 7.38 Fire streams should never be directed into ventilation exit openings.

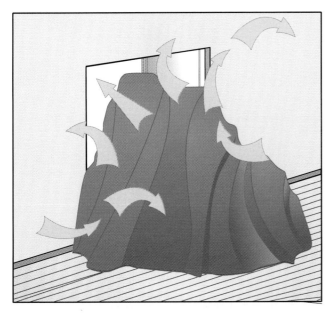

Figure 7.39 Salvaged goods stacked in front of openings can seriously impede airflow.

Building Construction and Contents

Even though a building may have become completely filled with smoke that has seeped through cracks and ventilator openings, horizontal ventilation can be obstructed by walls, partitions, closed doors, and stacks of stored material (**Figure 7.40**). If buildings contain a large number of rooms or are heavily loaded with contents, they may be very difficult to ventilate horizontally because of poor air circulation.

Wind

Under ideal circumstances, the wind can provide all the air circulation necessary for effective horizontal ventilation. Opening the structure on the windward side and ventilating on the leeward side often works very well. However, as mentioned earlier, if the seat of the fire is on the windward side of the building, the wind would tend to spread the fire into uninvolved areas (**Figure 7.41**).

Depending on the size and efficiency of the blower(s) used, winds of up to 25 mph (40 km/h) may be overcome with positive-pressure ventilation (**Figure 7.42**). With higher wind speeds and if vertical ventilation is impractical or impossible, delaying ventilation until after the fire is knocked down may be the only available option. If ventilation is to be delayed, firefighters must be aware of the danger of a rollover and should stay as low as possible when approaching and attacking the fire.

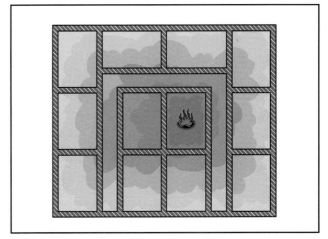

Figure 7.40 Interior walls and closed doors can also impede ventilation efforts.

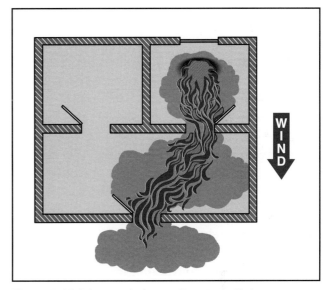

Figure 7.41 Adverse winds can disrupt ventilation operations and spread the fire.

Figure 7.42 PPV can overcome adverse winds of up to 25 mph (40 km/h).

Natural Horizontal Ventilation

Of all the various methods of ventilating structures, natural horizontal ventilation is by far the most often used. Unaided by any mechanical means, this method depends entirely on the buoyancy of the smoke, the prevailing wind, and the layout and design of the building. Natural horizontal ventilation is most often done through existing openings such as doors and windows.

Doors

Both exterior and interior doors can play an important role in horizontal ventilation. Because exterior doors are the most likely points of entry for search and rescue or fire attack, they may become part of the ventilation operation whether intentional or not. They may have to be forced before they can be opened for ventilation or entry, and this can sometimes be a frustrating and time-consuming task. The doors may be metal clad, have heavy security bars, or be otherwise reinforced for security purposes. If metal roll-up doors resist being forced open, cutting a large hole in them may be the only choice. However, before any door is forced, the old rule of *"try before you pry"* should always be followed.

If a door that has been opened for ventilation should suddenly close for any reason during a critical phase of the operation, the dynamics of the operation could change dramatically, perhaps endangering occupants and/or firefighters. Therefore, whenever any swinging door is opened for ventilation purposes, whether for natural or forced ventilation, the opening should be maintained by blocking the door open with wooden or rubber doorstops, pieces of furniture, or special hinge hooks (**Figure 7.43**). Or the door can be removed from its hinges (**Figure 7.44**).

Interior doors should be opened or closed in order to accomplish the objectives specified in the IAP. Doors will have to be opened to facilitate searching each room, but if there are open windows in the room, opening the door may have a detrimental effect on the ventilation airflow. It is good practice to mark interior doors and leave them closed after each room has been searched. For ventilation purposes, interior doors may be opened and closed one by one in a systematic process of ventilating an entire floor (**Figure 7.45**).

Figure 7.43 A hinge hook prevents a door from swinging shut.

Figure 7.44 If a bulkhead door cannot be locked open, it should be removed from its hinges.

Windows

When any window is opened for the purpose of ventilation, screens, curtains, drapes, or blinds should be removed because they will hinder airflow (**Figure 7.46**). If the seat of the fire is on the leeward side of the building, the correct procedure for ventilating horizontally (cross ventilation) is to first open the top windows on the leeward side, allowing the superheated gases to escape. The next step is to then open the lower windows on the windward side to introduce replacement air into the building (**Figure 7.47**). If the seat of the fire is on the windward side, natural horizontal ventilation probably will not work. In that case, before an exit opening is

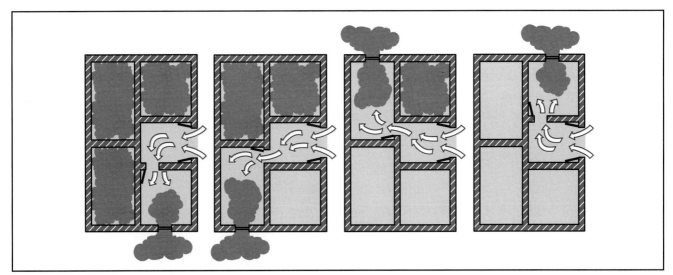

Figure 7.45 Opening and closing interior doors at the proper time can help clear a building of smoke.

Figure 7.46 To aid the ventilation of a room, the window coverings should be removed.

created on the windward side, the building should be pressurized as discussed in the next section on forced horizontal ventilation. If the building cannot be pressurized, opening windows on the windward side should be delayed until after initial knockdown of the fire.

Breaking Windows

Before breaking any window, try to open it first. If it is necessary to break the window, break out the

Figure 7.47 Opening windows at the top on the lee side and at the bottom on the windward side of a building helps natural horizontal ventilation.

entire pane and clear the sash of broken shards by scraping the sash with the breaking tool. As described in **Essentials**, the firefighter breaking the glass should be in full protective clothing, including hand and eye protection, and should be upwind of the window. If using an axe to break the window, the firefighter should use the flat side of the blade (**Figure 7.48**). Regardless of which tool is used, the handle should be held higher than the blade to prevent glass from sliding down the handle. When working aboveground, windows should be broken inward whenever possible to avoid the "flying guillotine" hazard that may injure anyone working below and may cut hoselines.

Figure 7.48 Windows may be broken out with an axe.

CAUTION

Using the tip of a ground ladder to break a second-story window is dangerous and *not* recommended.

Thermoplastic Windows. As discussed in previous chapters, Plexiglas® acrylic, Lexan® polycarbonate, and other thermoplastic windows may have to be opened for horizontal ventilation. A rotary saw with a medium (40 tooth) carbide-tipped blade is most effective when entry must be made through these windows (**Figure 7.49**). Eye protection is critically important whenever a rotary saw is used.

If a rotary saw is not available and the plastic is very thin (⅛ inch [3 mm] or less), it may be possible

Figure 7.49 A rotary saw can be used to cut plastic windows.

to shatter an acrylic plastic window by scoring an "X" on the pane and then striking the intersection of the "X" with the point of a pick-head axe (**Figure 7.50**). The pane may break along the "X," and if so, the pieces can be pulled or bent out. Another method is to strike the pane in the center with a sledgehammer (**Figure 7.51**). This will not break the pane, but it may bow it enough to allow it to slip out of its frame. This technique *will not* work on polycarbonate plastic windows so they will have to be cut with a rotary saw.

Figure 7.50 Plastic windows can be broken with the point of an axe.

Figure 7.51 A sledgehammer can be used to break plastic windowpanes.

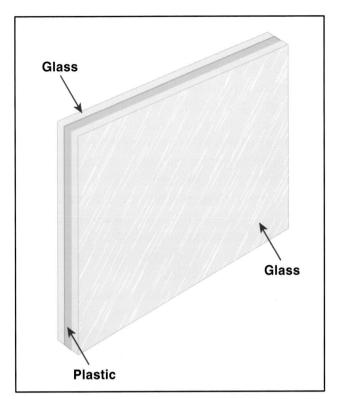

Figure 7.52 Laminated glass is two sheets of glass bonded to a plastic layer.

Laminated Windows. Many security windows are glazed with laminated glass similar to that in automobile windshields. A sheet of plastic is sandwiched between two sheets of plate glass (**Figure 7.52**). When broken, the glass shards cling to the plastic laminate. Firefighters can take advantage of this characteristic and simply cut out the panes of glass with an axe, hatchet, or a glass saw such as is used in vehicle extrication.

Wired-Glass Windows. Another common form of security window uses wire mesh imbedded in the glass panes (**Figure 7.53**). Like laminated glass, the pieces of broken glass cling to the wire mesh and therefore can be cut out in one piece. The same tools used to cut laminated glass can be used to cut wired-glass.

Film-Coated Glass. The windows on the west and south walls of many buildings have a reflective film applied to the inside of the windows to reduce glare from the sun (**Figure 7.54**). When broken, film-coated windows will sometimes behave in a manner similar to laminated windows. That is, the glass shards will cling to the film and the window will fall out in one large piece. When breaking these windows, firefighters must be careful to not allow the glass to fall on them.

Figure 7.53 A typical wired glass window.

Figure 7.54 Some windows have a reflective film coating.

Forced Horizontal Ventilation

Whether in horizontal or vertical ventilation operations, forced (mechanical) ventilation is primarily a means of supplementing or augmenting natural ventilation. Horizontal ventilation has traditionally been the area where smoke ejectors and/or nozzles have been used. Both of these methods are applied at the point of exit for the heat and smoke and are almost always applied from inside the structure. More recently, blowers have begun to be used to force replacement air into a structure from the outside at the point of entry.

Using Smoke Ejectors

Smoke ejectors are capable of being set up to blow air into a structure, but this is not the purpose for which they were designed. These units were designed to withstand the heat and contamination of drawing smoke through the fan in the process of exhausting it to the outside.

While smoke and heated air may pass harmlessly through the unit, actual flame passing through it can seriously damage or destroy it. Unless they are equipped with intrinsically safe motors, smoke ejectors are capable of igniting certain combustible gases encountered in fires. For these reasons, smoke ejectors are most often employed after initial knockdown of the fire and not as part of the fire attack.

Smoke ejectors are usually set up in openings on the lee side of the building. They may be suspended in window or doorway openings, set up on the floor, or elevated on a door, ladder, or some other object. Using a platform with bolt-on telescoping legs, smoke ejectors can be made freestanding, and their height can be adjusted to the most effective level.

When smoke ejectors are placed in doorways, windows, or other exterior openings, they should be positioned near the top of the opening because natural convection causes the majority of the heat and smoke to rise to the top of the compartment (**Figure 7.55**). In addition, the open area around the units should be sealed with salvage covers or

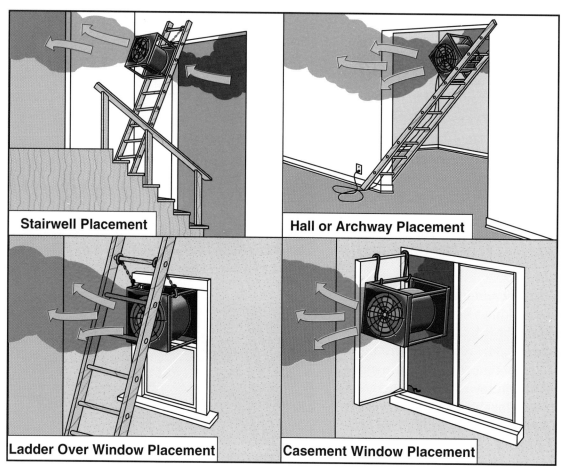

Stairwell Placement

Hall or Archway Placement

Ladder Over Window Placement

Casement Window Placement

Figure 7.55
Smoke ejectors should be positioned at the top of the window or doorway opening.

some similar means to prevent churning (**Figure 7.56**). *Churning* (sometimes called *recirculation*) is the phenomenon of smoke being blown out the top of the opening, only to be drawn back into the compartment at the bottom of the opening by the slight negative pressure (vacuum) created by the action of the ejector. Churning is obviously counterproductive to clearing the building of smoke.

Figure 7.57a A gasoline-powered blower. *Courtesy of Tempest Technology.*

Figure 7.56 Churning may occur if the area below the ejector is not properly sealed.

Using Blowers

Blowers can be extremely effective adjuncts to natural horizontal ventilation. Slightly larger than smoke ejectors, blowers are most often powered by gasoline-driven engines but may be powered by electric motors or by water pressure from a hoseline (**Figures 7.57 a-c**). Because gasoline engines require fresh air to operate, these units are not well suited for being set up in a contaminated atmosphere. Blowers are almost always set up about six feet (2 m) outside the point of entry into the building so they are not subject to being damaged by the fire (**Figure 7.58**). Properly applied, they can effectively support the efforts of the search and rescue and fire attack crews by enhancing visibility and reducing interior temperatures. For these reasons, they are often used as part of the initial attack.

Figure 7.57b A typical electric blower. *Courtesy of Tempest Technology.*

Figure 7.57c A water-powered blower. *Courtesy of Ramfan Corp.*

Figure 7.58 Firefighters set up PPV on the porch of a residence.

Figure 7.59 Blowers are sometimes set up in tandem.

Blowers function by creating a slight positive pressure within the structure, thus forcing the heat and smoke out the exit opening. A single blower is often sufficient to pressurize a building, but two blowers working in tandem can be used if needed (**Figure 7.59**). The keys to effective use of blowers are to apply positive-pressure ventilation (PPV) as soon as the first attack crew is ready to enter and to maintain the size of the exit opening in proportion to the size of the entry opening.

CAUTION
PPV can be used to help determine the location and extent of the fire, but SOPs in many departments specify that these facts be known before PPV is initiated.

Fire departments are encouraged to experiment with PPV in a safe, controlled training environment before developing SOPs for its use. Once the capabilities and limitations of PPV are understood, all fireground personnel should be thoroughly trained in its use before PPV is implemented on the fireground.

Using Nozzles (Hydraulic Ventilation)
The terms *fog stream* and *spray stream* are used interchangeably in this section. As described in **Essentials**, a fog or spray stream directed through a window or door opening will draw large quantities of heat and smoke in the direction in which the stream is pointed. Compared with mechanical smoke ejectors, fog streams are capable of removing two to four times more smoke, depending on the type and size of the nozzle, the angle of the spray pattern, and the location of the nozzle in relation to the ventilation opening.

A fog or spray stream directed through a window or doorway with a 60-degree pattern covering 85 to 90 percent of the opening provides the best results for ventilation. The ideal nozzle position will vary, but in most cases it should be about 2 feet (60 cm) inside the room being cleared. Regardless of the size of the opening, the spray pattern should not exceed 60 degrees because it will lose efficiency at angles greater than that.

As with any other technique, there are disadvantages to using hydraulic ventilation. These disadvantages are as follows:

- There may be an increase in the amount of water damage within the structure.

- There will be a drain on the available water supply.

- In subfreezing temperatures, additional ice may form in the area immediately outside of the window being used.

- The nozzle operator must remain in the hostile environment during the operation (**Figure 7.60**).

- The operation may have to be interrupted each time the operator runs out of breathing air.

Figure 7.60 Working within the hostile environment is one disadvantage of hydraulic ventilation.

Summary

Since horizontal ventilation is the most frequently used way of channeling smoke and other products of combustion out of burning buildings, firefighters need to be well trained in its capabilities, limitations, and applications. They must know how to use the available horizontal ventilation tools and equipment to its best advantage. They should also know which occupancies within their response districts are most likely to require horizontal ventilation. Finally, firefighters need to be familiar with their department's SOPs regarding horizontal ventilation and with how to apply them.

Chapter 8
Vertical Ventilation

Chapter 8
Vertical Ventilation

Even though ventilation is not a method of fire extinguishment, it can be used to influence a fire and thereby facilitate firefighter access, prevent or reduce the loss of life, and prevent or reduce property damage. After the IC has sized up a structure fire, decided that ventilation is needed, determined that vertical ventilation is most appropriate, and made sure that fire attack and protection lines are ready, the next step is to open the building at its highest point or as close to the seat of the fire as safely possible.

Because a building is filled with smoke does not necessarily mean that there is danger of a backdraft or a flashover. However, releasing the heat, smoke and other products of combustion through the roof will reduce these potentials and will facilitate search and rescue and interior fire fighting.

While many structure fires contain elements that might lend themselves to either vertical or horizontal ventilation, only those conditions that relate to vertical ventilation are discussed in this chapter. This chapter discusses the most commonly used vertical ventilation tools, establishing and supporting vertical ventilation, and safety considerations. Building construction related to vertical ventilation is also discussed, including existing roof openings, roof construction, lightweight roofs, and roof coverings. Finally, the various ways of opening a roof are discussed.

Vertical Ventilation Tools

Just as in horizontal ventilation, almost any forcible entry tool may also be used for vertical ventilation, and most of them are. However, some tools are better suited to this task than others. The specific applications of those tools more commonly used for vertical ventilation are discussed in the following sections.

Cutting Tools

Using any cutting tool can be a somewhat dangerous operation, both for the operator and others nearby. Cutting tools can be especially hazardous in vertical ventilation operations because they must often be used on steeply pitched roofs, while working from roof ladders, and for cutting materials that were never intended to be cut. One of the most important safety points to remember is that a safe distance should always be maintained between a firefighter using a cutting tool and other firefighters. While local protocols must be followed, it is recommended that a clear space of at least 10 feet (3 m) be maintained in all directions from anyone using a cutting tool for vertical ventilation. One exception to this rule is the use of a guide or backup who watches where the operator is going, clears the path of obstructions, and provides safety and support during cutting operations. The most common cutting tools used for vertical ventilation are the rotary saw, chain saw, and the pick-head axe.

Rotary Saw

As with any gasoline-powered tool, the rotary saw should be started and run briefly at the ground or street level, and then shut off, before it is carried or hoisted aloft (**Figure 8.1**). Also at the street level, the blade should be changed if the material to be cut requires something other than the multipurpose blade normally carried on these saws. When using this or any other power tool, the firefighter should wear full protective clothing (especially eye and ear protection).

After determining the location for the ventilation hole, the operator places the saw flat on the roof surface, revs it up to cutting speed, and then slowly rocks the saw forward until the blade contacts and cuts the roof covering to the required depth (**Figure 8.2**). The saw continues cutting as it is being drawn back toward the operator. When the saw blade comes into contact with a rafter, the saw should be rocked back slightly to decrease the depth of cut until the blade is clear of the rafter (**Figure 8.3**). The operator moves backward in a shuffle step — that is, both feet remain in contact with the roof surface at all times. The operator's back foot slides and stops

and the other foot slides to meet the back foot, and this process is repeated until the destination is reached. Some firefighters believe that it is more difficult to feel the rafters with a rotary saw than with a chain saw.

Chain Saw

All the safety precautions applicable to the rotary saw also apply to the chain saw. Because of its versatility and safety, the chain saw is the preferred cutting tool among many fireground support personnel (**Figure 8.4**). Chain saws used for forcible entry or ventilation are usually equipped with car-

Figure 8.1 Saws should be started at the apparatus.

Figure 8.3 The operator rocks the saw back far enough to avoid cutting the rafter.

Figure 8.2 The operator rocks the saw forward to make the cut.

Figure 8.4 Chain saws are effective ventilation tools.

bide-tipped chains to allow cutting through nails and light-gauge metal components. They may also be equipped with an adjustable depth gauge to reduce the chances of cutting through rafters (**Figure 8.5**).

The procedure used with chain saws is very similar to that used with rotary saws. The operator should first make sure that the chain oiler is working (**Figure 8.6**). Then the chain speed is increased to cutting speed before engaging the material to be cut, and the saw is drawn back toward the operator (**Figure 8.7**). Unlike the technique used when cutting logs, limbs, or structural members, which uses the area of the bar closest to the saw motor, roof cuts are made using only the last few inches (cm) at the tip of the cutting bar. Also, cutting is done using the bottom of the bar, not the top. One of the advantages of the chain saw is said to be that, compared to a rotary saw, it allows the operator to have a better "feel" for what is being cut, thereby reducing the risk of accidentally cutting through joists or rafters.

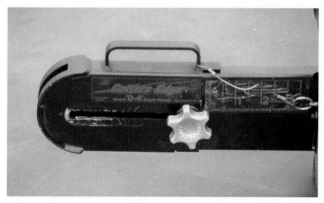

Figure 8.5 A typical depth gauge on a chain saw.

Figure 8.6 The function of the chain oiler should be checked before cutting.

Chain saws are generally safer to use than rotary saws because they do not twist in the operator's hand when revved up as rotary saws tend to do. Many chain saws also have some form of chain brake to instantly stop the movement of the chain if it jams and "bucks" out of the material being cut (**Figure 8.8**). However, as with any cutting tool, careful and responsible operation by well-trained personnel is still the best safety device.

Figure 8.7 The saw should be drawn back toward the operator.

Figure 8.8 The chain brake is an important safety feature.

Pick-Head Axe

To keep both hands free for other work, many firefighters wear their axes in scabbards strapped around their waists (**Figure 8.9**). When power saws are unavailable or inoperative, a pick-head axe can be used effectively to open some types of roofs. Another use of the pick-head axe is scraping away pea gravel from areas to be cut with a power saw. Cutting a roof with an axe should be done as close to the rafters as possible to minimize the tendency of the roof surface to deflect when struck (because of the springiness of the surface between the rafters)

Figure 8.9 Many firefighters carry their axes in scabbards. *Courtesy of Wes Kitchel.*

and to keep the axe from bouncing. Using a sharp axe also makes the job easier, but at best, opening a roof with a pick-head axe is a very arduous task. The safest way to cut with an axe is to use short, controlled strokes, with the axe head cutting to the side of the firefighter's feet, not between them (**Figure 8.10**). On roofs covered with wooden shakes or shingles, it is usually more efficient for firefighters to strike the roof surface with the point of the pick head and pull the axe toward them in short, quick strokes (**Figure 8.11**). Rather than attempting to cut the shakes or shingles, this technique scrapes them off.

Figure 8.10 The angle of the cut should not be toward the firefighter's feet.

Figure 8.11 The point of an axe can be used to strip shingles from skip-sheathed roofs. *Courtesy of Greg Terrill.*

Stripping Tools

In some cases, once the roofing material has been cut around the perimeter of a ventilation exit opening, the roof covering may have to be stripped back to expose the sheathing. While some departments have created their own specially designed stripping tools, the most common ones are the pick-head axe, the pike pole, and the rubbish hook. A sledgehammer performs the equivalent function on tile or slate roofs if the tiles cannot be removed intact.

Pick-Head Axe

The pick-head axe can be used to strip the roof covering from the sheathing and then the sheathing from the rafters after the appropriate cuts have been made. A firefighter is first positioned on each side of the cuts. Facing leeward and working as a team, the firefighters insert the picks of their axes into the leeward crosscut and pull the roof covering toward them as they back away (**Figure 8.12**). Then, they repeat the process to pull the sheathing.

Figure 8.12 Working as a team, firefighters pull the coverings from a roof.

Pike Pole

Pike poles can be used to strip roofing in much the same way as pick-head axes are used. The hook is inserted into the leeward crosscut, and the roofing is pulled back. Pike poles have longer handles than axes, and their length allows firefighters to position themselves farther away from the point from which heat, smoke, and perhaps fire may be issuing. Also, if there is a ceiling below the roof, its removal may be necessary in order to release the contaminants, and the handle of the pike pole is an excellent tool for this purpose (**Figure 8.13**).

Rubbish Hook

The rubbish hook is used in exactly the same way as the pike pole when stripping roofing. One further advantage of the rubbish hook is that it has two hooks instead of one, giving the tool twice the purchase on the material being pulled. Another advantage is the D-handle, which allows the operator a much more positive grip and therefore a stronger pull (**Figure 8.14**). Finally, the width of the tool head makes pushing a ceiling down from above much more efficient than with a pike pole.

Figure 8.14 A rubbish hook is a very effective ventilation tool.

Figure 8.13 The handle of a pike pole may be used to break out the ceiling below.

Sledgehammer

While not normally thought of as a stripping tool, the sledgehammer can be used on tile- or slate-covered roofs in much the same way that the pick-head axe is used with other roof coverings. Short, controlled blows with the sledgehammer will shatter the tiles without the head of the tool penetrating deeply enough to become lodged between the sheathing boards. If a sledgehammer is not available, a flat-head or pick-head axe can be used for this purpose.

Establishing and Supporting Vertical Ventilation

Even after the type of building involved has been considered, the location and extent of the fire has been determined, personnel and equipment have been moved to the roof, safety precautions have been observed, and the place to ventilate has been selected, the operation has only begun. Vertical ventilation involves all these factors and many other precautions that must be considered and procedures that must be performed if the operation is to be successful. Before and during the actual opening of the roof, the following items must be considered:

- Maintaining the safety of the firefighters
- Providing a second means of egress from the roof
- Having charged attack and protection lines ready
- Observing weather (temperature, humidity, visibility, wind direction/speed)
- Noting any obstructions or dead loads on the roof
- Reading (observing) the roof continually
- Locating the seat of the fire
- Coordinating with fire attack crews
- Using existing roof openings when appropriate
- Cutting one large opening, not several small ones
- Enlarging the original opening instead of cutting an additional hole if more ventilation is needed
- Evaluating roof construction type and condition (visibility, footing, stability)
- Tracking elapsed time into the incident

Vertical ventilation is intended to allow the heat, smoke, and other fire gases to escape harmlessly into the atmosphere, especially in potential backdraft situations. In performing vertical ventilation, firefighters should attempt to give the contaminants the most direct path out of the structure that is safely possible, without spreading the fire or interfering with occupants exiting the building. Ideally, the ventilation exit opening should be made directly over the seat of the fire. This is the preferred location, *but only if it is judged to be a safe one* (**Figure 8.15**).

Figure 8.15 If it is safe to do so, the ventilation opening should be made directly over the seat of the fire. *Courtesy of Dr. George McClary.*

Roof features can either help or hinder vertical ventilation operations. Some features, such as solar panels, are obstructions. Others, such as air-handling units, process vents, machinery vents, and dust-collection units, may lend themselves to aiding ventilation efforts under certain conditions. All such roof features should be assessed during pre-incident planning inspections. If it is determined that a particular feature cannot be used for fire-related ventilation purposes, alternative methods of ventilation can and should be devised and written into pre-incident operational plans.

Vertical Ventilation Safety

Because there are numerous ways in which firefighter safety can be compromised during vertical ventilation operations, these are potentially some of the most hazardous operations at structure fires. Vision on rooftops is often obscured by weather, smoke, or darkness. The tools that firefighters use to cut ventilation holes in roofs can be dangerous for the operator and for other firefighters nearby. Fire-weakened roofs may collapse — sometimes without warning **(Figure 8.16)**. Creating an opening through which the products of combustion may escape can expose firefighters to extremely toxic substances and to a considerable amount of fire. These and other conditions encountered during vertical ventilation operations make the following discussion of firefighter safety especially important.

Figure 8.16 Fire-weakened roofs can collapse without warning.

Identifying Vertical Ventilation Hazards

One of the most important safety considerations for firefighters actually performing vertical ventilation is the fact that they are usually standing on a roof that is being weakened by fire below them. Therefore, they must become familiar with the various types of roof construction and the effects that fire exposure is likely to have on each. Before stepping onto any roof, firefighters should read (observe the condition of) and sound (test the condition of) the roof, and they should continue to do so as long as they are on the roof (see more detailed descriptions in the sections on Reading a Roof and Sounding a Roof). These techniques reduce the chances of firefighters getting on or remaining on a roof that is structurally unstable. Smoke or darkness may reduce visibility and make reading the roof difficult. Except with tile/slate roofs, firefighters should sound the roof with a hand tool as they advance. Rain, snow, and ice may also interfere with accurately reading a roof and will increase the live load on the roof and make the

Figure 8.17 Snow and ice on a roof can make it very slippery. *Courtesy of Peter Sells.*

surface slippery **(Figure 8.17)**. As soon as ventilation is completed, or when conditions indicate that the roof is unstable, firefighters should immediately leave the roof.

While there are numerous hazards involved in vertical ventilation operations, the primary ones are that personnel must work aboveground (often far above) on sometimes steeply sloped surfaces that can lead to slips and falls. They also face the possibility of roof collapse. Personnel must beware of the possibility of falling onto roofs from high parapet walls, of falling off roofs because of tripping over low parapets, and of poor footing on steep roofs. They must also beware of the toxic products of combustion released through their ventilation efforts and of the dangers of fire spread beneath them.

CAUTION

Firefighters should never get on a roof wearing anything less than full protective clothing, SCBA, and a PASS device. As a minimum, the officer in charge of the vent group/sector should also be equipped with a portable radio.

Getting Firefighters to the Roof

Because truck-company personnel (or those responsible for performing truck functions in the absence of an actual truck company) are responsible for performing vertical ventilation when it is deemed necessary, they should be trained to automatically determine the best means of access to the roof of a burning building. As discussed in Chapter 2, Firefighter Survival, if on-scene resources permit, a burning building should be laddered on all sides (**Figure 8.18**). Some of these ladders may be used for roof access. Aerial devices may also be used for roof access if they are not already committed to rescue operations. A good standard procedure is to automatically position an aerial device for best access to the roof at every structure fire (**Figure 8.19**). This can save valuable time in ventilation and fire suppression operations. In those cases where firefighters cannot reach the roof by using fire department ladders,

Figure 8.18 Burning buildings should be laddered on all sides.

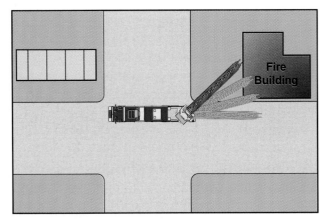

Figure 8.19 Aerial devices should be positioned for greatest advantage.

they may have to use the interior stairway, the building's fire escapes, or those on adjoining buildings if they can be used safely.

CAUTION

Whenever firefighters ascend to the roof, by whatever means, a secondary means of egress from the roof *must* be provided. This can be accomplished by placing ladders on two sides of the building.

Reading a Roof

To *read a roof* means to observe certain construction features and other signs that can warn firefighters of potentially unsafe conditions. By being familiar with standard local roof and building construction design practices, firefighters can learn to "read" a roof while observing it from a position of safety such as a parapet wall or an aerial device.

Construction features that can be read before venturing onto a roof include the age of the building, the type of roof structure, the location and most likely orientation of supporting members, the type and condition of the roof coverings, and the existence of heavy objects and/or other dead or live loads on the roof (**Figure 8.20**). Because vents, skylights, and other features penetrate a roof *between* the rafters or joists, they offer another clue to the location and orientation of roof supports (**Figure 8.21**). Also, the weathering of roof coverings over time will often reveal where rafters are located and the direction in which they run. If a thermal imager is available, it can be used to locate hot spots and to identify the location and orientation of roof supports (**Figure 8.22**).

Other factors that firefighters should look for before getting onto a roof include:

- Sagging roof surface
- Roof vents that appear to be getting taller (indicates that the roof is sagging)
- An accumulation of water or snow
- Fire/smoke coming from roof vents
- Heavy dead or live loads
- Drop-offs due to varying roof elevations

Figure 8.20 Heavy dead loads are among the things that reading a roof will reveal.

Figure 8.21 Skylights can show the location and orientation of roof supports.

All of these signs and conditions will help firefighters decide whether the roof is stable enough to walk on or whether ventilation work *must* be done from an aerial device or other position of safety such as from the roof of an adjoining building (**Figure 8.23**). If the roof appears stable, the factors observed while reading the roof can help identify the strongest and weakest areas of the roof and the safest routes of travel on it. If the roof appears unstable, the IC must be notified immediately so that consideration can be given to withdrawing interior crews.

Sounding a Roof

Before stepping off a ladder, parapet wall, or other place of safety onto the roof of a burning building, especially if the roof surface is obscured by smoke or darkness, firefighters should sound the roof (if possible) by striking the roof surface with the blunt end of a pike pole, rubbish hook, or axe (**Figure 8.24**). When struck by a tool, some roofs will feel solid over structural supports, and the tool will tend to bounce off the surface. Between the supports, the roof may feel softer and less rigid. The roof may also *sound* solid when struck over a rafter or joist and produce a hollow sound when struck between the supports. By practicing on structurally sound roofs,

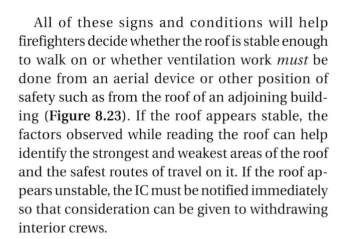

Figure 8.22 Thermal imaging cameras can be used to locate roof supports.

Figure 8.23 Firefighters may have to work from an adjacent roof.

Figure 8.24 A firefighter sounds the roof with a tool.

firefighters can learn to recognize the difference in the feel and the sound of supported and unsupported areas of a roof.

However, roofs that have several layers of composition shingles or other roof coverings may not respond to sounding as just described. They may sound quite solid when struck with a tool, but the roof supports may have been severely damaged by the fire. Also, roofs covered with tile or slate cannot be sounded, the tiles/slates must be removed to reveal the underlying structure.

When vertically ventilating a burning building, firefighters should:

- Place ladders away from windows.
- Place ladders away from electrical wires.
- Sound the roof with a tool in one hand while holding onto the ladder with the other hand.
- Progress from a safe area toward the unsafe.
- Work between the unsafe area and the egress route.
- Get off the roof as soon as the assignment is finished.

As mentioned earlier, as long as firefighters remain on the roof of a burning building, they should continue to read the roof for changes in its stability. They should also continue sounding the roof whenever they move about on it. If they must walk the ridge of a peaked roof, they should walk with one foot on either side of the ridge.

Working on a Roof

In general, the strongest points of any roof are directly over roof supports, at ridges or valleys, and where the roof meets the outside walls. The weakest points are between the supports. Firefighters can reduce the risk of falling through a fire-weakened roof by walking only over roof supports.

> # WARNING!
> Because roof supports always run perpendicular to the outside walls, firefighters should *never* walk diagonally across the roof of a burning building.

In addition, fire-weakened roofs will sometimes fail under the weight of a heavy snow accumulation. They may even fail under the weight of a single firefighter jumping from a ladder or parapet wall onto the surface because the firefighter's weight is concentrated in one spot. However, firefighters should never use a roof ladder on a fire-weakened roof to spread their weight over a greater area. Roof ladders should only be used to give the firefighter more secure footing on pitched roofs.

> # CAUTION
> Working on a roof that is known to be weakened is very risky and is *not* recommended.

The officer in charge of the vent group/sector must size up the roof very carefully and give the incident commander the benefit of his best judgment so that the risks and benefits of ordering firefighters onto the roof can be weighed. Whenever there is any doubt about the structural integrity of a roof, vertical ventilation operations *must* be limited to those that can be done from an aerial device or other position of safety (**Figure 8.25**).

Working with Protective Hoselines

Ideally, ventilation should be performed with the wind at the firefighters' backs. However, this is not always possible such as when the seat of the fire is at the windward end of a building. Wind that may

Figure 8.25 When roof stability is questionable, firefighters should work from the safety of an aerial device.

be fanning the fire may also push the fire and smoke toward the ventilation crew. Under these circumstances, it may be necessary to have a charged hoseline on the roof with the ventilation crew for their protection. The need for a charged hoseline on a roof should be based on the need to protect the vent crew. Pertinent safety considerations are as follows:

- Wind direction and intensity
- Size of the roof
- Type of roof covering
- Time needed to cut the hole

A hoseline may not be required on the roof of a single-family residence because firefighters can cut the hole and exit the roof in a relatively short time. However, a charged hoseline may be necessary to push heat and smoke away from the vent crew while they cut an exit opening on the roof of a large-area building. The protective hoseline is also useful for putting out spot fires that may occur in combustible roof coverings.

The hose stream may also be used to cool the thermal column rising from the ventilation exit opening. When the hoseline is used for this purpose, it is important that the spray stream be directed horizontally or at a slight upward angle across the opening but *never into the exit opening itself* (**Figure 8.26**). If the hose stream is directed into the opening, it will counteract the natural convection currents and push steam and smoke down into the building toward the firefighters working inside.

CAUTION

While a charged hoseline may be a useful and necessary item to have on the roof during ventilation operations, firefighters must realize its limitations and not become overconfident and careless because it is close at hand.

Existing Roof Openings

Instead of having to cut through roof coverings to create a ventilation exit opening, roof openings may already exist in the form of scuttle hatches, pent-houses, skylights, monitors, turbine vents, light and/or ventilation shafts, ridge vents, and clerestory windows. With the exception of light and ventilation shafts, all such openings are likely to be locked or secured in some manner against entry. All existing roof openings should be identified and evaluated during pre-incident planning inspections.

Figure 8.26 Firefighters should never direct a hose stream into a ventilation opening.

Scuttle Hatches

Scuttle hatches are normally square or rectangular metal-covered hatches that provide an exit from an attic or cockloft onto the roof and are often accessed from the top floor or the attic by a ladder (**Figure 8.27**). If the scuttle hatch is opened from

Figure 8.27 A typical roof scuttle.

the outside for ventilation purposes, the ceiling directly beneath the hatch may require removal, as well as any walls enclosing the scuttle access.

Penthouses (Bulkheads)

These structures often enclose the tops of stairways that terminate on the roof, and they usually have a metal-clad exterior door of standard size. Penthouse doors may be forced open in the same manner as other doors of similar type. Once the door is opened, it should be blocked open or removed to prevent it from closing and thereby disrupting the ventilation operation (**Figure 8.28**).

Figure 8.29 Some skylights can be tilted open for ventilation.

Figure 8.28 Penthouse (bulkhead) doors should be blocked open during ventilation operations.

Skylights

Whether covering roof openings or atria, skylights may be used effectively to ventilate heat and smoke. In fact, some skylights are thermoplastic units that are designed to melt out from the heat of a fire and thereby ventilate the building. Other types of skylights will have to be removed or broken out. They should be removed if possible. In many cases, the skylight can be lifted off if the flashings on all sides are pried loose. An alternative is to pry loose three sides and use the fourth side as a hinge (**Figure 8.29**). Skylights equipped with thermoplastic panels or ordinary window glass can act as automatic vents because the temperature of a fire will melt the plastic or cause the glass to break and fall out. However, skylights equipped with wired glass may have to be removed for ventilation purposes as they resist being broken.

Figure 8.30 Some metal roofs have translucent plastic panels.

In some buildings, especially those with corrugated metal roofs, translucent fiberglass panels may be installed to act as a form of skylight (**Figure 8.30**). If such a roof is covered by snow, or if visibility is reduced by smoke or darkness, firefighters can step on these panels and fall through the roof.

WARNING!
If visibility is obscured by smoke or darkness, skylights that have been opened or removed for ventilation purposes represent a potentially fatal fall hazard for firefighters working on the roof.

Monitors

Monitor vents are square or rectangular structures that penetrate the roofs of single-story or multistory buildings to provide additional natural light and/

or ventilation (**Figure 8.31**). A monitor may have metal, glass, wired glass, or louvered sides. During a fire, those with glass sides provide ventilation when the glass breaks. If the fire has not yet generated enough heat to break the glass, the glass will have to be broken or removed by firefighters. Monitors with solid walls usually have at least two opposite sides hinged at the bottom and held closed at the top with a fusible link that will allow them to open automatically in a fire.

Turbine (Rotary Vane) Vents

Many commercial and residential structures have turbine vents on their roofs (**Figure 8.32**). In most cases, it is not necessary to remove the turbine for ventilation purposes — and removing it may even be counterproductive. Many fire fighting texts have recommended that turbine vents be removed to increase ventilation efficiency. However, current practice in some of the most experienced truck companies is to leave turbine vents alone. According to these firefighters, removing the turbines can actually reduce the ventilation efficiency of these openings. Turbines are designed to vent the spaces below them, and during a fire they should be allowed to do that for which they were intended.

Light and Ventilation Shafts

Light and ventilation shafts in buildings can act as natural chimneys during a fire. This can cut off one possible means of egress for the occupants of the building. Except for breaking windows within the shaft, light and/or ventilation shafts usually do not require opening or enlarging for fire ventilation purposes. To break the windows, an axe or other heavy tool is lowered to the level of the window. The tool is then hoisted up far enough for it to be thrown outward from the wall, allowing the tool to swing back and strike the window (**Figure 8.33**).

Figure 8.33 A tool tied to the end of a rope can be used to break windows for ventilation.

Figure 8.31 A typical rooftop monitor vent.

Figure 8.32 A typical rotary vent.

If these shafts are not protected by a parapet wall or railing, they can present a potentially fatal fall hazard to firefighters on the roof (**Figure 8.34**). If vision is obscured by smoke or darkness, firefighters can fall into unprotected shafts — another reason why sounding the roof is especially important.

Ridge Vents

Some newer buildings with pitched roofs have narrow, plastic attic vents that run the entire length of the ridge. Because the vent opening is very narrow, these vents are almost impossible to see from the ground under normal circumstances (**Figure 8.35**). When there is smoke in an attic equipped with these vents, the vent's presence is obvious because of the smoke issuing from the entire length of the ridge. In some cases, simply pulling off the ridge vent with a pike pole or other tool will provide an opening large enough to vent the fire below.

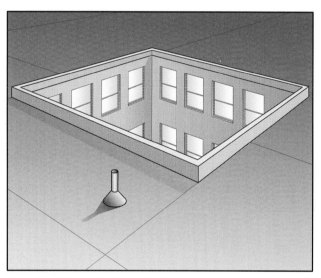

Figure 8.34 Light wells without railings around them are potential fall hazards for firefighters.

Figure 8.35 One type of ridge vent.

Clerestory Windows

Some residential and small office buildings have a horizontal row of windows installed on a vertical wall between two offset roof sections (**Figure 8.36**). These windows are designed to add natural light and ventilation to the buildings under normal circumstances. Under fire conditions, these windows can be opened or broken out faster than a vent hole can be cut in the roof and will be more economical to repair after the fire.

Figure 8.36 Clerestory windows make excellent ventilation openings.

Roof Construction

The extent to which firefighters are able to safely and efficiently ventilate a building through its roof will depend to some degree on their knowledge of roof construction. Construction practices and materials vary in different regions, so firefighters need to inspect buildings under construction in their response districts to become familiar with local construction materials and methods. In most areas of North America, there are several types of pitched roofs, flat roofs, and arched roofs.

Pitched Roofs

The angle or degree of slope (pitch) of pitched roofs tend to vary with climate and aesthetic considerations. The pitch is expressed in inches fall per horizontal foot. A roof that decreases 5 inches (125 mm) vertically for each foot (300 mm) horizontally from the ridge would be described as a "five-in-twelve" roof — the most common pitch on residential roofs (**Figure 8.37**). A roof designed to withstand a heavy snow load might have a twelve-in-twelve pitch (45-degree angle). Some church roofs are even steeper.

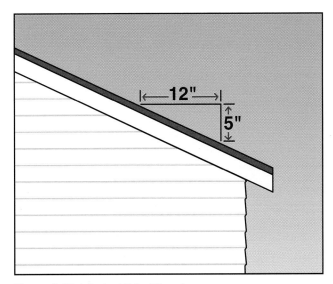

Figure 8.37 A typical 5-in-12 roof.

Pitched roofs are usually supported by wooden or metal rafters, laminated beams, or engineered trusses spanning the shortest distance between bearing walls. Where ceiling joists are used, they are fastened to the top plate and the rafters so that the entire assembly forms a series of triangles (**Figure 8.38**). In *post-and-beam* construction, the ceiling is often omitted and the rafters become part of the interior décor (**Figure 8.39**). The supporting structure carries the roof sheathing, which can be any of various materials such as plywood, oriented strand board (OSB), or planking. The sheathing is then covered by some form of weather-resistant material (**Figure 8.40**).

In many structures with pitched roofs, the space between the roof members and the ceiling forms an attic space, which may be vented by louvers at each gable end, turbine vents, or ridge vents (**Figure 8.41**). Other types of pitched roofs (hip roofs) have no gables so the attic spaces either have turbine

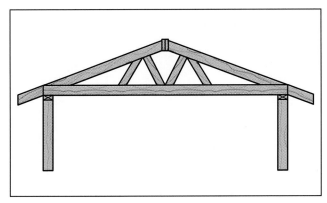

Figure 8.38 Typical pitched roof framing.

vents, eyebrow vents, or ridge vents (**Figure 8.42**). Access to attic spaces can usually be gained through a small attic scuttle in the ceiling of a hallway or closet, or there may be a stairway or ladder leading into the space (**Figure 8.43**). Insulation material, which may or may not be combustible, is sometimes found between the framing under the

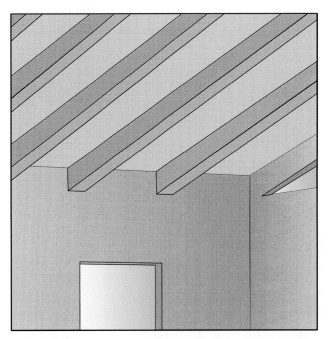

Figure 8.39 A typical open beam ceiling.

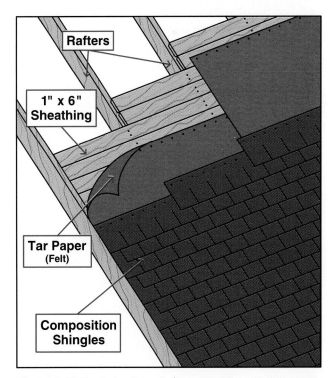

Figure 8.40 Roof sheathing is covered with a weatherproof material.

Figure 8.41 A typical gable vent.

Figure 8.42 One type of eyebrow vent. *Courtesy of Francine DeLanty.*

Figure 8.43 A typical attic scuttle.

roof or on top of the ceiling. There may also be a considerable amount of ductwork in the attic, which can impede access.

Types of Pitched Roofs

The most common examples of pitched roofs are the gable, hip, lantern, and shed styles. However, there are also bridge truss, mansard, modern mansard, gambrel, sawtooth, and butterfly styles.

Gable roof. The gable roof is perhaps the most common style of roof construction and can be found on most small residential dwellings and many commercial structures (**Figure 8.44**). The pitch of this type of roof ranges from nearly flat to very steep, and the points where the rafters meet the outside walls and the ridge beam provide the most support. Its A-frame configuration consists of rafters that run perpendicular to the ridge beam and down to and usually beyond the outside walls. The ridge and rafters are often 2- × 6-inch (50 mm by 150 mm) lumber or larger in stick-built roofs (those built on site), but in prefabricated assemblies. These components are commonly 2- × 4-inch (50 mm by 100

mm). In both types of roof assemblies, the rafters are commonly spaced at 16 to 24 inches (400 m to 600 mm) on center. The size and spacing of the rafters will vary with the horizontal distance being spanned. Additional support may be provided by collar beams and ceiling joists. Valley rafters are used where two ridgelines intersect (**Figure 8.45**). The trussed pitched roof is designed to cover a considerable span, and its rafters can be made of timber or metal (**Figure 8.46**).

Figure 8.44 A typical gable roof.

Figure 8.45 A typical valley rafter.

Figure 8.46 Typical trussed gable roof framing.

Hip roof. The hip roof is similar to the gabled roof in every respect except that the ends of the roof terminate in a "hip" configuration rather than a gable. In other words, the roof slopes down to meet every outside wall (**Figure 8.47**).

Hip roof construction consists of a ridge beam with conventional rafters running perpendicular to the ridge and hip rafters running from the ends of the ridge beam, at a compound angle of 45-degrees laterally, and some lesser vertical angle down to and beyond the outside walls at the corners (**Figure 8.48**). The rafters in the hip sections run in the same direction as the ridge beam. The dimensions and spacing of hip roof structural members follow the same engineering rules as those for gabled roof construction. The strongest parts of this roof system are the ridges, valleys, hips, and at the outside walls.

Lantern roof. The lantern roof consists of a high gabled roof with a vertical wall above a downward-pitched shed roof section on either side. This roof style is found on many barns, churches, and commercial buildings with rural-style construction (**Figure 8.49**).

This roof may be difficult to ventilate without an aerial device because of the difficulty in gaining access to the upper roof from either lower roof. The peak of the upper roof may also be beyond the reach of available ground ladders.

Figure 8.48 Typical hip roof framing.

Figure 8.47 A typical hip roof.

Figure 8.49 A typical lantern roof.

Shed roof. The shed roof can be seen as half of a standard gable roof or as a slightly pitched flat roof sloped from only one side — usually from the front of the building down to the back. This type of roof may be constructed with mono-pitch trusses, which employ only a single web member (**Figure 8.50**). These trusses may be more prone to early collapse than other lightweight wooden trusses.

Bridge-truss roof. Bridge trusses are heavy-duty trusses with sloping ends (**Figure 8.51**). The top chord is shorter than the bottom chord, and when installed, the bottom chord is supported. When constructed of wood, the trusses are usually made from 2- × 12-inch (50 mm by 300 mm) lumber, and vertical metal tie rods may be used for additional support. Joists are usually 2- × 6-inch (50 mm by 150 mm) or 2- × 8-inch (50 mm by 200 mm) lumber covered with 1- × 6-inch (25 mm by 150 mm) sheathing. Truss spacing may be as much as 16 to 20 feet (5 m to 6 m) on center. Composition roofing may be used throughout this type of roof, or the sloping sections may be shingled. Because of the shape of bridge trusses, they form a roof that is very similar to the modern mansard roof discussed later in this section.

The strongest areas of bridge-trussed roofs are at the perimeter of the building where the bottom chord of the trusses rest on the outside bearing walls. Trusses are in constant tension and compression and will fail under severe fire conditions, but the likelihood of roof collapse is dependent on the dimensions of the materials used, the span of the trusses, and the duration of fire exposure. If vertical metal tie rods are used, early failure of the rods will also affect the stability of these trusses.

Mansard roof. The mansard roof has a double slope on each of its four sides. In other words, instead of the roof pitch being a constant angle, there are two angles. One angle forms a steep pitch running from the eaves to a certain height, and the other produces a flatter pitch to the ridge of the roof.

This style is similar to the gambrel roof (see gambrel roofs later in this section) in that the lower pitch is steeper than the upper pitch. The difference between the mansard and the modern mansard (see

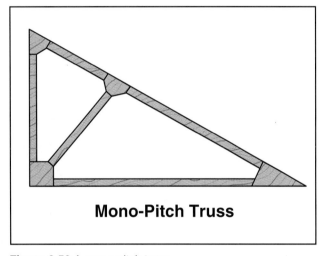

Mono-Pitch Truss

Figure 8.50 A mono-pitch truss.

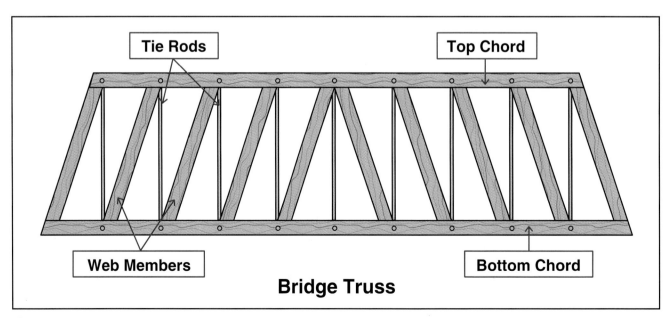

Bridge Truss

Figure 8.51 A typical bridge truss.

following paragraph) is the way in which the four sides meet in the middle. The true mansard forms a slight hipped peak or ridge (**Figure 8.52**). On the other hand, the modern mansard has a flat central portion.

Modern mansard roof. The modern mansard roof possesses characteristics of both flat and pitched roofs: four steeply sloped sides rise to meet a flat top called a *deck* (**Figure 8.53**). This roof type may utilize bridge trusses or K-trusses as supporting members, both of which allow for the creation of an ample void space between the roof and the ceiling, as well as a potential for early collapse under fire conditions. In addition, the modern mansard style roof may include overhangs that form concealed spaces through which fire and smoke can spread quickly (see *modern mansard roofs* under Types of Flat Roofs section).

Gambrel roof. A gambrel roof is most often found on barns and other outbuildings. This roof is essentially a gable type with two different slopes on each side of the peak and with the lower slope being steeper than the upper slope (**Figure 8.54**). Such a design can make getting to the top of the roof difficult with ground and roof ladders, so an aerial device may be the preferred method of access. Because this roof design permits efficient use of the attic space under the roof, firefighters must consider that additional weight resulting from maximum interior attic storage could hasten the failure of the roof assembly during a fire.

Sawtooth roof. This type of roof is used in industrial and institutional buildings to maximize light and ventilation. The sawtooth roof consists of a series of inclined planes similar in shape to the teeth of a saw (**Figure 8.55**). The rafters are 2- × 8- inch (50 mm by 200 mm) lumber or larger and use wood or metal supports for bracing. The vertical walls in-

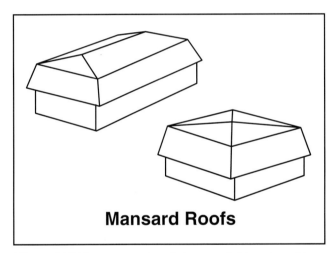

Mansard Roofs

Figure 8.52 True mansard roofs have a slight peak or ridge.

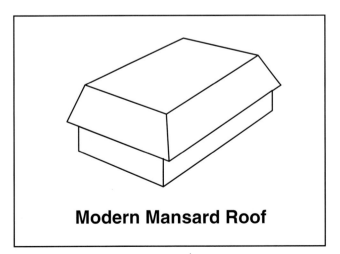

Modern Mansard Roof

Figure 8.53 A modern mansard roof has a flat deck in the middle.

Figure 8.54 A typical gambrel roof.

Figure 8.55 A typical sawtooth roof.

clude openable windows along their entire length, usually containing panes of wired glass. Pitched roofs are sheathed with plywood, OSB, or planked sheathing and covered with roofing material.

Butterfly roof. The butterfly roof may be seen as two opposing shed roofs that meet at their lower edges in the middle of the building (**Figure 8.56**). The same hazards and operational and safety considerations of all other pitched roofs also apply to butterfly roofs with one exception. A firefighter who slips and falls on a butterfly roof is not in danger of sliding off the edge of the roof as might happen on other types of pitched roofs.

Figure 8.56 A typical butterfly roof.

Hazards of Pitched Roofs

Pitched roofs are designed to shed water and snow, and one of their major hazards is the steepness of the roof and the lack of secure footing for firefighters working on them. This problem is increased when the roof is wet or covered with ice, snow, wet leaves, moss, etc., but footing may even be a problem when dry because of the loose granular texture of some roof coverings. Loose roof tiles, slate, or broken pieces can also be hazardous to firefighters working on the roof and on the ground. Loose tiles and broken shards may cause firefighters on the roof to slip, and the loose pieces can fall on firefighters working on the ground.

In addition to the hazards presented by the pitch (slope) of the roof and by falling debris, the growing use of lightweight roof assemblies can present an even greater hazard to firefighters. These assemblies are often held together with metal gusset plates that can warp and pull out of the material when

Figure 8.57 Lightweight roofs can fail without warning. *Courtesy of Mark Pedroia.*

exposed to direct flame impingement. Therefore, these roof assemblies offer little fire resistance and can fail early in a fire, resulting in sudden roof collapse with little or no warning (**Figure 8.57**). As one way of mitigating this hazard, a growing number of fire departments track the elapsed time into an incident at 5-, 10-, 15-, and 20-minute intervals. This helps the IC decide if and when vent crews should be ordered off of a roof and interior crews out of a burning building. For more information on metal gusset plates, see the discussion later in this chapter after the heading Pitched Roof Trusses.

Venting Pitched Roofs

As described in **Essentials**, pitched roofs should be vented at the highest point on the leeward side directly over the fire or as close to it as safely possible. The ventilation opening should be cut parallel to the rafters and perpendicular to the ridge (**Figure 8.58**). To help identify where the rafters are located, the first cut should be parallel to the ridge. The ventilation opening should be at least 4 × 4 feet (120 cm by 120 cm), and in many cases may need to be larger. Generally, one large ventilation opening is better than several smaller ones. In some cases, as

Figure 8.58 A typical pitched roof vent.

with plank sheathing, it may be advantageous to strip the roof covering before cutting and pulling the planking. In other cases, especially when using the center-rafter technique on plywood or OSB decking, leaving the roof covering attached works well and saves time and effort (**Figure 8.59**). On metal-covered roofs it may be possible to remove an entire section at one time by cutting or prying along the edges, pulling screws or nails as necessary, and removing the panel.

Because of the steep pitch of many roofs, the task of cutting a ventilation opening can be difficult and dangerous. Firefighters should use roof ladders to prevent themselves from sliding down the roof (**Figure 8.60**). When working from a roof ladder, firefighters will often need to reach as far as safely possible laterally from the ladder in order to cut the largest possible ventilation opening. To provide more secure footing and extend their reach, the pick of an axe or Halligan can be embedded in the roof and the tool head used as a foothold (**Figure 8.61**). Long pike poles or rubbish hooks may also be

needed when ventilating this type of roof because the ceiling can be several feet (meters) below the roof level, and sections of the ceiling may have to be removed for complete ventilation (**Figure 8.62**).

Figure 8.61 An axe head imbedded in the roof makes a good foothold.

Figure 8.59 Some older roofs have many layers of roofing material.

Figure 8.60 On steep roofs, firefighters must work from a ladder.

Figure 8.62 A rubbish hook may be needed to break out the ceiling below.

Flat Roofs

Flat roofs are more common on mercantile and industrial buildings, multiple dwellings, and apartment complexes than on single-family dwellings. This type of roof ordinarily has a slight slope (two-in-twelve pitch or less) from the front toward the rear of the building to promote drainage (**Figure 8.63**). Flat roofs are frequently penetrated by chimneys, vent pipes, shafts, scuttles, bulkheads, and skylights. These roofs may be surrounded by a mansard-type facade that overhangs the outside walls, or they may be surrounded and divided by parapet walls (**Figure 8.64**). These roofs may also support water tanks, HVAC equipment, antennas, solar panels, billboards, and other dead loads that may interfere with ventilation operations and increase the likelihood of roof collapse (**Figure 8.65**). If firefighters observe new dead loads (HVAC, water tanks, etc.) on the roof of an old building, they should be aware of the increased collapse potential created by the additional weight.

Flat roofs are commonly supported by horizontal joists or rafters similar to the joists used in floor systems. The structural elements of flat roofs consist of a wooden, concrete, or metal substructure covered with sheathing (**Figure 8.66**). The sheathing is, in some cases, covered with a layer of dense foam insulation under the weatherproof finish layer. There is often a concealed space between a flat roof and the ceiling of the top floor below. This space is referred to as an *attic*, *cockloft*, *crawl space*, or *interstitial space*. The underside of the roof assembly is often unprotected and will be exposed to the effects of any fire in this concealed void, which may contribute to early roof failure.

Types of Flat Roofs

The general category of flat roofs includes several common styles and some less common. Sufficiently common to warrant discussion here are the inverted roof, rain roof, wooden deck roof, metal deck roof, concrete roof, poured gypsum roof, modern mansard roof, and panelized roof.

Inverted roof. Inverted roofs differ from conventional flat roofs primarily in the location of their main roof beams. In a conventional roof system the main joists are set at the final roof level, sheathing is attached to the tops of the joists, and a ceiling

Figure 8.63 Flat roofs actually have a slight slope (pitch).

Figure 8.64 Many flat roofs have parapet walls around them.

Figure 8.65 Heavy dead loads increase the collapse potential of flat roofs.

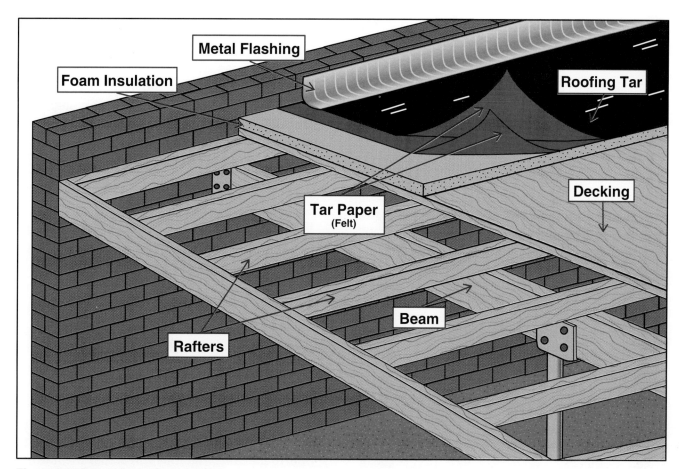

Figure 8.66 Typical flat roof construction.

may be attached to the bottoms of the joists, or more commonly, it is suspended below the joists, creating a concealed space. In the inverted roof, the main roof joists are set at the level of the ceiling, and a framework of 2- × 4-inch (50 mm by 100 mm) members is constructed above the main joists. The sheathing is attached to this framework, and the weatherproof covering is applied over the sheathing (**Figure 8.67**). This roof is a fairly solid roof system that retains its structural integrity during a fire until the upright members burn through.

From the outside, the inverted roof looks like any other flat roof, but the surface usually feels "springy" or "spongy" to anyone walking on it. The design of the inverted roof creates a concealed space several feet (meters) in height between the ceiling and the roof deck. The unprotected structural members within this concealed space are exposed on all four sides, so they are subject to severe damage from a fire within the space. Firefighters should familiarize themselves with any of these roofs in their districts by making thorough pre-incident planning inspections.

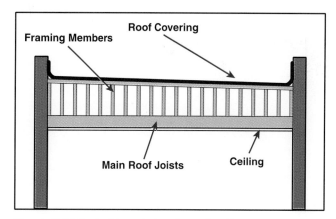

Figure 8.67 Typical inverted roof construction.

Rain roof. One dangerous relative of the inverted roof is the so-called "rain roof." While this oddity can be found over any type of roof, it is most common on buildings with flat or arched roofs. The rain roof is built *over* an existing roof that has become so porous it does not keep out the rain and/or it sags sufficiently to allow rainwater to collect on the roof. The existing roof is left in place, and the new roof is built on a raised framework above the original roof (**Figure 8.68**).

Rain roofs create some potential problems. First, the void created between the two roofs may allow fire to burn undetected for some time and could result in an inaccurate size-up of the fire. Second, the existence of two separate roofs can seriously impede effective ventilation or prevent it entirely. Finally, the original roof was not designed to support the additional weight, and therefore the entire roof assembly may be more susceptible to collapse.

Wooden deck roof. Wooden deck roofs may present a hazard if lightweight plywood or OSB decking is used. Panels of ⅜- to ⅝-inch (9 mm to 17 mm) thickness offer little fire resistance, and it may be difficult to remove for ventilation purposes (**Figure 8.69**).

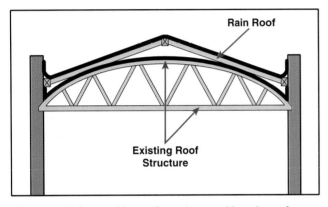

Figure 8.68 Some older roofs are covered by rain roofs.

Figure 8.69 The underside of a typical wooden deck roof.

CAUTION
Some types of fire-resistant plywood delaminate and weaken over time, resulting in a deck that a firefighter can step through without it having suffered any fire damage. Identifying these hazardous roofs during pre-incident planning inspections is critical to firefighter safety.

Roofs sheathed with wooden planks are easier to strip but may be somewhat less wieldy when making louver vents or trench cuts. The structural stability of the joists will vary depending on the span, the size and spacing of the joists, and whether the joists are suspended by metal hangers.

Metal deck roof. Metal deck roofs consist of metal bar joists, which usually run across the narrow dimension of the building, and metal decking that is laid perpendicular to the joists (**Figure 8.70**). In most cases, the metal decking is spot welded to the joists. Large-area metal deck roofs consist of large supporting beams that may run across the narrow dimension of the building or parallel to the long dimension, and bar joists that run perpendicular to the beams (**Figure 8.71**).

CAUTION
Unprotected metal deck roofs can be expected to fail within a very few minutes of flame impingement. Because the heat of a fire will soften metal and make it more pliable, metal decking around roof vents and other openings may not support the weight of a firefighter.

Concrete roof. Concrete roofs are constructed in a variety of ways. One of the most common is lightweight concrete poured over metal decking (**Figure 8.72**). Another common concrete roof consists of precast Double-T panels (**Figure 8.73**). Concrete roofs provide a smooth, hard surface that is structurally strong and highly resistant to fire, but it may be extremely difficult to breach for ventilation purposes. Opening these roofs may require special

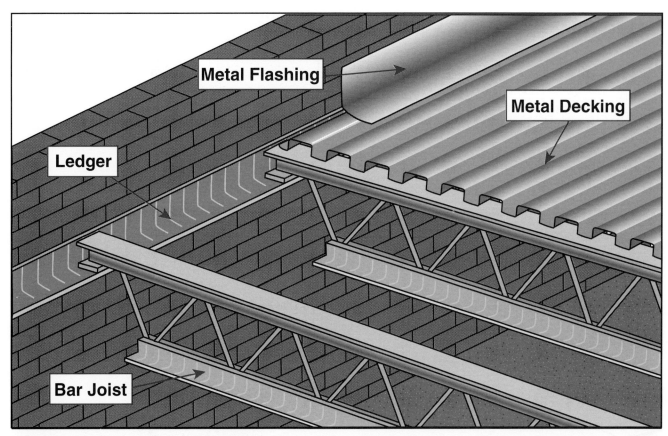

Figure 8.70 Typical metal deck roof construction.

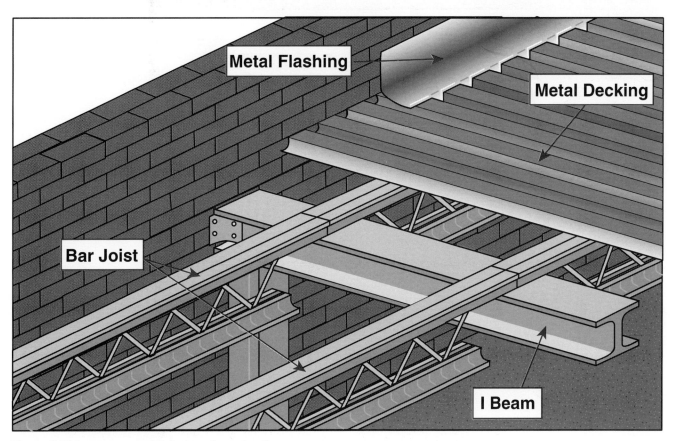

Figure 8.71 Large area metal deck roof construction.

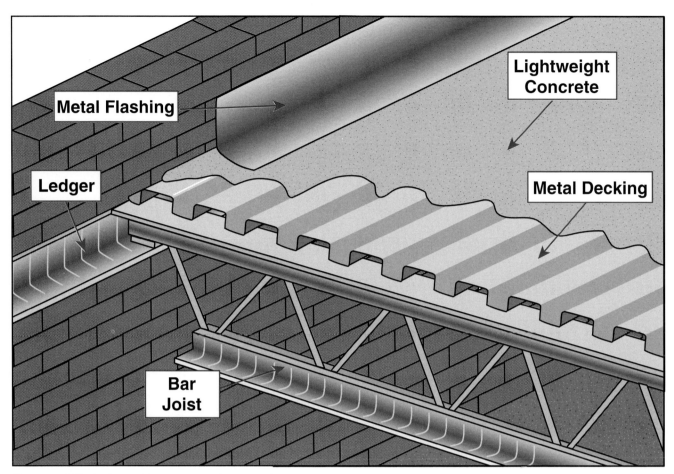

Figure 8.72 Typical poured concrete roof construction.

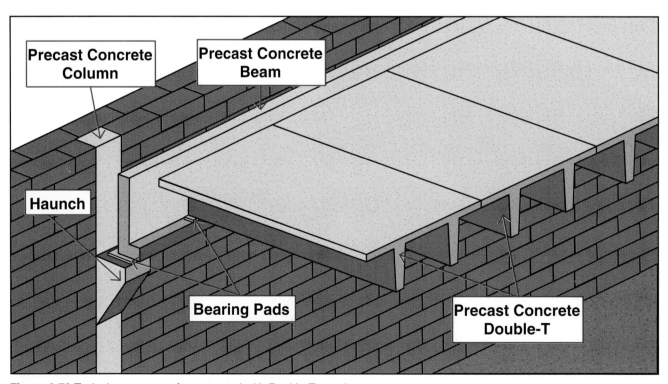

Figure 8.73 Typical concrete roof constructed with Double-T panels.

tools, such as jackhammers, core drills, or burning bars, and will be a laborious and time-consuming operation. Because they are so difficult to breach, some concrete roofs have built-in knockout panels similar to those discussed in Chapter 4 regarding concrete walls. The presence of these roofs should be identified during pre-incident planning inspections.

Lightweight concrete roofs may be cut using a rotary saw with a masonry blade. Because it is difficult and time consuming to cut concrete roofs that are over 4 inches (100 mm) thick, they are often designed with built-in access panels that can be lifted out in an emergency. Using existing openings, such as bulkheads, ventilators, or scuttles, will certainly be the fastest way to ventilate these roofs and may be the only practical way. Once again, thorough pre-incident familiarization will greatly speed the process of ventilating these roofs.

Poured gypsum roof. Poured gypsum roofs consist of bar joists or I-beams with brackets tack welded to the joists. Gypsum board is placed upon the brackets and is covered with a layer of gypsum cement up to 2½ inches (65 mm) thick to which wire mesh reinforcement is added. The gypsum board is then sealed with a weatherproof covering.

Because these roofs are constructed of materials that are highly resistant to fire, they retain their structural stability longer than some other roof types. The roof covering is easily cut with a power saw using a metal-cutting blade, and the covering can then be rolled back to open the hole.

Modern mansard roof. This type of roof has characteristics of both pitched and flat roofs. The perimeter of the roof consists of steeply pitched sections that surround a flat roof area in the middle (**Figure 8.74**). These roofs are most commonly supported by bridge trusses, and the same operational and safety considerations apply to these roofs as to any other pitched or flat roof — with two exceptions.

First, some modern mansard roofs are actually only facades, each consisting of a wall (with a triangular cross section) that has been added to the perimeter of a flat roof for aesthetic reasons. This creates a depressed area in the middle of the roof

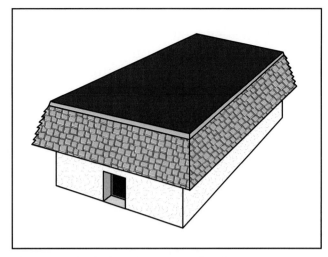

Figure 8.74 Typical modern mansard roof.

that can range from a few feet to several feet (meters) deep. Unsuspecting firefighters can fall from the top of this facade onto the actual flat roof if visibility is obscured by smoke and/or darkness.

Second, in building these facade structures, an uninterrupted concealed space that may run the entire perimeter of the roof is often created. This can allow fire to travel around the entire roof undetected. These facades usually extend beyond the exterior wall, creating an overhang that can collapse if fire weakens the bracing on the original roof.

Panelized roof. Many modern buildings have panelized flat roofs. These increasingly common roofs are discussed in the Lightweight Construction section later in this chapter.

Hazards of Flat Roofs

Firefighters preparing to ventilate a flat roof should look for hot spots or sagging of the roof area prior to walking on the roof surface and should continually look for these signs during ventilation operations. A sagging roof will often reveal itself when the vent pipes that penetrate the roof appear to be getting taller. Firefighters should always sound the roof before stepping onto it and repeatedly sound it while they are moving about on the roof.

WARNING!
Never step on any area of a flat roof that has not been sounded.

In some cases, hot spots can be identified by patches of melting snow and ice or by heat waves rising from specific areas. Sagging of the roof's surface indicates damage to the substructure of the roof assembly. However, these observations are not always reliable; therefore, if available, a thermal imager should be used. A thermal imager will not only reveal the hottest areas of the roof, it will also show the location and direction of roof supports. In the absence of a thermal imager, firefighters may have to cut one or more inspection (smoke indicator) holes to locate the seat of the fire (**Figure 8.75**). Each of the signs just discussed indicates severe heat and fire conditions directly below the roof and suggests that the roof may be ready to collapse, either partially or totally. Crews working on flat roofs must exercise extreme caution if these signs exist or develop while work is in progress. In addition, firefighters should not congregate in any particular area as this increases the live load on that section.

Figure 8.75 An inspection hole may have to be cut to find roof supports.

Some older buildings with flat roofs may have wooden or metal access ladders built onto the side of the structure (**Figure 8.76**). These ladders should generally not be used by firefighters because age and weathering may have made the ladders unsafe. If access from an adjacent roof is not possible, ground ladders or aerial devices should be used to gain roof access for ventilation.

As mentioned earlier, overhangs are often added to flat-roofed buildings to give the appearance of a mansard roof. These overhangs form concealed spaces through which fire and smoke can quickly spread undetected.

Inverted flat roofs create special hazards as well. This design also creates a concealed space, often several feet (meters) in height, which includes many unprotected wooden structural members. Heavy fire conditions can burn quickly through the 2- × 4-inch (50 mm by 100 mm) supporting members, causing the roof deck to collapse onto the roof joists. Likewise, roofs supported by unprotected steel members will often fail with relatively little direct fire exposure.

Other hazards encountered on flat roofs are the security measures that some building owners have taken to deter burglars from entering through skylights and other roof openings. Some have installed barbed wire or razor ribbon around the perimeter

Figure 8.76 Firefighters should not use old, weathered access ladders.

of the roof (**Figure 8.77**). Guard dogs can also be found on flat roofs of business and apartment buildings in high-crime areas. These dogs can delay or prevent access to a roof, so their presence should be determined during pre-incident planning in-

Figure 8.77 Roofs of buildings in high-crime areas may have security devices.

Figure 8.78 Some flat roofs have dangerously low parapet walls.

spections. All of these security measures can injure firefighters and/or delay access to the roof for ventilation.

Many buildings with flat roofs also have parapet walls that can be a help as well as a hazard to firefighters during ventilation operations. These walls may extend from a few inches (cm) to several feet (meters) above the roof's surface. Properly constructed parapet walls can help prevent the spread of fire from building to building and can help prevent firefighters from accidentally falling or walking off the roof. However, high parapet walls create a potential fall hazard, and walls that are too low may cause firefighters to trip and fall over them (**Figure 8.78**). Because the heights of parapet walls vary so much from building to building, firefighters must become familiar with those in their response districts through pre-incident planning inspections.

Before stepping off a parapet wall or ladder onto a flat roof, especially if the roof surface is obscured

by smoke or darkness, firefighters should always sound the roof by striking it with the blunt end of an axe, rubbish hook, pike pole, or other tool. This will reveal the condition of the roof as well as the vertical distance from the top of the wall to the roof. If firefighters must work on a roof when their vision is obscured by smoke or darkness, they should continually sound the roof as they shuffle-step on areas supported by structural members. Whenever these near zero visibility conditions are encountered during an incident, this information should be communicated to the IC.

Venting Flat Roofs

As with pitched roofs, flat roofs should be vented as close to directly over the seat of the fire as safely possible. Flat roofs may be vented by cutting a large square or rectangular ventilation hole, cutting a strip or trench ventilation opening, or by using existing roof openings such as roof vents, skylights, or monitors. However, for a variety of reasons, existing roof openings must be used with discretion.

Existing roof openings may or may not be in the most desirable location. If not, opening them may draw fire, heat, and smoke to previously uninvolved areas of the building. This can threaten any remaining building occupants or fire attack crews working inside, and it may cause additional sprinklers to open, which can reduce the efficiency of these openings. Also, existing openings may or may not be large enough to provide the needed ventilation. If not, they can be used to supplement openings cut in the roof.

Cutting holes in flat roofs. To create sufficiently large openings for the efficient ventilation of buildings with flat roofs, and to locate those openings where they will vent the fire without drawing it into uninvolved areas, cutting ventilation holes is usually the most effective method. Many flat roofs have a thick covering of tar and gravel or other material that may need to be removed or cut before cutting the sheathing. An axe can be used to cut the roof covering or to scrape away some of the gravel to facilitate cutting with a power saw (**Figure 8.79**). Thick tar coverings tend to gum up chain saws, so a rotary saw may be a better choice.

Ventilation holes in flat roofs should be cut parallel to the rafters and perpendicular to the outside walls of the building. Rafters or purlins can sometimes be located by sounding the roof. However, in many cases it will be necessary to make a diagonal cut in the roof until a structural member is intersected (**Figure 8.80**). Then, another cut is made to determine rafter direction (**Figure 8.81**). This process may also reveal the condition of the roof itself. If so, the roof's condition and stability should be communicated to the IC.

Once rafter location and direction have been determined, firefighters are ready to move to the desired location and begin cutting the ventilation opening. When cutting the ventilation opening, firefighters should work with the wind at their backs. They should start by making a cut across the leeward end. This should be followed by making parallel side cuts approximately 4 feet (120 cm) apart between the rafters (**Figure 8.82**). These cuts should start at the ends of the first cut and be made as long as necessary to create an exit opening of the required size. The roof covering and the sheathing may then be pulled back, together or separately, with two pick-head axes, pike poles, or rubbish hooks (**Figure 8.83**). If it is necessary to break out a section of ceiling below the exit opening, a rubbish hook or the butt of a pike pole will work.

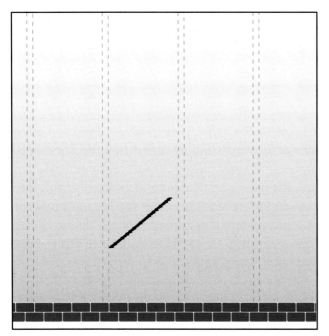

Figure 8.79 An axe is used to clear away gravel where saw cuts will be made.

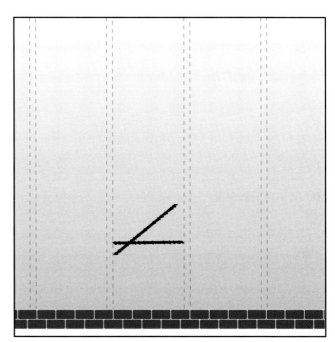

Figure 8.81 A second cut is made across the first.

Figure 8.80 A diagonal cut is made until a roof support is found.

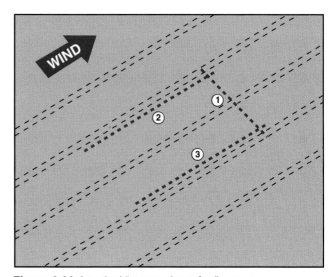

Figure 8.82 A typical "across-the-rafter" cut.

Figure 8.83 Firefighters work together to pull the roof covering.

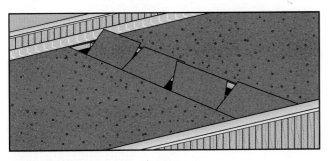

Figure 8.84 A typical trench vent.

Center rafter or louver vents may be cut in flat roofs in the same manner as described previously but with the addition of a fourth cut connecting the other ends of the side cuts. If it is necessary to cut a strip or trench vent, the louver vents may simply be extended from one outer wall to the other across the full width of the building (**Figure 8.84**).

Using existing openings. When smoke under pressure is issuing from a turbine vent, it is more efficient to leave the vent alone. The ventilator is doing what it was designed to do and, in most cases, will expel smoke and heat more efficiently with the rotary vane in place than if it were removed. Re-

moving the turbine takes time, does not increase the vent's efficiency, and can damage the vent pipe.

Roof monitors can also be used for vertical ventilation. To maximize their effect, at least two sides of the monitor housing should be removed.

If bubble skylights need to be opened for ventilation, the plastic bubble should be removed rather than broken. Likewise, the panes in wired glass skylights should be removed if possible, but they may have to be broken.

CAUTION
Interior crews should be warned before any glass skylights are broken.

When glass skylights must be broken, firefighters should break a single pane first and then pause before breaking out the remaining panes. The pause will give firefighters who did not hear the warning an opportunity to move out of the way or to alert the vent crew of the need to delay breaking the remainder of the panes.

Arched Roofs

Arched construction is typically used to support roofs with large, open spaces unobstructed by pillars or other supports. Structures with this type of roof are typically those used at convention centers, exhibition halls, sports arenas, and similar occupancies.

Arched roofs may be supported with bowstring trusses, or arches of steel, concrete, or laminated wood. Steel arches can be made from plate girders or trusses (**Figure 8.85**). Some wooden arches are

Figure 8.85 A typical steel truss arched roof.

laminated and glued at the factory. Others are constructed similar to trusses. Typically, arches are spaced at 16 to 20 foot (5 m to 6 m) centers.

Horizontal as well as vertical forces continuously act on an arched roof. As gravity attempts to flatten the arch, vertical forces bear down on the top of the arch. The resulting horizontal forces act on the ends of the arch, attempting to force them apart. These forces are resisted by abutments or buttresses at the ends of the arch or by tension cables or tie rods between the ends of the arch (**Figure 8.86**). The presence of tie rods is often obvious from the metal star plates on the exterior of the building (**Figure 8.87**). While the buttresses are usually stable, tension cables will lose their strength and integrity if exposed to fire. Arches may also contain hinges that permit some flexibility to allow for thermal expansion and contraction. These hinges can be found at the top of the arch or at the abutments.

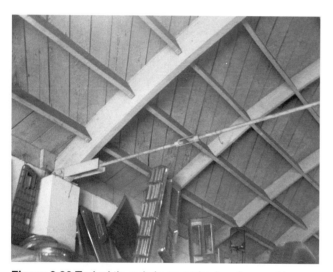

Figure 8.86 Typical tie rods in an arched roof assembly. *Courtesy of Wes Kitchel.*

Figure 8.87 Metal stars on the outside of a building are a clue that it has an arched roof.

Types of Arched Roofs

There are a variety of arched roofs. The two most common types are the bowstring and lamella arches.

Bowstring arch roof. The bowstring arch roof, commonly found in older bowling centers and supermarkets, uses a wooden bottom chord or a steel tie rod for lateral support with turnbuckles to maintain proper tension (**Figure 8.88**). The main supporting members are easy to locate from the outside if the tie rods pass through the exterior wall to a plate or reinforcement star. The chords of these arch members are usually laminated 2- × 12-inch (50 mm by 300 mm) or larger lumber. The rafters (usually 2 × 10 inches [50 mm by 250 mm]) are covered by 1- × 6-inch (25 mm by 150 mm) sheathing and composition roofing material. The perimeter of the building and the arch members are the strongest points.

This roof is normally quite strong because of the size of the lumber used in its construction. However, bowstring arches with steel tie rods have a history of early and sudden collapse when the tie rods are exposed to fire. Because the tie rods act to hold the outer walls together, the walls can be pushed outward when the tie rods fail, causing the entire building to collapse (**Figure 8.89**).

> # WARNING!
> Because of the potential for sudden collapse associated with bowstring arch roofs, incident commanders must be extremely cautious about placing crews inside these buildings and must carefully monitor elapsed time when deciding when to withdraw the crews.

Lamella roof. The lamella roof is made up of a geometric, egg-crate or modified diamond-pattern framework on which plank sheathing is laid (**Figure 8.90**). The framework is constructed of 2- × 12-inch (50 mm by 300 mm) wooden members bolted together at the intersections with steel gusset plates. The roof decking is 1- × 6-inch (25 mm by 150 mm) planking covered with composition roofing material.

Figure 8.88 A typical bowstring arched roof. *Courtesy of Greg Terrill.*

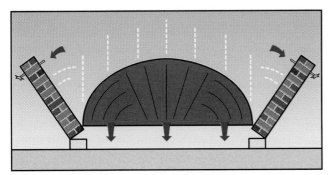

Figure 8.89 When tie rods fail, the walls fall outward and the roof comes down.

Figure 8.90 The distinctive pattern of a lamella roof.

Support is provided by exterior buttresses or internal tie rods with turnbuckles. The perimeter of the building is the strongest area. The lamella roof system shares many characteristics with the bowstring-type roof, and the same operational and safety considerations apply.

Hazards of Arched Roofs

Firefighters can estimate the hazards of arched roofs by the size of the lumber and the span of the arches. In trussed arch roofs, the lower chord of the truss may be covered with a ceiling to form an enclosed cockloft or attic space. These concealed spaces are a definite impediment to effective ventilation and may contribute to the spread of fire.

The single biggest hazard of arched roofs, however, is the danger of sudden and total collapse, often without warning (**Figure 8.91**). Because of this potential and because the rounded surface makes the use of roof ladders difficult, it is recommended that personnel work only from aerial devices when ventilating arched roofs.

Figure 8.91 Arched roofs can collapse without warning. *Courtesy of Mark Pedroia.*

> # WARNING!
> Fire involvement in the truss area should prompt the IC to consider the immediate withdrawal of all personnel from the roof and from the interior of the building.

Venting Arched Roofs

Arched roofs should be ventilated at the top of the arch directly over the fire or by a long, narrow strip vent along the centerline of the roof. A conventional square opening can be cut perpendicular to and

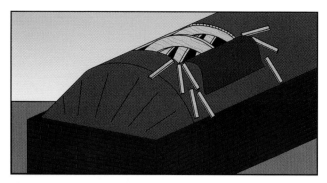
Figure 8.92 A typical square opening is often effective in this type of roof.

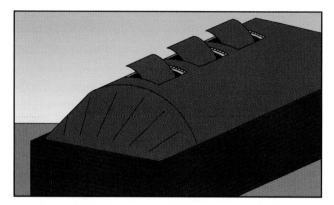
Figure 8.93 A series of louver vents may be necessary in this type of roof.

between main arch supports (**Figure 8.92**), or a louver vent (which will probably be faster) can be made. If a strip vent is to be cut along the centerline of the roof, a series of louver vents may be the best choice (**Figure 8.93**).

Lightweight Construction

Because of the costs of labor and building materials, lightweight building and roof construction has become much more common in recent years. In many modern buildings, heavy timber and 1- × 6-inch (25 mm by 150 mm) sheathing have given way to laminated beams and 2- × 4-inch (50 mm by 100 mm) lumber covered by ½-inch (13 mm) plywood or OSB, regardless of building size. Because these lightweight materials are less fire resistive than traditional materials, firefighters have less time in which to ventilate before the roof becomes dangerously unstable. This section focuses on the three major types of lightweight roof construction: *panelized roofs, trussed roofs,* and those supported by *wooden I-beams.*

Panelized Roofs

Panelized roof construction consists of laminated beams of various sizes (commonly 6 × 36 inches [15 cm by 90 cm]) that span the length or width of the building. These beams are supported at their ends by pilasters, wooden or steel posts, or saddles. Additional wooden or steel posts may provide support at intervals along the span. The beams may be bolted together to form lengths well in excess of 100 feet (30 m) and may be spaced between 12 feet (4 m) and 40 feet (12 m) apart. Wooden purlins (usually 4 × 12 inches [10 cm by 30 cm) with metal hangers are installed on 8-foot (240 cm) centers between and perpendicular to the beams (**Figure 8.94**). Wooden joists (usually 2 × 4 inches by 8 feet [5 cm by 10 cm by 240 cm]) are installed with metal hangers on 2-foot (60 cm) centers between and perpendicular to the purlins (**Figure 8.95**). Sheets of plywood or OSB (4 feet × 8 feet × ½ inch [120 cm by 240 cm by 13 mm]) are nailed over this framework and then covered with composition roofing material. The strongest parts of this construction are the beams, the purlins, and the perimeter of the building where the roof meets the exterior walls.

A three-layer, laminated insulation paper is used on the underside of panelized roof decking. This material offers little protection to the joists and plywood decking because it consists of a tar-impregnated layer covered on either side by a layer of thin aluminum foil. When the insulation paper is subjected to fire, the foil peels away from the tar-impregnated paper and disintegrates, allowing the joists and decking to be exposed to fire.

Trussed Roofs

There are several common types of trusses used in roof construction, each with unique characteristics. However, all trusses have certain characteristics in common. Among their common characteristics are that all trusses, regardless of configuration or application, are designed as a series of triangles — the strongest geometric shape known. All trusses also have a top chord and a bottom chord, connected by other components known as the "web." Some trusses are designed as horizontal assemblies; others are designed with a pitch. The most common types of roof trusses are *parallel chord trusses* and *pitched roof trusses.*

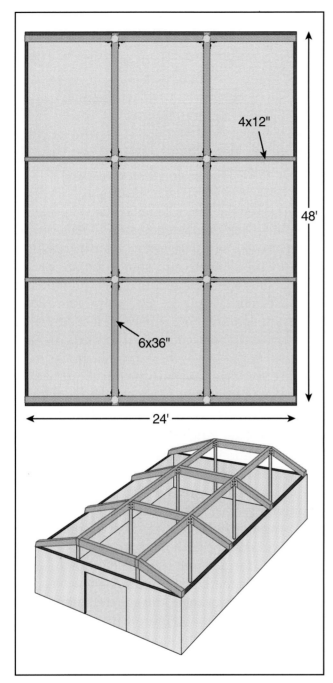

Figure 8.94 A basic panelized roof assembly.

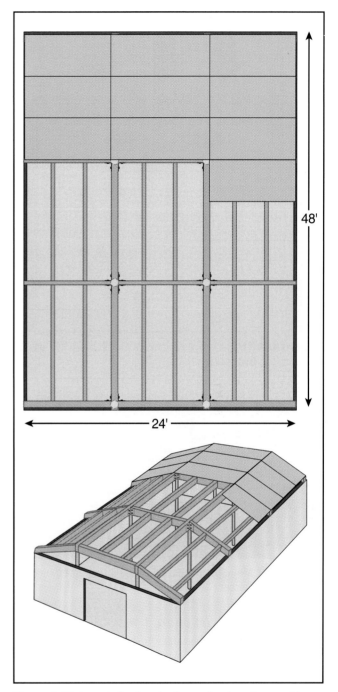

Figure 8.95 A partially sheathed panelized roof assembly.

Parallel Chord Trusses

Parallel chord trusses are constructed of metal or a combination of wood and metal. As the name implies, these trusses are designed with horizontal top and bottom chords that run parallel to each other. The top and bottom chords are connected by one or more web components. All parallel chord trusses are designed with web components that cause the space between the top and bottom chords to be mostly open. This design reduces the weight of the truss and allows easy penetration by ductwork, wir-

ing, and plumbing. However, it also allows for the rapid and unimpeded spread of heat, smoke, and fire. The bridging effect of parallel chord trusses causes the top chord to always be in compression and the bottom chord in tension (**Figure 8.96**). Because parallel chord trusses are capable of spanning large open spaces unsupported, they are used in a variety of applications and occupancies. The area where these trusses intersect with the outside bearing walls is the strongest point.

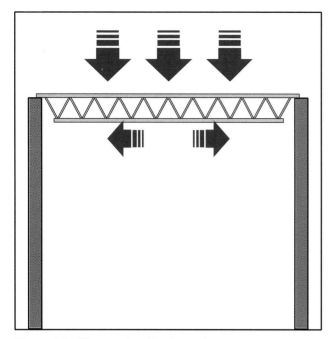

Figure 8.96 The top chord is always in compression and the bottom chord in tension.

Figure 8.97 Metal gusset plates connect truss members where they intersect.

Wooden parallel chord trusses. Some parallel chord trusses are constructed of wooden components held together with metal gusset plates, also known as *gang nails* (**Figure 8.97**). These gusset plates vary in size, thickness, and depth of penetration, but plates with ⅜-inch (9 mm) prongs are most common. Unless they are also corner-nailed, gusset plates often warp and pull out when exposed to fire. Like wooden I-beams (discussed later in this section), the bottom chords on wooden parallel chord trusses rest on and are supported by other beams or bearing walls (**Figure 8.98**).

Wooden/metal trusses. Other parallel chord trusses consist of wooden top and bottom chords that are cross-connected by web members made of steel tubing. The web members are usually made of 1-inch (25 mm) cold-rolled steel tubing with the

Figure 8.98 A typical wooden parallel chord truss.

ends pressed flat into a semicircular shape. Holes are punched in the flattened ends to receive connecting pins. These flattened ends are inserted into slots in the chords, and steel pins are driven through holes in the chord members and the web members, completing the assembly (**Figure 8.99**). Normal spacing of these trusses is 2 feet (60 cm) on center, and the area where the roof meets the exterior wall is the strongest point. Like most other parallel chord trusses, only the top chords rest on and are supported by a beam or bearing wall, and the bottom chords are unsupported (**Figure 8.100**).

Metal trusses. Still other parallel chord trusses are made entirely of steel components welded together. Also known as *bar joists*, these extremely strong assemblies often consist of top and bottom chords that are each made of two angle irons set in opposing directions. The web material may consist of individual members or a continuous piece of steel stock formed into a zigzag pattern. In either case, the web material is sandwiched between the opposing pieces of angle iron and the entire assembly is welded together (**Figure 8.101**). Bar joists are most often used to support a steel deck roof that is spot welded to the joists, and the joists may span as much as 144 feet (44 m). Other steel trusses are made of angle iron components that are welded or bolted together (**Figure 8.102**). These massive trusses are most often found in large commercial or industrial occmupancies.

> # WARNING!
> Case studies suggest that there is a potential for sudden collapse of this type of roof if interior crews inadvertently pull on the bottom chord of fire-weakened parallel chord trusses when pulling ceilings.

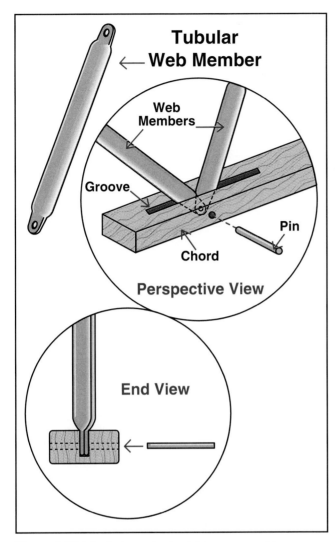

Figure 8.99 A typical wooden/metal truss assembly.

Figure 8.101 A typical bar joist.

Figure 8.102 A typical heavy metal truss.

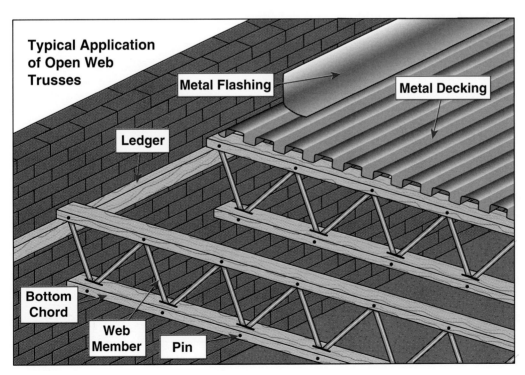

Figure 8.100 A typical wooden/metal truss installation.

Pitched Roof Trusses

Used mostly in residential construction, pitched roof trusses are known by a variety of names depending upon their configuration and are made from a variety of materials. Common pitched roof truss configurations are the Howe, Pratt, and Fink trusses. Each of these trusses, and other less common ones, can be made of wood, metal, or a combination of the two. While each of these trusses has certain unique characteristics, they are all similar enough to fall under the following discussion of pitched roof trusses.

Like many parallel chord trusses, the most common pitched roof trusses are prefabricated of relatively small dimension wood, usually 2- × 4-inch (50 mm by 100 mm) lumber held together with metal gusset plates where the components intersect (**Figure 8.103**). Pitched roof trusses are normally supported only by the outside bearing walls. In this type of construction, interior partition walls are essentially freestanding walls that do not actually support the truss at any point. However, to provide lateral support for partition walls, truss clips may be nailed to the bottom chord of the truss and to the top plate of a partition wall where the bottom chord crosses the wall. Even without the support of interior walls, spans of up to 55 feet (17 m) are possible using 2- × 4-inch (50 mm by 100 mm) components. The most common spacing between these trusses is 2 to 4 feet (60 cm to 120 cm) on center, and ½-inch (13 mm) plywood or OSB is commonly used as sheathing.

Unless the metal gusset plates with which these trusses are made are corner-nailed, these trusses offer less fire resistance than conventional (stick built) roof systems, and early roof collapse is possible. In addition, roof failure can occur when the bottom chord or webbing fails, either from direct fire damage or from connected interior walls falling and pulling them down.

Wooden I-Beams

Some roof and floor assemblies are supported by prefabricated wooden beams that incorporate a solid piece of material to connect the top and bottom chords. These assemblies are usually referred to as wooden I-beams. Wooden I-beams consist of three main components: a top chord, a bottom chord, and a solid ⅜-inch (10 mm) plywood or OSB web (**Figure 8.104**). The web is connected to the top and bottom chords by a continuous, glued joint. The chords may be made of 2- × 3-inch (50 mm by 75 mm) lumber, 2- × 4-inch (50 mm by 100 mm) lumber, or a wooden laminate called "micro-lam." Common spacing for this type of beam is 2 feet (60 cm) on center, and the area where the beams rest on the outside walls is the strongest point.

Because the web in a wooden I-beam has relatively little mass and a large surface area for combustion, it can burn through and weaken quickly, causing collapse of the beam and the roof or floor system it supports. If electrical conduits, plumbing, or heating and air conditioning ducts

Figure 8.103 Gable trusses with metal gusset plates.

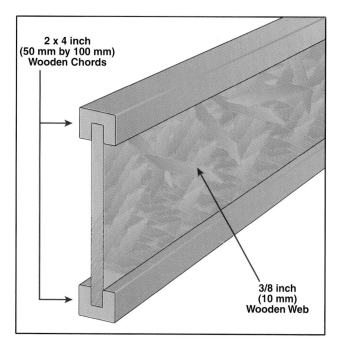

Figure 8.104 Components of a typical wooden I-beam.

2 x 4 inch (50 mm by 100 mm) Wooden Chords

3/8 inch (10 mm) Wooden Web

penetrate the web, some of the beam's strength is lost, and an avenue for fire spread is created (**Figure 8.105**). If the web remains intact during a fire, backdraft conditions may develop in the spaces between the I-beams. In a normal installation, the bottom chords on wooden I-beams are supported by other beams or by bearing walls.

Figure 8.105 Penetrations for plumbing and wiring create a path for fire spread.

Roof Coverings

Roof coverings are the weather-resistant materials applied over the roof decking or sheathing. They usually consist of one or more layers of underlayment (also called *substrate*) as a vapor barrier and/or insulation over which a weather-resistant covering is laid. The most common substrate is tar paper (also called *roofing felt*). Roof coverings may be combustible or noncombustible, depending on the application and local code requirements. Roof coverings are classified in NFPA 203, *Guidelines on Roof Coverings and Roof Deck Construction.* The coverings most commonly used on pitched roofs are wooden shingles or shakes, composition shingles or roll roofing, tile/slate, and light-gauge metal or fiberglass. On flat roofs, the most common coverings are tar and gravel, urethane/isocyanate foam, synthetic membrane, and steel in a variety of forms.

Wooden Shingles and Shakes

Wooden shingles come in a variety of sizes and are made from a number of different woods. Cedar and redwood shingles are the most common because of their appearance and inherent durability (**Figure**

8.106). Because these wafer-thin, wooden slabs have so little mass, they tend to be highly combustible when dehydrated by time and weather. Consequently, many jurisdictions allow wooden shingles to be used only if they have been pressure-treated with an approved fire retardant.

There are two main differences between wooden shingles and shakes. Shingles are sawn from large rectangular blocks of wood, so the shingles tend to be uniform in shape and thickness. Shakes, which are much thicker than shingles, are split from large blocks of wood, so their shape and thickness are much less uniform (**Figure 8.107**). Because of their additional mass, shakes are somewhat less susceptible to ignition than shingles, but many jurisdictions still require them to be treated with fire retardant before installation.

Shingles or shakes are usually nailed to wooden 1- by 4-inch (25 mm by 100 mm) or 1- × 6-inch (25 mm by 150 mm) planked sheathing with a space of about 1 inch (25 mm) between the planks. For

Figure 8.106 A weathered wooden shingle roof.

Figure 8.107 A typical shake roof.

Figure 8.108 Typical skip-sheathed roof.

obvious reasons, this form of sheathing is called *spaced sheathing* or *skip sheathing* (**Figure 8.108**). There is usually a single layer of tar paper between the sheathing and the shingles or shakes.

For ventilation purposes, the shingles/shakes can be quickly stripped from spaced sheathing by inserting the pick of an axe into the space between the planks and pulling the axe laterally in quick, short strokes. This alone may provide sufficient ventilation, but if not, the sheathing planks will have to be cut and stripped away as described earlier.

CAUTION

Wooden shakes and shingles can be very slippery when wet or covered by ice, snow, or moss. A roof ladder may be needed to provide safe footing during roof operations.

Composition Roofing/Shingles

Composition roofing also comes in a variety of materials and shapes. The most common forms are shingles (in rectangular strips) and rolls of various widths, but the 36-inch (90 cm) width is most common (**Figure 8.109**). As the name implies, they are usually made from a composite of an asphalt-base material and a granular mineral coating. The mineral coating provides weather resistance and acts as a fire retardant. In recent years, composition roofing containing fiberglass has also become available.

Composition roof coverings are also usually installed over a layer of tar paper. The roof covering is nailed through the tar paper to solid plywood or OSB decking or butted plank sheathing.

While much less combustible than wooden roof coverings, composition roofing materials will burn. Once any part of this material has burned, the surrounding roof covering must be stripped far enough to expose unburned sheathing all around the burned area. This may require that the roof covering be stripped from the entire roof. A flat shovel works well for this operation (**Figure 8.110**). How-

Figure 8.109 Composition roofing being installed.

Figure 8.110 A flat shovel can be used to strip shingles from a roof.

ever, one of the most troublesome aspects of composition roofing for firefighters is that it is a common practice for a new layer of roofing to be applied over an existing one when a building is re-roofed. This process can continue over the life of a building, resulting in multiple layers of roofing accumulating on the roof. This can make the roofing much more difficult to cut for ventilation purposes because the thick asphaltic material tends to gum up the blades of power saws. When multiple layers of roofing are found while ventilating a building during a fire, it indicates that the building is probably quite old and the added weight of the roofing materials combined with the effects of the fire may make the roof prone to early collapse.

Tar and Gravel

Tar and gravel roof coverings (also called *built-up roofs*) are very common on flat or nearly flat roofs. They are found on many types of buildings, ranging from single-family residences to large commercial or industrial buildings. During construction, melted roofing tar is "hot mopped" onto one or more layers of a tar paper substrate over plywood, OSB, or butted plank sheathing. Pea-sized gravel or crushed slag is most commonly broadcast onto the melted tar to add durability and weather resistance (**Figure 8.111**). Regardless of what mineral material is used on the roof, the mineral covering should be scraped away to protect the blade of the cutting tool before the roof covering is cut. Because the tar is thermoplastic, it will again soften and liquefy when exposed to the heat of a fire or that generated by a saw blade.

A single layer of tar and gravel roofing can be cut easily with a power saw or an axe, but this type of roofing is often found in multiple layers on the roofs of older buildings just as with the composition types of roof coverings. Older tar and gravel roofs may also be covered with a thick coating of foamed roofing (see following section), which often has a silver-colored finish layer. In either case, this type of roof covering can be cut and rolled back as a unit, or it may be louver cut.

Urethane/Isocyanate Foam

Urethane/isocyanate foams are applied to roofs in two forms. One is in the form of 4- × 8-foot (120 cm by 240 cm) sheets of foam insulation (**Figure 8.112**). The other is in what is called foamed-in-place applications. In either application, the foam is sealed by one or more layers of a weather-resistant covering. While these foams may be applied to new roofs, they are often applied over older existing roof coverings. The latter may result in an unusually thick roof covering that slows cutting ventilation openings. These thick, heavily insulated roofs tend to hold heat longer than other roof coverings, which increases the likelihood of flashover or backdraft conditions developing. Because of the toxic products these materials liberate when exposed to fire, firefighters should *always* wear SCBA when ventilating these roofs.

Single-Ply/Synthetic Membrane

Several liquid elastomers (rubber-like substances) are approved for application on new roofs or over existing built-up roofs after the gravel has been

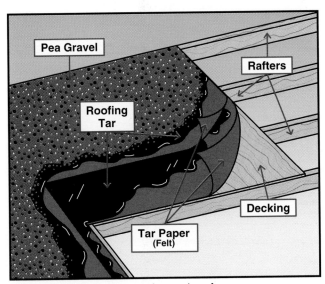

Figure 8.111 Typical tar-and-gravel roof.

Figure 8.112 A stack of foam insulation sheets.

scraped away. These coatings are then sealed with a single layer of any of a variety of approved flexible, water-resistant synthetic membranes (also known as *single-ply roofs*). These membranes are made of neoprene, polyvinyl chloride, chlorinated polyethylene, or bituminous sheets reinforced with polyester or fiberglass (**Figure 8.113**). The sheets are then sealed to the substrates below with an adhesive or by heating the underside of the sheet with an electric heat sealer gun or a propane torch. The seams in the membranes are overlapped and welded together by heating in the same way.

From a ventilation standpoint, these single-ply roof coverings can present some serious problems for firefighters. While the membranes and their substrates are easily cut with common ventilation tools, they are highly combustible and liberate toxic products when they burn.

> # WARNING!
> Single-ply/synthetic membrane roofing materials liberate highly toxic products of combustion when they burn. Firefighters must protect themselves with SCBA, and people downwind of the fire may need to be evacuated.

Tile/Slate

Terra-cotta tile (sometimes called *Spanish* tile) roofs are common in some areas. They are made of either semicircular or S-shaped tiles that are "nested" on the roof, usually over a single layer of tar paper on wooden sheathing (**Figure 8.114**). Concrete, clay, or ceramic tile roofs use tiles that are usually flat, interlocking pieces that hook over 1- × 2-inch (25 mm by 50 mm) battens (sometimes called *furring strips*) nailed to the sheathing or directly to the rafters (**Figure 8.115**). Slate roofs are most common on churches and some larger, single-family dwellings. Slates are usually nailed directly to the roof sheathing.

Figure 8.114 A typical terra-cotta tile roof.

Figure 8.115 A typical concrete tile roof.

Figure 8.113 A typical single-ply membrane roof.

Tile/slate roofs are somewhat fragile and often cannot be walked on without breaking the tiles. Firefighters walking on the roof may cause considerable damage while getting to the area to be ventilated. To reduce breakage, firefighters should step only on the lower half of the tiles, and they may spread their weight by working from roof ladders.

CAUTION

Since tile/slate roofs cannot be sounded in the same ways as other roofs, firefighters must remove tiles to identify where roof supports are located. To ensure that they remain on roof supports as they move about on these roofs, tiles/slates must be removed ahead of them.

Ideally, ventilating these roofs involves removing the individual tiles or slate. If possible, tiles should be removed and stacked, not broken. However, conditions may necessitate shattering the tiles or slate over the appropriate area. This is best accomplished with a sledgehammer, although a flat-head or pick-head axe can also be used. The sheathing can then be cut using an axe or power saw. Broken pieces of tile/slate may slide off the roof creating a safety hazard below; therefore, close coordination between ventilation crews and those working on the ground is critical. In addition, tile/slate roofs carry more weight per unit of surface area than any other roof style and may therefore be susceptible to early roof collapse. In addition, when some buildings are remodeled, tile or slate is used to cover roof assemblies that were not designed to support the weight of these materials. Unless the roof assembly in reinforced, the extra dead load makes these roofs susceptible to collapse.

Light-Gauge Metal/Fiberglass

This type of roof covering consists of aluminum, fiberglass, or 18- to 20-gauge steel panels over a wooden or metal substructure. The panels may be corrugated, ribbed, or shaped to simulate tiles or shakes (**Figure 8.116**). Buildings with corrugated metal roofs often have plastic or fiberglass panels as skylights in shed and gable roof configurations (**Figure 8.117**). If these panels are obscured by

Figure 8.116 Typical metal roof styles.

Figure 8.117 A metal roof with a plastic skylight.

smoke, darkness, or snow, or if they have been painted over, firefighters stepping on the panels can fall through the roof. The ridge and the area where the roof crosses the outside bearing walls are the strongest points. Because these roof coverings are commonly used over the most lightweight substructures, this roof system has little fire resistance and is subject to early collapse. These roofing materials can be cut with an axe or a tin roof tool (**Figure 8.118**). However, using a power saw with a metal-cutting blade or a chain saw is far more efficient.

Figure 8.118 A roof cutter can be used to open a metal roof.

Steel Clad

In an attempt to secure their property against entry through the roof, some property owners cover their roofs with steel grids or plates. The entire roof surface, including the steel components, is then resealed under a layer of tar. This seal coat sometimes makes the steel difficult to see and the roof nearly impossible to ventilate in a timely manner. Two types of these steel-clad roofs are commonly installed.

The first type consists of ¼-inch (6 mm) thick by 2-inch (50 mm) wide steel strips laid out side-by-side on the roof. A second layer of strips crosses the first layer at right angles, and the strips are welded together at each intersection. The grid thus formed leaves small openings of from 6 to 8 inches (15 cm to 20 cm) square. The entire grid is lag-bolted through the roof to the joists below (**Figure 8.119**). The entire system is then covered with hot tar to restore weather resistance.

The second type consists of laying 4- × 8-foot (120 cm by 240 cm) sheets of steel, ranging from ⅛ to ¼ inch (3 mm to 6 mm) thick, over the en-

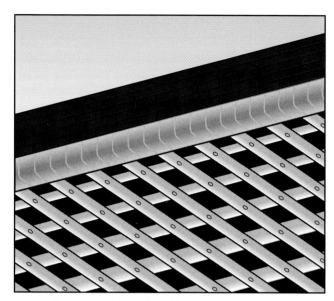

Figure 8.119 The finished roof is coated with roofing tar.

tire roof surface. The plates are then welded together to form a continuous layer of steel. Again, hot tar is applied to restore weather resistance.

Steel-clad roofs hold in heat and smoke, promote the development of flashover and backdraft conditions, impede ventilation efforts, and increase the chances of roof collapse due to the added weight. Because a ¼-inch (6 mm) steel plate weighs about 10 pounds per square foot (49 kg/m²), a 20- × 50-foot (7 m by 17 m) roof would have approximately 10,000 pounds (4 536 kg) added to it. The only effective way to prevent this type of construction from interfering with ventilation operations is to learn of its existence through pre-incident planning inspections and then to develop procedures for dealing with it.

The buildings most likely to have these measures will be high-value occupancies, although in high-crime areas they will also be found on ordinary commercial and industrial buildings. Because it may also discourage potential burglars, some building owners/occupants may be willing to post a prominent sign on the front of the building stating that the building has a steel-clad roof. This sign can alert firefighters during a fire so that the steel roof protection can be taken into account during size-up and planning.

Opening a Roof

The location for the ventilation exit opening will generally be determined by several factors such as a familiarity with the roof structure, the layout of the building, coordination with interior operations, and an initial size-up of the fire situation. Other clues that may be helpful in locating the spot for the ventilation exit opening are smoke coming from existing openings, smoke or fire coming through the roof covering, blisters in the roof covering, or a sagging roof. After determining the best place for the ventilation hole, firefighters can begin opening the roof.

Once the need to open the roof has been determined and the location for the opening has been selected, firefighters should not hesitate to cut a hole to open the roof, especially if there are no existing openings or if they are too small or in the wrong location. However, in most departments, this decision is reserved to the officer in charge of the vent group/sector in coordination with the IC.

Before accessing the roof, firefighters should establish primary and secondary escape routes from the roof. Once these routes are established, firefighters should *read* the roof from a position of safety. Unless it is a tile/slate roof, they should also sound the roof with a hand tool to make certain that the roof is stable before stepping off the ladder onto the roof. Once on the roof, they should get a feel for the roof by bouncing on it while holding onto the ladder with one hand (**Figure 8.120**). They should continue reading and sounding the roof as they walk on it. They should also stop frequently and bounce on the roof to see if the feel of it has changed. Any difference in the feel of the roof may indicate that they are on a weakened section of the roof.

CAUTION

Firefighters should never walk diagonally across a roof but should walk only over the main roof supports.

A key factor in opening roofs safely and efficiently is knowing the location and extent of the fire and the location and direction of the rafters. Most roof assemblies employ a parallel rafter system with rafters spaced from 12 to 24 inches (30 cm to 60 cm) on center, spanning the shortest distance between bearing walls. Exceptions to this rule are panelized

roofs and specialty roofs using wood or metal trusses or laminated beams. If a thermal imager is available, it can be used to reveal the location and direction of the rafters and other roof supports. If a thermal imager is not available and all other signs indicate that the roof is stable, the roof should be sounded. If sounding does not reveal the location and direction of the rafters, a diagonal cut through the roof covering can be made with a chain saw or rotary saw at an angle of 45 degrees to any exterior wall. The blade will usually encounter a rafter before the cut is 3 feet (1 m) long. If, after the rafter is located, its direction is still unknown, a cut parallel to a sidewall should be made, crossing the first cut. This cut should be 2 to 3 feet (60 cm to 90 cm) long. If no rafters are found, then rafter direction is parallel to the second cut. A triangular hole can be completed to determine spacing, roof thickness, and possible fire/smoke conditions in the attic. Many experienced firefighters prefer to make these cuts with a chain saw because it allows the operator to "feel" the rafters better than with a rotary saw.

Figure 8.120 Bouncing on a roof tells the firefighter what the roof feels like when supported.

When firefighters reach the point where the ventilation opening is to be made, every cutting and pulling operation should allow them to continually work back toward an area of safety (**Figure 8.121**). Once the first cut is made in the roof, the firefighters should avoid putting themselves between that first cut and the seat of the fire. The following precautions should be considered when ventilating any roof:

- Know the emergency escape routes and be prepared to use them.

- When appropriate, use existing openings to limit damage to the roof.

- Maintain a safe distance between crew members and cutting tools.

- Do not make the opening between a crew member and the escape route or in the normal path of travel.

- Cut the roof covering and decking—not the supporting structural members.

- Begin the opening on the leeward side and work against the wind whenever possible so that smoke and hot gases are blown away from the vent crew.

- Remove the ceiling below the roof to ensure adequate ventilation.

Figure 8.121 Firefighters should work with the wind at their backs when venting a roof.

Cutting the Hole

As previously mentioned, before the ventilation exit opening is cut, the location of the fire should be determined and the opening made as close to the seat of the fire as can be done safely. Ideally, the ventilation exit opening should be made directly over the seat of the fire; however, this can be *extremely dangerous*. The location of the ventilation exit opening must be based upon the type of roof construction, condition of the roof, fire conditions, available tools and equipment, and the experience and capabilities of the vent crew.

> # WARNING!
> If there is any doubt about the structural integrity of the roof or a section of it, firefighters should not be allowed in the questionable area. Ventilation operations in that area should be limited to those that can be performed from an aerial device.

When an exit opening is cut, it should be cut large enough to do the job because the time required to enlarge it or to cut several smaller holes is greater than that for making one large one. For example, one 8- × 8-foot (240 cm by 240 cm) hole is equal in area to four 4- × 4-foot (120 cm by 120 cm) holes (**Figure 8.122**). When cutting through a roof, firefighters should make the opening square or rectangular and at right angles to the bearing walls to

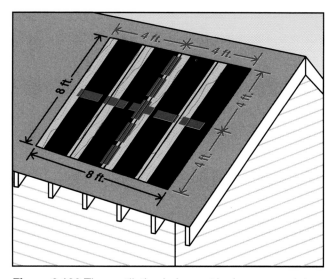

Figure 8.122 The ventilation hole must be large enough to be effective.

increase firefighter safety and to facilitate repairs after the fire.

Although one large hole is better for ventilation than several small holes, the holes do not necessarily have to be square. Even though firefighters may use a power saw to cut the traditional large, square hole, they may still have to contend with the nails in two or more rafters in order to pull the sheathing (**Figure 8.123**). This can be a slow and very physically taxing task. On the other hand, rectangular, louver vents can be made very quickly and with much less effort (**Figure 8.124**). If a larger opening is needed, the hole can be lengthened and used for trench ventilation (described later in this chapter), or a closely grouped series of holes can be cut.

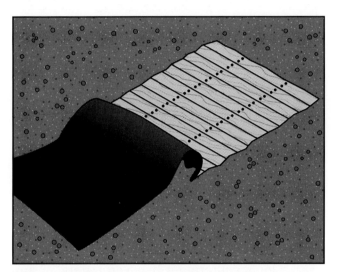

Figure 8.123 Sheathing can be difficult to pull if two or more rows of nails must be pulled as well.

Figure 8.124 A typical louver vent.

Louver Vents

Cutting louver vents is often the fastest and most efficient way of opening a roof. Unlike large, square openings, in louver vents there is always a rafter in the center of the sheathing being cut so that a constant reference point is maintained with the rafters. Knowing the location and direction of the rafters and the type of sheathing are critical to safe and efficient roof cutting operations.

Basically, there are two methods that have proven effective for cutting louver vents in roofs. Both methods employ the center-rafter principle and take advantage of the roof's construction to facilitate opening the roof. In the first and most common method, the longest cuts are made parallel to the rafters; in the other method, the longest cuts are made across the rafters.

Center- Rafter Cut

The first of these methods involves cutting a long, rectangular center-rafter vent. This method is sometimes referred to as "cutting with the rafters." With a rafter spacing of 2 feet (60 cm) on center, the hole will be approximately 4 feet (120 cm) wide and at least 4 feet (120 cm) long (**Figure 8.125**).

The following steps outline the procedures for a center-rafter cut:

Step 1: Make the first cut parallel to rafter "A," cutting 2 to 3 inches (50 mm to 75 mm) from the rafter to miss any metal joist hangers.

Step 2: If the roof is sheathed with plywood or OSB or if there are multiple layers of roof covering, make the second cut by starting near rafter "A," rolling over rafter "B" without cutting it, and stopping just short of rafter "C."

   NOTE: If the roof covering is thin and if the roof is sheathed with plank sheathing, it may not be necessary to make this end cut because the sheathing provides a break at each joint.

CAUTION
It is critical that the rafters not be cut as this will weaken the roof.

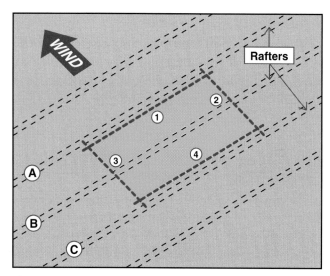

Figure 8.125 A typical "center rafter" cut.

Step 6: If it is necessary to enlarge the hole, repeat either Steps 1, 2, and 4 or Steps 1, 3, and 4 depending on whether the original hole is enlarged to the right or the left.

A center-rafter cut works equally well on pitched or flat roofs, particularly in newer buildings with 2- × 4-inch (50 mm by 100 mm) trusses set on 24-inch (600 mm) centers.

Dicing

A second method of louver venting, sometimes called "rolling the rafters," involves making the two longest cuts perpendicular to the rafters. Subsequent cuts are made parallel to the rafters but in the center between the rafters instead of adjacent to them (**Figure 8.127**).

The following steps outline the procedures for the dicing method:

Step 1: If the roof is sheathed with diagonal planks, plywood or OSB, or if there are multiple layers of roof covering, start the first cut centered between rafters "A" and "B." Cut across rafters "B" and "C" without cutting them, stopping halfway between rafters "C" and "D."

NOTE: If the covering is thin and the roof is over perpendicular plank sheathing, you may not need to make this cut because the sheathing provides a break at each joint.

Step 2: Make the second cut about 4 feet (1.22 m) long, centering it between rafters "A" and "B."

Step 3: Make the third cut by starting at rafter "A," rolling over rafter "B" without cutting it, and stopping short of rafter "C."

NOTE: Again, this end cut may not be necessary if there is thin roof covering over plank sheathing.

Step 4: Make the fourth and final cut parallel to rafter "C," cutting as close to the rafter as possible without hitting any joist hangers.

Step 5: Push down on the near edge of the louver to expose the far edge, and then pull the far edge to fold back the sheathing and open the vent away from the crew (**Figure 8.126**).

NOTE: If conditions dictate, plank sheathing can be stripped away with rubbish hooks instead of being tilted into a louver vent.

Figure 8.126 Firefighters should simultaneously push and pull the louver to open it.

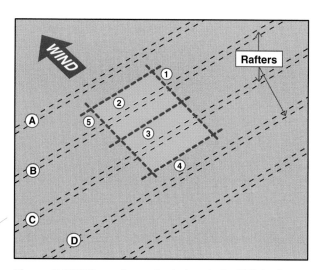

Figure 8.127 The pattern of cuts in a typical "dicing" operation.

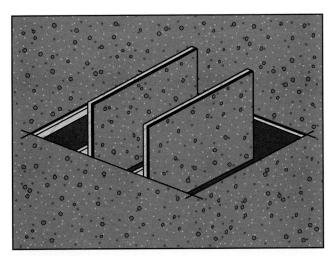

Figure 8.128 When all cuts are completed, the louvers can be tilted up.

Step 3: Make the third cut centered between rafters "B" and "C," making it the same length as the second cut.

Step 4: Make the fourth cut centered between rafters "C" and "D," making it the same length as the second and third cuts.

Step 5: Make the fifth and final cut in the same manner as the first cut, except make it at the opposite ends of the second, third, and fourth cuts.

Step 6: Once all the cuts are completed, tilt the sheathing between the cuts to open the louvers (**Figure 8.128**).

> **NOTE:** Regardless of the cutting tool used, it is generally best to complete as many cuts as possible before pulling or folding back the sheathing. This will help reduce the firefighters' exposure to heat and smoke during the cutting operations.

Step 7: To enlarge the opening, repeat either Steps 1-4 or Steps 2-5 to widen it, or repeat Steps 1, 2, 3, and 5 to lengthen it. In either case, repeat Step 6 to tilt the louvers.

Trench (Strip) Ventilation

Primarily a defensive maneuver, *trench ventilation* is sometimes referred to as *strip ventilation*. In some departments the term *strip vent* is used to describe a *louver vent*; however, the terms *strip* and *trench* are used interchangeably here to indicate a relatively narrow ventilation exit opening that extends from one outside wall to the other. The term *trench* may be somewhat misleading. If firefighters infer a long, *deep* hole and cut the rafters, purlins, or other supporting members, the roof system may be seriously weakened in the process. Rather than making a deep cut, firefighters should cut only the roof covering and sheathing and not the members supporting the roof when cutting a hole for trench ventilation.

When done properly, trench ventilation will often help confine a fire to one section of a building by preventing the horizontal spread of heat, smoke, and fire. Trench ventilation has proven to be particularly effective in cutting off running attic fires in strip malls and other buildings with long, narrow, undivided attics.

Trench ventilation is accomplished by making an opening in the roof, approximately 4 feet (120 cm) wide, across the entire width of the building (**Figure 8.129**). It is imperative that the vent extends fully from one outside wall to the other. If any part of the

Figure 8.129 A typical trench vent.

roof within the vent opening is left intact, the fire can burn past the trench vent and involve the rest of the building. If the fire being cut off is not in the attic, the ceiling below must also be breached once the roof has been opened. In most cases a center-rafter (louver) cut is fastest for making a trench vent. However, depending upon roof construction and rafter orientation, other methods may be more appropriate.

> **CAUTION**
>
> Because cutting a strip vent takes time, it is imperative that the trench be located far enough ahead of the advancing fire to allow sufficient time to complete the opening before the fire reaches it.

Summary

Vertical ventilation offers a number of benefits to the overall fireground operation at structure fires. Properly done, vertical ventilation can influence the behavior of an interior structure fire to protect firefighters and other occupants by channeling heat and smoke away from them. Vertical ventilation can also reduce property damage by limiting the horizontal spread of a fire. Done at the right time, vertical ventilation can prevent both flashovers and backdrafts by allowing heat and smoke to vent harmlessly into the atmosphere.

However, vertical ventilation is also a potentially very dangerous operation. Whenever firefighters must operate on fire-weakened roofs that may collapse without warning, they may be in serious jeopardy. Firefighters may also fall from steeply pitched roofs that are slippery from rain, snow, or ice, and they may stumble over low parapets or into open light wells. Firefighters can be overcome by heat and fatigue while performing strenuous tasks on hot, wind-protected roofs surrounded by high parapet walls. Therefore, firefighters must protect themselves by learning as much as possible about the construction of the buildings within their response districts and devising plans for dealing with known hazards safely. They must know and apply the most efficient use of their ventilation tools and equipment. In every situation, they must function as a team and look out for each other. And, finally, they must develop and maintain the physical and psychological strength and stamina required to perform vertical ventilation safely and effectively.

Chapter 9
Special Ventilation Operations

Chapter 9
Special Ventilation Operations

As the cost of undeveloped land in urban areas has risen, economic considerations have forced builders to erect structures with a relatively small footprint and that are two or more stories high — often many stories high. High-rise structures are being built even in suburban and rural communities, presenting a new fire fighting challenge for many small fire departments. Departments that previously had to deal with only one- and two-story buildings are now faced with having to perform rescues or fight fires well above the reach of their longest ladders (**Figure 9.1**).

Some of the same economic factors that have created the need for high-rise buildings have also spurred the development of highly secure windowless and underground structures. To deal with these extraordinary structures, fire departments must develop new strategies based upon the construction of the buildings and the available resources. This chapter deals with the problems associated with ventilating high-rise buildings and other unusual structures such as windowless and underground structures, highly secure buildings, and remodeled buildings.

Figure 9.1 Small departments can be unprepared when high-rise buildings are constructed in their districts.

Fire Operations in High-Rise Buildings

High-rise fires present numerous challenges for firefighters — limited access, large numbers of offices or apartments, heavy occupant loads, falling glass and other debris, smoke and fire spread through vertical shafts, locked interior doors, low water pressure, and crews having to climb an extraordinary number of stairs. These are but a few examples of what firefighters can expect when fighting a high-rise fire. Crews may also have to deal with stranded occupants, unfamiliar floor layouts, complex elevator and HVAC systems, built-in fire protection equipment, and difficult communications — each of which may complicate fireground operations.

Staffing
The staffing required for operations in this type of building may be several times as great as that required for similar fires in smaller structures. The problems of communication and coordination between attack and ventilation crews can be compounded as the number of involved personnel increases. In addition to the extra personnel required to handle the logistics of fighting a high-rise fire, the physical exertion required to merely reach the fire floor or the roof may mean that crews will have less energy left to perform their assigned tasks (**Figure 9.2**). Consequently, crews will have to be relieved sooner than they normally would, and they will have to be rotated more frequently.

Fire Attack
Most fire departments attack a high-rise fire from the floor below the fire and concentrate relief crews

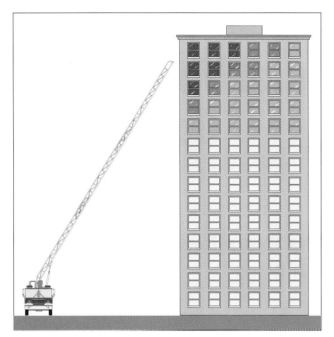

Figure 9.2 Just reaching the roof can be a challenge for vent crews.

and spare equipment in *Staging*, two floors below the fire floor. During a high-rise fire, firefighters (including fireground support personnel) should never enter the building empty-handed. If they do not have to carry forcible entry or ventilation tools and equipment, they should carry spare SCBA cylinders, hose, tools, lights, etc., to Staging (**Figure 9.3**).

Figure 9.3 When entering a burning high-rise building, firefighters should carry extra equipment to Staging.

Elevators

High-rise buildings often have a variety of elevators. These include the following types:

- *Low-rise elevators* — Serving the lower floors of the building. For example, they may serve floors 1 through 10.

- *Mid-rise elevators* — Serving only those floors between the low-rise and high-rise elevators. For example, they may serve floors 1 and 10 through 20.

- *High-rise elevators* — Serving only the upper floors. For example, they may serve floors 1 and 20 through 30.

- *Express elevators* — Usually serving only the ground floor and the uppermost floor of the building. For example, they may serve only floors 1 and 31 or whatever the highest floor happens to be.

- *Freight elevators* — Serving some or all floors.

When it is deemed safe to do so, some departments allow their firefighters to use freight elevators to ascend part way to the fire floor and to transport additional equipment. Departments that allow this do so because these elevators are usually not in blind shafts, and they are designed to carry heavier loads than ordinary passenger elevators. A fully equipped firefighter, especially one wearing a full tool belt or carrying spare air tanks, can exceed 300 pounds (135 kg). Obviously, a half-dozen fully equipped firefighters and any spare equipment could weigh a ton (1 000 kg) or more. A group of fully equipped firefighters carrying additional equipment will be less likely to overload freight elevators than passenger elevators. However, freight elevators should only be used when authorized by the officer in charge on the fire floor.

WARNING!

Elevators that serve the fire floor or above should not be used by occupants or firefighters unless the officer in charge on the fire floor has determined that it is safe to do so.

An elevator control malfunction could automatically call the elevator car to the fire floor, or a power failure could strand the elevator car above the fire or between floors. Therefore, those assigned to *Lobby Control* should bring all elevators to the ground floor and lock them there. Elevators that do not serve the fire floor or above and are equipped with manual fire department controls may then be used for evacuating occupants and for shuttling firefighters and equipment partway to the fire floor.

Fire Behavior

Because of structural characteristics that are unique to very tall buildings, regardless of their use or occupancy, fires may behave differently in these structures than in those of more modest dimensions. For example, fires in grain elevators or buildings with multistory stairwells or tall elevator shafts are subject to fire extension to a degree that shorter structures are not. Fire behavior in high-rise buildings is most affected by *stack effect* and *mushrooming*.

Stack Effect

As described in **Essentials**, *stack effect* is the natural vertical movement of heat and smoke (convection) in tall structures. Because of differences in the density of the air inside and outside of these buildings, resulting from differences in inside and outside temperatures, heat and smoke rise as if in a smoke stack — thus, the name. The greater the difference is between the inside and outside temperature and the greater the building height is, the greater the stack effect will be (**Figure 9.4**).

If a high-rise building is vented at the roof and at the street level, the direction and intensity of airflow within the building depends primarily on the relative temperature differences. If it is hotter inside than outside, the airflow will be inward at the bottom and outward at the top. But if the outside air is hotter than the air inside, the flow will be reversed. If there is only a short distance between the upper and lower openings and if the inside and outside temperatures are equal, no natural airflow takes place.

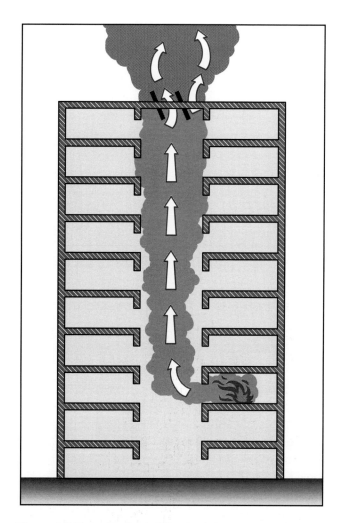

Figure 9.4 The taller the building is, the greater the stack effect.

Mushrooming

The mushrooming effect that commonly occurs on the top floors of smaller buildings does not always occur in the same way in very tall buildings if insufficient heat is generated to move the smoke and fire gases to the top of the building. As smoke and fire gases rise within the building, heat dissipates into the environment, cooling the smoke and other gases. These products of combustion rise through any vertical opening until they encounter a horizontal obstruction or until their temperature is reduced to the temperature of the surrounding air. When this equalization of temperature occurs, the smoke and fire gases lose their buoyancy, cease to rise, and *stratify* — forming layers or clouds of smoke within the building (**Figure 9.5**). Stratification can occur several floors below the top floor of the building. The products of combustion then

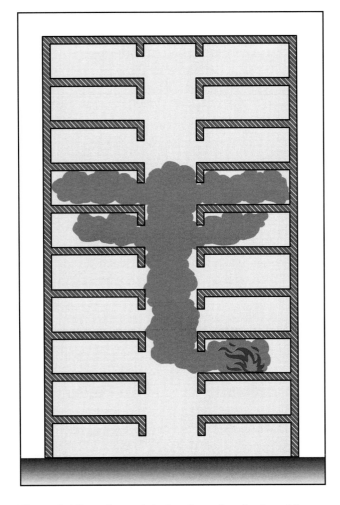

Figure 9.5 If smoke cools before it reaches the top of the building, it will stratify at some level.

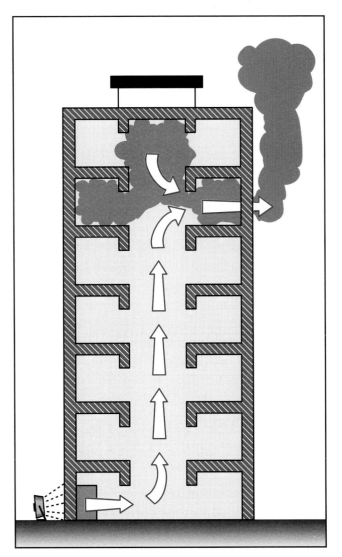

Figure 9.6 PPV can be used to vent cold smoke from a building.

spread laterally and downward until the building is ventilated. In very hot climates, it is also common to see a "reverse stack effect." Because of the extreme heat outside, the smoke actually migrates downward.

Stratification of smoke and fire gases can create a highly toxic atmosphere many floors above the fire, even where there is little heat. Ventilating this cooled, stratified smoke out of the building can be accomplished by using positive-pressure blowers to create a controlled flow of air up the stairwell and horizontally across the smoke-filled floors (**Figure 9.6**). However, there are limits to the effectiveness of positive pressure ventilation (PPV) in high-rise buildings. PPV blowers positioned at street level are effective up to about 22 floors. If ventilation is required above that level, additional blowers will have to be positioned at about the 22nd floor, smoke ejectors will have to be positioned at the highest level to be ventilated, or both may be required.

High-Rise Ventilation

High-rise buildings may be ventilated in several ways. Vertical (top) ventilation, horizontal ventilation of the fire floor, and horizontal ventilation above and below the fire floor are the options available at a high-rise fire. Because of the numerous factors affecting smoke movement in a high-rise fire and the need to channel heat and smoke away from egress routes, it may be necessary to employ more than one of these methods. The following discussion of airflow within high-rise buildings relates primarily to *natural* ventilation. The natural airflow within a high-rise building can be enhanced or even reversed through mechanical means, especially when *positive-pressure* ventilation is used.

In high-rise buildings, fire and smoke may spread rapidly through pipe shafts, stairways, elevator shafts, air-handling systems, and other vertical openings because of convection. In some instances, ventilation must be accomplished horizontally on the fire floor or on the floors immediately above the fire where smoke and heat may have spread. Despite the danger of the fire lapping into floors above the fire and the hazards of shards of broken glass falling onto those in the street below, horizontal ventilation may be the most appropriate method in some situations. For example, if ventilating vertically would endanger occupants attempting to leave the building, horizontal ventilation must be used. In other situations, the fire can and should be vented vertically through stairwells or other vertical shafts, taking advantage of the stack effect described earlier.

CAUTION

Elevator shafts should not be used for ventilation because of the fall hazard created if shaft doors are left open and visibility is reduced by smoke or darkness.

Vertical (Top) Ventilation

During pre-incident planning, the potential for vertically ventilating serious fires in high-rise buildings should be considered. Top ventilation can prevent or reduce mushrooming on the upper floors and does not promote lapping, which is always a danger when venting horizontally in multistory buildings. A pre-incident inspection of the roof will reveal the existence of any roof vents that may lend themselves to the fire ventilation process or of any automatic smoke vents that may reduce or eliminate the need for additional top ventilation by firefighters.

Getting Firefighters to the Roof

One of the biggest challenges in top venting high-rise buildings is getting the vent crew and their equipment to the roof. The roofs of most high-rise and even some low-rise buildings are beyond the reach of aerial devices; therefore, some alternative

means of getting to the roof must be found. The various ways of reaching the roof of a high-rise building involve using an aerial device whenever possible, using an interior stairway, using elevators that do not serve the fire floor and then using the interior stairway, and using helicopters. Each of these methods has certain advantages and disadvantages.

Aerial devices. When an aerial device is able to reach the roof of a high-rise building, using it is the preferred method of getting to the roof because it is the fastest, safest, and most direct route (**Figure 9.7**). Firefighters using an aerial device will not have to contend with the congestion of personnel and equipment that often develops in the interior stairways of high-rise buildings during a fire. In many cases aerial devices will not reach the roof. However, they can be used as far as they will reach to access an exterior fire escape or to provide a platform from which entry can be forced into an upper floor of the building. The vent crew can then continue to the roof via the interior stairway.

Figure 9.7 An aerial device is the best way for firefighters to reach the roof.

Interior stairway. While many high-rise buildings have more than one interior stairway, few have more than one that terminates on the roof and would be useful for ventilation purposes. In this context, references to the *interior stairway* assume that the stairway terminates on the roof. Pre-incident inspection of the building should reveal which stairway leads to the roof, whether it is a smokeproof tower, whether it can be pressurized from below, and whether it is likely to be available for access during fire attack. During a fire, the interior stairway may be relatively free of smoke but can be heavily congested with occupants leaving upper floors, with firefighters carrying equipment to Staging, and with charged attack lines. Vent crews should communicate with attack crews before deciding which interior stairway to use.

Elevators. As mentioned earlier, any elevator that serves the fire floor(s) or above should *not* be used by occupants or firefighters unless the officer in charge *on the fire floor* determines that it is safe to do so. If local protocols allow, elevators that do not reach the fire floor may be used to shuttle firefighters and equipment to the highest floor served by the elevator. The vent group can then use an interior stairway to reach its destination. However, the vent group should assess heat and smoke conditions before committing to using the stairway.

Helicopters. One of the most direct means of moving personnel and equipment to the roof of a high-rise building, and of removing occupants stranded on the roof, is through the use of helicopters — weather and smoke conditions permitting. To use helicopters safely and most effectively during a fire requires close coordination between fireground personnel and the helicopter crew. This level of coordination can only be achieved through pre-incident planning and realistic training between the two groups (**Figure 9.8**).

Procedures must be developed for identifying safe landing zones, for transporting fire and rescue

Figure 9.8 To work effectively together, fire crews must train with helicopter crews.

personnel to the roof, and for removing occupants from the roof who may be injured. Once these procedures have been developed, they need to be tested in realistic exercises and revised as necessary. To maintain an adequate level of readiness, firefighters and helicopter crews need to train together on a regular, periodic basis.

Channeling the Smoke

In buildings having only one stairwell that terminates on the roof, this natural "chimney" may be used to ventilate smoke, heat, and fire gases from various floors. The bulkhead (penthouse) door on the roof must be blocked open or removed from its hinges before the stairway doors on the fire floors are opened. Removal of the bulkhead door ensures that it cannot be closed accidentally, upsetting the established ventilation process and allowing the shaft to become filled with super-heated gases.

Timing and coordination of ventilation with rescue and fire suppression operations are extremely important. Ventilation directed up the one stairwell that terminates on the roof must be delayed until all occupants above the fire floor are either evacuated or moved to an area of refuge within the building. Firefighters should also be in positions of safety prior to executing the ventilation order. Once the ventilation operation has begun, the stairway may be untenable, even for firefighters in full protective clothing.

Pressure Transfer

Just as heat flows spontaneously from a hotter object to a colder object until their temperatures are equal, pressure transfers from an area of higher pressure to another of lower pressure until the pressures equalize. If two compartments are connected by an opening and one of the compartments is pressurized as happens when a fire burns, air from the pressurized compartment moves into the other compartment, equalizing the pressure across both compartments (**Figure 9.9**).

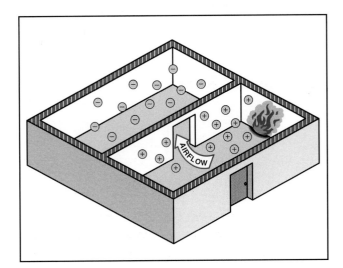

Figure 9.9 Pressure between connected compartments will equalize.

When gases within a structure are heated, they expand and become less dense than the surrounding atmosphere. This buoyancy causes the gases to rise. If the gases are confined, the internal pressure of the structure increases. However, if buoyancy forces are the only ones acting on the gases within a closed compartment, then in relation to atmospheric pressure, the pressure will be higher near the top of the compartment and lower near the bottom of the compartment (**Figure 9.10**).

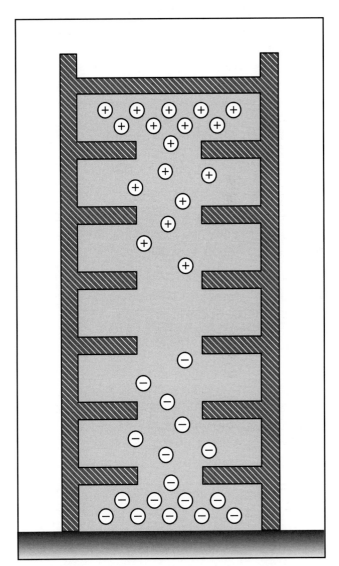

Figure 9.10 Atmospheric pressure is higher at the upper levels of the compartment.

Neutral Pressure Plane

Somewhere near the vertical midpoint of a closed compartment, there is a point called the *neutral pressure plane* where the interior pressure is equal to the pressure outside the space. This concept is important in understanding the stack effect discussed earlier. While the location of the neutral pressure plane can be calculated from engineering formulas, doing so on the fireground is neither practical nor necessary. However, a basic understanding of the pressure changes is needed to be able to understand certain ventilation practices, particularly those used in high-rise structures.

Assuming that the structure is closed, with little or no gases being vented to the atmosphere, a neutral pressure plane exists at the level of ambient atmospheric pressure, usually between 35 percent and 50 percent of the building height (**Figure 9.11**). As the distance away from this plane increases, the pressure difference also increases — positively above the plane and negatively below the plane.

Because there is little or no movement of gases in a closed structure, upper areas of the structure are under positive pressure, and negative pressure (vacuum) forms at the bottom of the structure.

This has a pronounced effect on tall structures, such as high-rise buildings, where the distances from the top and bottom to the neutral plane are extreme. If openings are made at the top and bottom of the structure, positive pressure located at the upper end of the structure escapes upward, and the negative pressure located at the bottom creates an inward pull of air, causing the entire structure to act as a chimney — the stack effect mentioned earlier (**Figure 9.12**). The efficiency of the stack effect is greater in situations where a significant difference in temperature exists between the inside and the outside of a building. Wind can also have a major

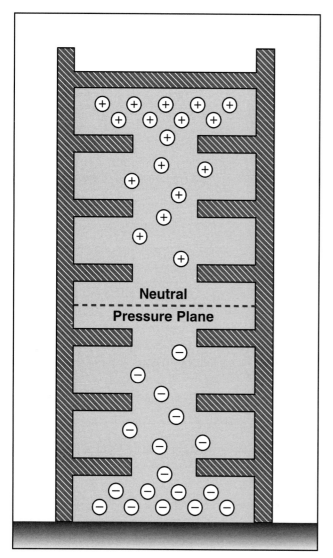

Figure 9.11 The neutral pressure plane will be near the vertical middle of the building.

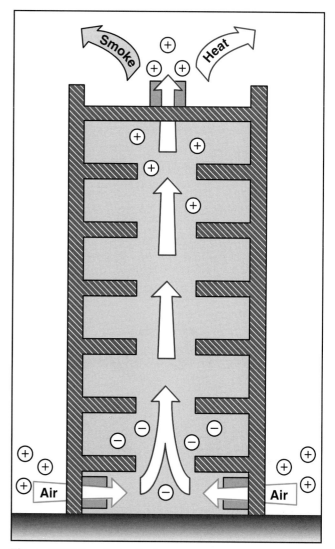

Figure 9.12 The stack effect.

influence on stack effect because of its ability to produce a positive pressure on the windward side of the building and a negative pressure on the leeward side.

Forced ventilation creates a pressure differential in the area being ventilated. When air is expelled, a low-pressure environment is created inside the structure, allowing replacement air to enter. When air is blown in, a high-pressure environment is created inside the structure, causing air to move to the outside (a low-pressure area). This difference in pressure is what enables firefighters to ventilate a structure.

Effects of Wind

Wind can raise or lower the neutral pressure plane within a building, which can have a major influence on high-rise ventilation. Wind produces a positive pressure on the windward side of the building (which tends to raise the neutral pressure plane) and a negative pressure on the leeward side of the

building (which tends to lower the neutral pressure plane) (**Figure 9.13**). Before venting the fire floor horizontally, it must be determined that air movement will be conducive to effective ventilation. For example, if the seat of the fire is located above the neutral pressure plane, ventilating on the leeward side of the building can make best use of the negative pressure condition created by the wind. However, ventilating on the windward side could work against effective ventilation and spread the fire into uninvolved areas.

Wind can influence the stack effect in two ways. Wind blowing across the roof of a building can increase the stack effect if there is a ventilation opening in the roof (**Figure 9.14**). And, as just discussed, wind also influences the stack effect by

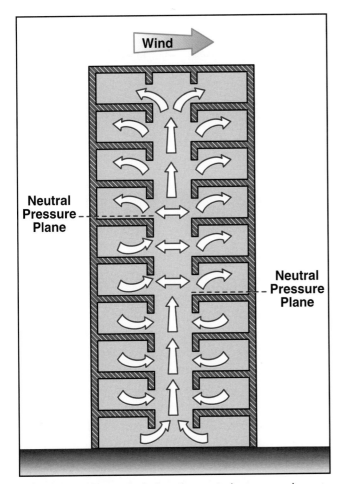

Figure 9.13 Effects of wind on the neutral pressure plane.

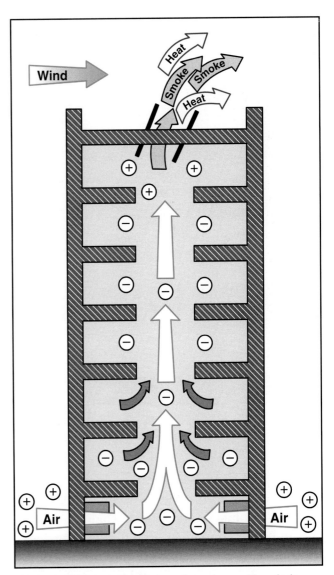

Figure 9.14 The stack effect can be enhanced by winds across the top of the building.

raising or lowering the neutral pressure plane. Positive wind pressure causes the neutral pressure plane to rise, and negative pressure causes it to fall. Ventilating horizontally below the neutral pressure plane draws air into the building, thus spreading the smoke throughout the interior rather than ejecting it to the outside. On the other hand, ventilating above the neutral pressure plane allows the smoke to escape to the outside (**Figures 9.15 a and b**). The closer that ventilation takes place to the neutral pressure plane, the less positive or negative effects wind will exert.

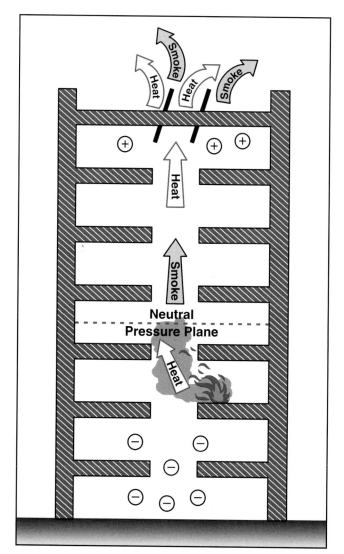

Figure 9.15b The effects of venting above the neutral pressure plane.

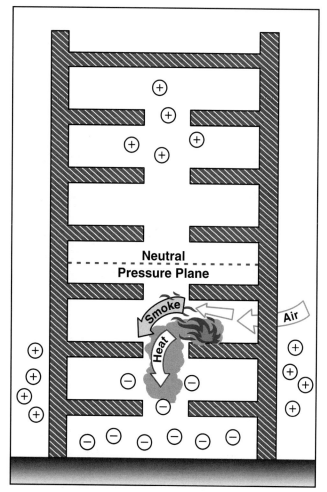

Figure 9.15a The effects of venting below the neutral pressure plane.

Ventilating Below the Fire

Ventilating below the fire floor is not a common practice but may be necessary when smoke has spread to the floors below the fire due to reverse stack effect or mushrooming. The most common technique, venting these floors horizontally, can be enhanced by pressurizing the entire building with blowers. As mentioned earlier, PPV may have to be supplemented if the fire floor is above the 22nd floor.

Ventilating the Fire Floor

Prior knowledge of the layout of the building is extremely important. Attempting to ventilate through a stairwell that does not terminate on the roof or through a dead-end corridor can seriously delay the extinguishment of the fire and increase fire and smoke damage. Many modern high-rises are sealed buildings with windows designed to remain closed. Therefore, horizontal ventilation may necessitate breaking windows. Because this task is difficult, time consuming, and potentially quite dangerous to those in the street below, horizontal ventilation of the fire floor should be done only when there is no other choice.

To avoid the risks associated with horizontally ventilating sealed high-rise buildings, vertical ventilation should be used whenever possible. This can sometimes be accomplished by mechanically ventilating up a stairwell, across the smoke-filled fire floor, and out through the roof via another stairwell (**Figure 9.16**).

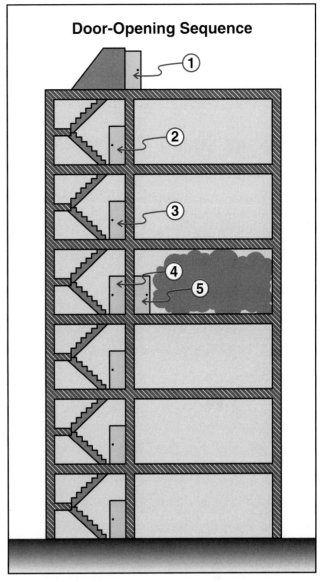

Door-Opening Sequence

Figure 9.17 Venting above the fire floor should be started at the top of the building.

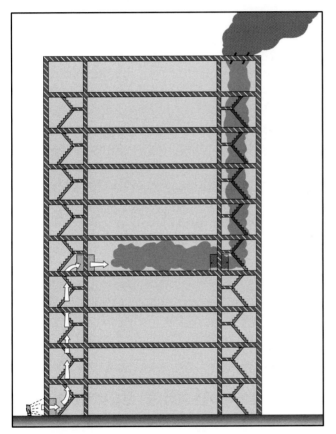

Figure 9.16 One way to vertically ventilate a high-rise building.

Ventilating Above the Fire

Ventilating above the fire floor will be most effective if the process is started at the top of the building (**Figure 9.17**). This provides a clear exit path for the smoke and gases when doors on the fire floor are opened. Starting at the fire floor and working upward is less efficient, may contribute to increased fire spread and smoke damage, and may place ventilation personnel in greater jeopardy.

Following extinguishment, when only cold smoke is left to be expelled, venting vertically eliminates the need for breaking windows for horizontal ventilation. Also, opening up floors near the neutral pressure plane only minimally affects smoke removal unless mechanical ventilation is added.

HVAC and Smoke-Control Systems

Early HVAC systems were designed around the demands for controlling the environment of high-rise buildings under normal conditions. Little thought was given to how such systems might affect a fire or to how they might contribute to the spread of smoke and fire throughout a building. Modern systems have many improvements including controllable dampers that can be selectively opened and closed. With these features, HVAC systems are more easily adapted to also serve as smoke-control systems.

Correct and effective use of an HVAC system can limit the spread of smoke and fire gases, improve operating conditions for firefighters, and increase the likelihood of survival for building occupants. Although the actual manipulation of a building's HVAC system for smoke control should be left to the building engineer, firefighters should have an understanding of the HVAC system's capabilities and limitations. The building engineer should be consulted during pre-incident planning to help firefighters work more effectively with the engineer to use the system to best advantage during a fire. This planning also provides firefighters an opportunity to inform the building engineer that during a fire he would be expected to remain available to the IC for consultation and for actual manipulation of the HVAC system under fire department direction.

CAUTION

Because elevators, stairwell pressurization fans, and other vital equipment require electricity to operate, the building's utilities should *not* be shut down arbitrarily when a fire is burning within the building.

To effectively use an HVAC system to control smoke movement, firefighters should use the following guidelines:

- The HVAC system should be operated by a qualified building engineer, not by firefighters.
- The HVAC system may be used to assist in locating the seat of the fire.
- The HVAC system should be used to limit the extension of fire and smoke to the smallest possible area.
- The HVAC system should not be allowed to spread the fire or smoke beyond the area of origin.
- The HVAC system should provide fresh, uncontaminated air to any occupants who are trapped or are located in a designated safe refuge area within the building.

The HVAC system should have smoke detectors in the ducts to shut down the system in the event smoke enters the ducts. If not, smoke from a fire in a high-rise may spread to several floors before the HVAC system can be shut down manually. To accomplish a manual shutdown with the least possible delay, contact must be made with the building engineer as soon as fire department units arrive. Under the direction of the incident commander, the building engineer may be able to use the HVAC system for exhausting smoke from the building.

Some heavy-duty HVAC systems can be of considerable assistance in removing cold smoke following a fire. These systems are varied in design and complexity, so, just as during a fire, firefighters should not attempt to manually control these systems.

Built-In Ventilation Devices

Roof vents and curtain boards are most common in large buildings having wide, unbroken expanses of floor space. Some industrial or warehouse facilities are so large that their floor space is measured in acres (hectares). If these structures are not properly vented and/or protected by other permanently installed systems for limiting fire spread, the entire contents are vulnerable to smoke and fire damage.

Roof vents and curtain boards have proven to be effective in limiting the spread of fire, releasing heated fire gases, and reducing smoke damage. The standard that provides guidelines for the design and installation of smoke and heat venting equipment, NFPA 204, *Guide for Smoke and Heat Venting*, recommends using automatic heat-activated roof vents and curtain boards. The following is general information on various types of vents and curtain boards; however, firefighters need to become familiar with the specific types in use in their local areas.

Automatic Roof Vents

Automatic roof vents are intended to limit the spread of fire within a building by releasing heat and smoke to the outside before the fire mushrooms throughout the building. Because they work automatically, these vents may reduce or eliminate the need for additional ventilation by fire department personnel.

Automatic roof vents take advantage of the fact that fire gases rise due to convection; therefore, they are placed at the highest point of the roof. Although some are now activated by smoke detectors, most still operate through the use of fusible links connected to spring-loaded or counterweighted cover assemblies. When the fusible link reaches its designed fusing temperature, it separates, allowing the vent covers to open (**Figure 9.18**). Automatic locking devices help to ensure that the covers remain open, even in gusty winds. Under some conditions, prevailing winds may prevent heat and smoke from exiting through automatic roof vents. When this occurs, closing the roof vents and using horizontal ventilation may be necessary.

Figure 9.18 An automatic smoke vent in operation. *Courtesy of the Bilco Company.*

> # CAUTION
> In darkness or heavy smoke, firefighters should be extremely careful when working on roofs with automatic vents to avoid falling into them. Pre-incident familiarization is essential so that firefighters know that automatic vents are present.

Heat-activated roof vents may not open automatically when sprinkler heads discharge near them because the sprinklers may prevent the fire from developing enough heat to activate the vents. Attempting to force automatic roof vents open from the exterior can do extensive damage to their operating mechanisms, and spring-operated covers may be dangerous to firefighters. Therefore, firefighters should become familiar with the manual release mechanisms of automatic roof vents in their areas (**Figure 9.19**).

Figure 9.19 A firefighter uses the pull-handle to open the vent.

Atrium Vents

Many high-rise hotels and office buildings are constructed with an atrium in the center of the structure. These large, vertical openings lend themselves to the stack effect. Therefore, building codes in most areas require that they be equipped with automatic vents. These automatic vents are usually designed to be activated by either smoke or heat. The potential consequences of a firefighter falling into an open vent over an atrium in a high-rise building are obvious, so the earlier caution about working on roofs in darkness and/or heavy smoke is especially important in these situations.

Monitors

Monitor vents are usually square or rectangular structures that penetrate the roofs of single-story buildings, but they may be found on high-rise buildings as well (**Figure 9.20**). The monitor may have metal, glass, wired glass, or louvered sides. Those with glass sides rely upon the glass breaking to provide ventilation in case of a fire. If the fire has not yet generated enough heat to break the glass, the glass will have to be removed by firefighters. Monitors with solid walls should have at least two opposite sides hinged at the bottom and held closed at the top with a fusible link that allows them to fall open by gravity in case of fire.

Figure 9.20 A typical monitor vent.

Skylights

As described in Chapter 8, Vertical Ventilation, skylights may be used to ventilate heat and smoke in the event of fire. Skylights equipped with thermoplastic panels or ordinary window glass can act as automatic vents because the temperature of a fire will melt the plastic or break the glass. In the absence of skylights with thermoplastic panels or those with automatic venting, firefighters will have to remove the skylight or break the glass panes to ventilate the building. In skylights equipped with wired glass, the panes may have to be removed from their frames for ventilation purposes.

Curtain Boards

Curtain boards, also known as *draft curtains*, are fire-resistive half-walls that extend down from the underside of the roof. They generally extend a distance equal to at least 20 percent of the vertical distance from the floor to the roof but not lower than 10 feet (3 m) above the floor. The areas encompassed by curtain boards will generally be those containing critical industrial processes and/or concentrations of flammable liquids or other hazardous materials with high fire potential.

The function of curtain boards is to limit the horizontal spread of heat and smoke by confining it to a relatively small area directly over its source. They also concentrate heat and smoke directly under automatic roof vents to accelerate their actuation. Curtain boards may also accelerate the activation of automatic sprinklers in the area, and this helps to get water onto the fire sooner. However, as mentioned earlier, operating sprinklers may also slow or prevent the actuation of automatic roof vents. If the roof vents do not open automatically, firefighters will have to open them manually.

Underground Structures

Basements, utility vaults, tunnels, and other underground structures rarely provide an opportunity for effective natural ventilation and usually require forced ventilation. In addition to the difficulties often encountered in gaining access for ventilation below grade, there is a much greater likelihood of having to work in an IDLH atmosphere.

> ## WARNING!
> All personnel working below grade *must* wear SCBA because of the possibility of oxygen deficiency in addition to whatever toxic gases may be present.

Because basements and cellars are the most common underground structures, this section deals primarily with ventilating them. While they may be defined differently in different codes and other sources, in this context both basements and cellars have an interior access, and basements have an additional access from the exterior of the building.

Both basements and cellars may contain furnaces, boilers, heating oil tanks, and main electrical panels. Usually, but not always, cellars are windowless, and basements have small windows between grade level and the first floor of the building. Cellars are most often unfinished areas used for storage. Basements used for storage are often unfinished, and those used for habitation (game rooms, spare bedrooms, etc.) are usually finished. In general, the same ventilation problems that exist in basements and cellars exist in other underground structures, therefore; the same tactics and techniques apply as well.

While all basements and cellars can be accessed by an interior stairway, some also have openings for elevators, chutes, or dumbwaiters. As mentioned earlier, some of these access openings are inside the buildings and others are outside. Opening these access ways for ventilation may be a slow and difficult process because they may be blocked or secured at the street level by iron gratings, steel shutters, security doors, or some combination of these. To achieve rapid access into basements, cellars, and other underground structures, firefighters need to be familiar with the access openings and any security measures employed so that forcible entry crews can bring the needed tools and equipment with them initially.

Building features, such as interior stairways, elevator shafts, pipe chases, laundry chutes, air-handling systems, and other vertical openings may contribute to the spread of fire and smoke from a basement to upper floors. Therefore, early and effective ventilation of below-grade fires is critically important to successful fireground operations.

To prevent or reduce the upward spread of smoke and fire from an involved basement or cellar, it must be ventilated as quickly as possible. If an opening of adequate size can be made opposite the interior point of entry into the space, the fastest way to ventilate the compartment is to set up positive-pressure blowers at the entry point (**Figure 9.21**). This allows the vent crew to stay out of the compartment while still ventilating it effectively. However, the rest of the structure (especially those with balloon frame construction) must be closely and continually monitored for signs of fire extension through walls or other vertical channels.

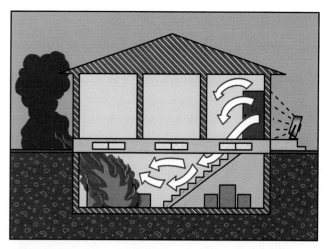

Figure 9.21 PPV can effectively ventilate a basement or cellar.

In some cases involving fires in cellars, it may be necessary to vent the cellar through the first floor of the building. In these cases, a ventilation exit opening is cut in the first floor near an exterior window. A smoke ejector is suspended in the window opening to facilitate the flow of heat and smoke to the outside (**Figure 9.22**). This technique risks fire spread to the first floor area and should only be used when there is no other means available to vent the cellar.

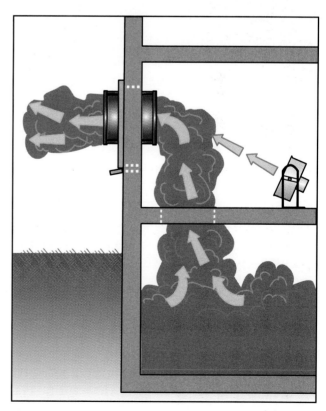

Figure 9.22 A cellar fire can be vented through the first floor and out a window.

Windowless Buildings

Many modern buildings have few, if any, windows and depend on skylights and artificial lighting for interior illumination (**Figure 9.23**). Some windowless buildings have various forms of translucent glass walls that admit light but that are of little value for ventilation purposes. These walls may appear to be fragile, but they can be as resistant to being breached as are many masonry walls.

The absence of exterior openings severely limits the opportunities for horizontal ventilation and increases the likelihood of backdraft conditions developing within these structures. Both of these problems underscore the need for fast and effective vertical ventilation of fires in windowless buildings.

Figure 9.23 A typical windowless building.

Highly Secure Buildings

In response to terrorist attacks such as the bombings of the federal office building in Oklahoma City and other buildings around the world, many public buildings (especially government buildings) have been retrofitted with barriers to keep vehicles away from them and with other security measures (**Figure 9.24**). Unfortunately, these security measures also keep emergency vehicles away and make it more difficult for firefighters to gain access into these buildings for ventilation and other fireground operations. Therefore, it is imperative that firefighters conduct pre-incident planning inspections of these buildings and develop effective operational plans for dealing with the security measures. They must identify what the impediments to access are, what tools and equipment are needed

Figure 9.24 A growing number of buildings are protected by security barriers.

to overcome these impediments, and how to get those and other needed resources to the scene in a timely manner.

However, government office buildings are not the only highly secure buildings that firefighters may have to ventilate. Jails, prisons, and other correctional facilities must necessarily be highly secure. As discussed in Chapter 4, Access Into Structures, entry into and movement within these buildings is best done with the aid of staff members accompanying the firefighters. Because the firefighters may need to go into parts of the building that are charged with heat and smoke, the staff members need to be equipped with appropriate PPE including SCBA. Therefore, pre-incident planning and training with the institution's fire department or fire brigade are highly desirable. Such cooperation and coordination allows fire operations to be conducted both safely and efficiently in these facilities.

Remodeled Buildings

Many older buildings have been remodeled numerous times over the years. These modifications are sometimes obvious from the outside of the building, sometimes not. As discussed in Chapter 4, some modifications are new sections added onto existing older buildings. Some modifications actually increase a building's structural stability and its fire resistance — others do quite the opposite. For example, the modifications that were made to the warehouse described in the Washington incident made the floor more susceptible to collapse and that resulted in the loss of four firefighters.

Firefighters should pay attention to all construction projects in their response districts, especially large-scale remodeling projects. They should visit these sites as often as possible during the construction or remodeling process (**Figure 9.25**). They

Figure 9.25 Firefighters should pay attention to changes within their districts.

should observe changes that could affect access to or into the building. They should pay particular attention to changes in bearing walls, roof assemblies, floor assemblies, and any other structural elements that might affect the building's structural stability. Finally, firefighters should familiarize themselves with the doors, windows, and roof coverings as these are the most likely points for ventilation openings.

Summary

Firefighters must familiarize themselves with the various types of buildings and construction features that exist in their response districts. Of particular importance are high-rise buildings, windowless buildings, underground structures, highly secure buildings, and those that have undergone extensive remodeling. Once these structures have been identified, firefighters should develop operational plans for using horizontal and/or vertical ventilation techniques to vent these structures safely and effectively should the need arise.

Chapter 10
Controlling Utilities

Chapter 10
Controlling Utilities

Historically, many firefighters and others have been injured or killed by fires and explosions that were either caused by or fueled by the flammable substances with which we heat our homes and other buildings, and with which we power a variety of industrial processes. Others have been injured by flash burns from electrical arcs or killed by electrocution. Still others have been scalded by fire-heated water, and victims trapped in basements or cellars have drowned because the water supply was not shut off. Unfortunately, such incidents continue to occur.

At working structure fires, securing a burning building's utilities is one of the best ways to protect the firefighters working in and around the building, and any occupants who may be trapped inside. However, arbitrarily securing all of a burning building's utilities may not always be the best choice. For example, arbitrarily shutting down all electrical power to a burning high-rise building can preclude the use of the building's elevators, HVAC systems, fire pumps, and lighting. As with every other aspect of fireground support operations, control of a burning building's utilities must be coordinated with the overall rescue and suppression efforts.

Securing a burning building's utilities is not always related to preventing explosions and electrocutions. For example, it may be necessary to secure a building's gas service because it is also supplying fuel to a malfunctioning industrial oven or other gas-fired device. Likewise, it may be necessary to shut down a building's electrical service to prevent machines or other appliances from accidentally being reenergized at a critical moment.

Not all gas and electrical emergencies are related to structure fires — some occur outside of buildings and other structures. For example, construction crews sometimes cut into gas mains, water mains, or underground electrical cables while excavating or trenching. These occurrences can create incidents that may be limited to the location where the service was damaged, or their effects may spread over a large area and impact a large population.

As mentioned earlier, uncontrolled utilities at structure fires and other emergency incidents can result in injuries, fatalities, and increased property damage. To prevent or reduce these traumatic injuries and excessive property losses, utility services must be controlled in a safe and timely manner. This chapter begins with a discussion of fuel control, which includes natural gas (methane), liquefied petroleum gas (LPG), and fuel oil. The chapter continues with discussions of controlling electrical utilities and water supplies.

Fuel Control

In January of 1998, a construction crew severed an underground gas main in the downtown commercial district of Phoenix, Arizona. The construction crew called 9-1-1 and because it was a confirmed natural gas leak, the PFD notified the utility company and dispatched two engines, a ladder truck, a rescue unit, and a chief officer to the scene. On arrival, PFD personnel established a perimeter, set up a protective hoseline, and stood by while waiting for utility company personnel and equipment to arrive.

Shortly after the utility crew arrived with a large truck and a backhoe, a huge orange fireball blew out the front windows of the nearest building. The open window area was apparently not large enough to completely relieve the overpressure created by the explosion because the walls and roof of the building also disintegrated, sending construction debris flying in every direction. The utility crew and several firefighters were knocked down by the blast, but no one was seriously hurt.

Had PFD personnel not secured the scene and controlled entry, the results might have been much worse. This incident is typical of countless other incidents in which firefighters and civilians have been injured or killed by explosions and fires. Many of these calamities were caused by or fueled by natural gas, LPG, or heating oil. Some of these incidents involved gas leaks that went undetected until the buildings exploded. Other incidents involved gas explosions that occurred as firefighters investigated a report of "an odor in the area." Still others involved gas explosions inside burning buildings as firefighters attempted to extinguish the fire.

Situational Differences

While the universal priorities — life safety, incident stabilization, and property conservation — remain the same, situational differences may necessitate different approaches to addressing these priorities. For example, the most common fuel control problem with which fireground support personnel must contend is making sure that the gas supply to a burning building is secured. Securing this utility reduces the chances of an explosion from accumulated fuel gas within the building and keeps the fuel from adding to the fire. Therefore, following the universal priorities in this situation is best done by securing the building's fuel supply as quickly as possible. In most cases, the tools and techniques described in **Essentials** can be used to accomplish this task.

On the other hand, if the call is to a reported gas leak without fire, the universal priorities dictate that the responding units approach the scene from upwind and stage a safe distance away. Of course, there are other considerations involved — establishing a

perimeter, eliminating sources of ignition, evacuating those downwind from the scene, etc., but the point is that how the universal fireground priorities are followed will vary with the situation.

The two most common gas control situations with which firefighters are faced are those in structure fires and those in which there is a gas leak without fire. As mentioned earlier, uncontrolled utilities can complicate a fire situation and perhaps result in injuries, fatalities, or increased property damage. Therefore, it is critically important that a burning building's utilities be secured in accordance with the situation at hand.

Controlling Natural Gas in Structure Fires

Stopping the flow of natural gas into a burning building is one of the most common gas control operations that firefighters perform. In many cases, the tools and techniques for securing a building's gas supply are as described in **Essentials** — but not always. For example, many industrial sites and some larger commercial buildings have gas meters that are much larger than those shown in **Essentials,** and they may have a different type of control valve.

The main control valve on heavy-duty gas meters may simply be larger versions of the crossbar, quarter-turn valve common to residential and light commercial buildings. However, some heavy-duty control valves are installed in a horizontal section of the main line close to the meter housing. In addition, the operating nut is usually square instead of the crossbar design found on most residential meters (**Figure 10.1**). Turning the square-operating

Figure 10.1 A typical shutoff valve on an industrial gas meter.

nut one-quarter turn in either direction closes the valve. Turning this nut requires a properly sized open-end or box wrench or an adjustable wrench. The type of shutoff valve should be identified during pre-incident planning inspections so that firefighters can take the correct tool to the meter initially.

Another item to verify during pre-incident planning is the location of the gas meter on the property. Where gas meters are located varies greatly from region to region. In some areas, gas meters are located at or near the curb making them easy to locate during an emergency (**Figure 10.2**). In other areas, meters are typically located at one of the front corners of the building making them accessible from the street — but not necessarily visible from the street — especially if the property owner plants shrubbery in front of the meter for esthetic reasons. In still other areas, gas meters may be located along the rear property line, in the basement, or under exterior stairways, making them more difficult to find during an emergency (**Figure 10.3**). In many industrial properties, gas meters are located in underground vaults or in utility rooms inside the buildings. Once again, familiarity with the property gained through pre-incident planning inspections is critically important to the process of cutting off a burning building's gas supply as quickly as possible.

In buildings with multiple occupancies, there is usually a gas meter for each occupancy or unit within the building (**Figure 10.4**). If the meters are not clearly labeled to identify which occupancy each meter serves, it may be necessary to shut off

Figure 10.3 Gas meters are sometimes found in obscure locations.

Figure 10.4 In some cases, gas meters are grouped together.

Figure 10.2 In some areas, gas meters are located near the curb line.

the gas service to the entire building. This can cause unnecessary disruption of service to those occupancies not affected by the fire and may result in critical industrial processes being interrupted needlessly. Therefore, firefighters should work with property owners during pre-incident planning to get each gas meter correctly labeled (**Figure 10.5**).

NOTE: During a working structure fire in a multiple-occupancy building, the meter for the affected occupancy can sometimes be identified by the fact that the needle on the dial is moving at a much faster rate than those on the other meters.

Figure 10.5 Identification is easier if individual gas meters are labeled.

Controlling LPG in Structure Fires

In areas not served by a natural gas distribution system, buildings of all types — residential, mercantile, agricultural, and industrial — often use LPG for heating and industrial processes. The quantities of LPG used at some of these sites require very large storage tanks on the premises (**Figure 10.6**).

Figure 10.6 A typical residential or light commercial LPG tank.

> # WARNING!
> Regardless of its size, if an LPG tank is exposed to the heat of direct flame impingement, it can BLEVE with devastating force.

Therefore, if a large horizontal tank is involved in fire and especially if LPG is venting from the tank, firefighters should not attempt to control the leak but should set up master streams to cool the tank and any adjacent exposures and withdraw a safe distance away. The *2000 Emergency Response Guidebook* (ERG2000) recommends pulling back one-half mile (800 m). However, any decision to approach a propane tank with direct flame impingement must be made on a case-by-case basis after weighing the risk/benefit and determining whether available water supply and pumping capacity are adequate.

At structure fires, there are two different scenarios with which firefighters may have to contend involving LPG tanks. The first is when the LPG tank is threatened by or involved in fire. The other very common scenario is when the LPG is or may be fueling a fire inside of an adjacent building but the LPG tank itself is not involved.

As just mentioned, when any LPG tank — regardless of size — is involved in fire, the possibility of an explosion or BLEVE is ever present. Therefore, if the fire has the potential of reaching a portable LPG tank, it may be prudent to disconnect the tank and move it away from the building. A forklift or similar vehicle may be needed to move the tank. Otherwise, these situations must be handled as described in **Essentials** and according to local protocols.

If the LPG tank is not threatened by or involved in the fire, the flow of gas can be stopped by turning off the valve located where the piping connects to the tank. On portable LPG tanks, the control valve is located on the top of the tank, sometimes protected by a hinged weatherproof cover (**Figure 10.7**). On larger, fixed installations with horizontal tanks, the control valve may be located on the side of the tank or in a manifold box at the end of the tank (**Figure 10.8**). Where multiple tanks are installed side by side, the flow from any or all of the tanks may be controlled from a central manifold location.

Figure 10.7 On some LPG tanks, the shutoff valve is located on top.

Figure 10.8 Controls are located at the side of commercial LPG tanks. *Courtesy of Keith Flood.*

Controlling Fuel Oil in Structure Fires

Many buildings in North America are heated with oil rather than natural gas or LPG. Some industrial boilers are fired with pulverized coal and a variety of other similar fuels. However, these other fuels are far less common than fuel oil so this discussion is confined to heaters and boilers using ordinary heating oil. Also called *bunker oil* or *#6 fuel oil*, heating oil is sometimes stored in underground tanks connected to the heating appliances by copper or aluminum tubing. In multifamily residential buildings there can be as much as 500 gallons of fuel oil located in the basement. Firefighters should be aware of this potential hazard when responding to a report of a leak or fire.

In other situations, heating oil tanks are mounted on stanchions aboveground to increase gravity pressure (**Figure 10.9**). These stanchions may or may not be fire resistive. Where the stanchions are made of wood or unprotected steel, jurisdictions usually require that an earthen dike or other containment surround the tanks. Even though a BLEVE of a fuel oil tank is theoretically possible, it is highly unlikely because fuel oil tanks are not pressure vessels. Fuel oil tanks usually rupture in a fire before the conditions required for a BLEVE develop. However, this does _not_ mean that fuel oil tanks are not dangerous when exposed to direct flame impingement. The fire-related rupture of a fuel oil tank can result in the spread of flaming oil over a large area around the tank.

As a combustible liquid, heating oil must be preheated before it will burn. The preheating process may increase the risk to firefighters because this is

Figure 10.9 Some fuel oil tanks are mounted on legs or stanchions. *Courtesy of Mark Pare.*

usually done with either electricity or steam. In most appliances, the oil is also atomized into a fine spray as it is introduced into the firebox. Some industrial heaters or boilers use steam or air atomizers, but most residential units use mechanical atomizers. However, considering that the oil pressure required for maximum efficiency ranges from 600 to 1,000 psi (4 137 kPa to 6 895 kPa), any of these systems may be dangerous to firefighters who are unfamiliar with them. For their own safety, firefighters must become familiar with the types of heating systems in use in their respective response districts.

If a fuel oil tank is not threatened by or involved in fire, the flow of oil can be stopped at the tank by closing the gate valve where the tubing connects to the tank (**Figure 10.10**). If the valve is inoperable for any reason, crimping the tubing can stop the flow of oil. The tubing can sometimes be crimped with heavy-duty pliers or with a hydraulic cutter equipped with crimping blades (**Figure 10.11**).

Perhaps the most dangerous phenomenon associated with oil-fired appliances is commonly called a *white ghost*. The name comes from the white cloud of fuel oil vapor that forms in and around an oil-fired appliance when the pilot light fails to ignite fuel oil introduced into an already heated firebox.

Figure 10.10 Fuel oil can often be shut off at the tank. *Courtesy of Mark Pare.*

WARNING!
A white ghost has a strong odor of fuel oil and is within its explosive range. If the cloud cannot be dissipated before it reaches an ignition source, it can explode with devastating force.

Figure 10.11 Fuel oil lines can be crimped with heavy-duty pliers. *Courtesy of Mark Pare.*

As all occupants of the building are being evacuated, the fuel oil should be shut off at the remote control switch (usually located near the utility room door), or at the tank. The utility room should be thoroughly ventilated.

Gas Leaks Without Fire

In December 1983, a large propane tank fell from a forklift that was moving it in the basement of a three-story warehouse building in New York. When the tank struck the concrete floor, the valve broke off and liquid propane began to leak. The fire department was called, and just as the firefighters arrived, the propane vapors reached an ignition source and a tremendous explosion followed. The explosion blew a ladder truck and two engines across the street. Five firefighters were killed, and nine others were seriously injured. Two civilians were killed and dozens more were injured.

The foregoing example is but one type of call involving an uncontrolled release of a flammable gas. A more common call that fire departments receive is a report of an odor of gas in a building or neighborhood, but the reporting party is unaware of its source. When investigating an odor of gas where the source of the leak cannot be determined immediately, adjacent buildings should also be checked because gas can migrate through the ground and emerge some distance from the leak. In addition, soil may filter out the additive that gives natural gas its odor; therefore, it is possible that buildings may be filling with gas that has no odor. The occupants of these buildings may be unaware of the danger until an explosion takes place. Therefore, firefighters must not become complacent when dealing with these incidents. They should establish a perimeter, charge one or more protective hoselines, and wear full PPE while investigating the source of the leak.

In other instances, such as the case history from Phoenix cited earlier, the source of the gas leak is definitely known. And, as in that incident, even though there is no fire when the leak is initially reported, this can change in an instant. Uncontrolled flammable gas leaks are never "routine." They are always potentially lethal, and firefighters should handle them that way. Safely handling these incidents involves using the correct approach, establishing and controlling the perimeter, assessing the hazard, and mitigating the hazard.

Approach

Because the responding fire apparatus could provide a source of ignition, the approach to the area of the reported odor should be from upwind. Apparatus responding from the downwind direction should stage beyond the affected area or detour around the area and approach from the upwind side. Depending upon the size and location of the leak, wind speed and direction, topography, and local protocols, apparatus should be staged as much as a block away and upwind from the leak. The ERG2000 recommends staying from 160 to 330 feet (50 m to 100 m) from the source for both LPG and natural gas leaks. Those assigned to assess the hazard can approach the leak source on foot (**Figure 10.12**).

Perimeter Control

One of the first-arriving units should be assigned to establish a perimeter around the hazard area and maintain control of that perimeter (**Figure 10.13**). As the incident progresses, it may be necessary or desirable to set up hot, warm, and cold zones as described in **Essentials**. Initially, the goal is to establish a perimeter a safe distance from the leak. What constitutes a "safe" distance is a judgment made by the IC based on information supplied by firefighters and others at the scene. One critical piece of information relating to the perimeter is an accurate assessment of the hazard, which is discussed in the next section. The perimeter should be marked with barrier tape, and only utility company personnel or those in full PPE should be allowed to enter the hazard area. Even though firefighters may have to be used to establish the perimeter initially, control of the perimeter should be passed to law enforcement as soon as possible (**Figure 10.14**).

Figure 10.13 The perimeter should be clearly marked.

Figure 10.12 Monitoring for combustible gas begins at the apparatus.

Figure 10.14 Crowd control should be assigned to law enforcement personnel.

These instructions are necessary to prevent people from inadvertently creating a spark (source of ignition) when an electrical switch is used, or an internal combustion engine is started. The instructions may be announced over a public address system or by handheld electronic bullhorns (**Figure 10.15**).

Figure 10.15 An electronic bullhorn may be used to give evacuation instructions.

Hazard Assessment

One of the best ways to assess a flammable gas leak is by using combustible gas indicators (CGI) (**Figure 10.16**). These handheld devices not only detect the presence of a combustible gas, but they indicate its concentration. Some of these units express the gas detected in parts per million (ppm) and others as a percentage of the lower explosive limit (LEL).

Figure 10.16 A typical combustible gas indicator.

When establishing a perimeter, the CGI operator moves from a point that registers no detectible concentration toward the assumed leak source, taking samples at frequent intervals until a reading is noted. Since natural gas is slightly lighter than air, the readings should not be taken near the ground. Instead, they should be taken at waist height or higher (**Figure 10.17**). Agency protocols (based on ERG2000) must be followed, but in general, the point at which the first detectible reading appears is one point at which the perimeter may be estab-

Figure 10.17 The position of the CGI is determined by the vapor density of the gas being monitored.

Figure 10.18 LPG, being heavier than air, hugs the ground.

lished. Since the LEL for natural gas is 5 percent (50,000 ppm), many fire departments establish the perimeter at 10 percent of that figure — 0.5 percent (5,000 ppm). However, because the lower explosive limit for propane is 1.5 percent (15,000 ppm), any reading above 0.15 percent (1500 ppm) may be too dangerous, and control points may have to be located where readings indicate a lower concentration. This process is repeated at various points around the leak until the entire hazard area has been defined and cordoned off.

One characteristic that makes assessing an LPG leak somewhat easier than assessing a natural gas leak is that LPG may form a white cloud in air when sufficient humidity is present. The white cloud makes the fuel vapor more visible. Because LPG is heavier than air, the cloud hugs the ground and collects in depressions and other low areas (**Figure 10.18**). The fact that LPG is heavier than air also makes it more likely that the gas will enter any open basement windows, and basements often contain heating appliances with pilot lights — a lethal combination. Firefighters should also be aware that the white cloud formed by an LPG leak is not the only dangerous area.

> ## WARNING!
> The visible cloud of LPG is surrounded by an invisible envelope of gas that is within its explosive range.

Hazard Mitigation

The main things that firefighters can do to follow the universal priorities in a gas leak without fire are to establish a safe perimeter, deny unauthorized entry, and prevent the gas leak from becoming a gas explosion. Preventing a leaking gas from reaching a source of ignition before the leak can be controlled may take a couple of forms.

Control of Natural Gas Leaks

Some natural gas leaks may be controlled by firefighters; others may have to be left to utility company personnel. Many fire departments allow their personnel (wearing full PPE) to shut off the flow of gas at above-grade gas meters but insist that utility company crews handle below-grade operations. Utility company emergency response personnel are trained and equipped to handle these contingencies. Even when utility company personnel control the flow of gas, firefighters may contribute to the successful disposition of the problem by assisting with the evacuation of those downwind of the leak, if this is what the IC orders. The IC may choose to shelter those people in place by using a public address system to instruct the occupants of buildings downwind of the leak to close all exterior windows and doors, remain indoors, but not to turn any electrical or electronic device on or off until notified otherwise.

The other way that firefighters may help reduce the hazard of a natural gas leak is by systematically eliminating sources of ignition downwind of the leak. This is usually done in areas from which the occupants have been evacuated. Starting from a point within the perimeter that is farthest from the leak source and working slowly toward it, firefighters turn off the gas supply to every building within the perimeter. This should extinguish any pilot lights within these buildings, but long gas distribution lines in large buildings or complexes may take some time to bleed down.

In general, fire departments do not allow their firefighters to restore gas service to buildings following a fire or other emergency. This task is usually left to the utility company since it involves making sure that there are no leaks, and relighting all pilot lights.

Control of LPG Leaks

In LPG leaks, firefighters can take more direct action to dispose of the problem. First, the company supplying the LPG may not have an emergency response team available for such contingencies. Therefore, it may be up to the firefighters to eliminate the sources of ignition as well as to control the leak. Because the buildings that use LPG tend to be remote from other buildings, the problem of pilot lights in nearby buildings is usually reduced. If this is the case, firefighters may be able to keep the gas cloud away from possible ignition sources by dispersing the cloud with hoselines (**Figure 10.19**). The nozzles should be set on a wide fog pattern.

Controlling the leak itself may be more difficult. As described briefly in **Essentials**, controlling an LPG leak at its source is most often accomplished by firefighters advancing two closely coordinated hoselines with the nozzles set on a wide fog pattern. Those directly involved in this evolution must be in full PPE, including SCBA. The officer in charge pro-

vides the required coordination and is positioned between the two firefighters operating the nozzles. The officer keeps one hand on the shoulder of each of the nozzle operators as they advance toward the source of the leak (**Figure 10.20**). A third hoseline should be charged and ready in case one of the first two lines fails for any reason. Ideally, each of the three lines should be supplied from a different source (pumper), but a minimum of two sources should be used.

When the LPG leak is in close proximity to the control valve, some departments use a slightly different approach. In this approach, two hoselines are still used, with a third backup line, but only one nozzle is set on a wide fog pattern for crew protection. The other nozzle is set on a straight stream that is applied directly onto the source of the leak. Otherwise, the two techniques are exactly the same.

In both of the foregoing evolutions, the firefighters backing up the nozzles should be positioned between the hoselines, and they should advance slowly using a *shuffle step* to maintain

Figure 10.19 An LPG cloud can be dispersed with hose streams.

Figure 10.20 Overlapping fog streams are used for safety.

maximum balance. Maintaining maximum balance is necessary in case the leaking fuel is suddenly ignited and the firefighters need to make a rapid but orderly retreat. To maintain their balance, firefighters should use the following technique:

Step 1: Slide the front foot forward.

Step 2: Slide the opposite foot up to the heel of the front foot without crossing the legs.

Step 3: Move the front foot forward and move the other foot up to meet the front foot, etc.

Once at the tank or valve, the officer can close the main supply valve or apply the necessary leak control device. When the flow of gas has been stopped, the crews maintain the protective fog curtain as they back away from the tank. They also use the reverse form of the shuffle step when backing away from the tank. As with natural gas, once the LPG supply to a building has been shut off, most fire departments do not allow their firefighters to restore gas service.

Electricity Control

According to an NFA report, in a 1995 incident firefighters advanced a charged hoseline through a residential garage to attack a fire in the interior of the house. Shortly thereafter, a sudden increase in the fire's intensity forced the crew to retreat back into the garage. However, because the electricity to the house had not been secured, the heavy wooden garage door had closed spontaneously cutting off their escape route. Unable to open the garage door from the inside, the members of the trapped crew pounded on the door and yelled for help. Firefighters on the outside were eventually able to cut through the garage door and rescue those inside. Unfortunately, the officer in charge of the hose crew later died of smoke inhalation, and two of the firefighters suffered serious smoke inhalation and burn injuries. Nine of the firefighters involved in rescuing the trapped crew suffered a variety of injuries. One of the rescuers was injured seriously enough to require hospitalization.

Situational Differences

The incident just described emphasizes the importance of quickly controlling the electrical service to a burning building and of propping open overhead-type doors with a pike pole or other device (**Figure**

10.21). But, as discussed in the preceding chapter, arbitrarily securing the electrical service is not always advisable. Just as in controlling gas service, there are situational differences that affect how and when electrical utilities should be controlled. For fireground support personnel, the two most common emergency situations involving electricity are structure fires and downed electrical wires.

Figure 10.21 Roll-up doors should be propped open. *Courtesy of Wes Kitchel.*

Controlling Electricity in Structure Fires

In many structure fires, one of the most important safety considerations is shutting down the burning building's electrical service. Eliminating the electrical supply to the building helps protect firefighters and others from electrical shocks or electrocution and prevents additional fires from being started by electrical arcs and overheated wiring or components. When the IC orders the electrical supply shut down, firefighters must know where and how to do so safely. Where and how to shut down a building's electrical service varies depending upon whether the building was designed for residential, commercial, or industrial occupancy.

Residential

Most single-family residences have only one main electrical panel, located with the electrical meter and main switch. Where power distribution in the neighborhood is through overhead wires, the building's main electrical panel is usually located directly below the weather head where the power from the pole-mounted transformer enters the building (**Figure 10.22**). In many areas, newer subdivisions have underground power lines. In these areas, firefighters must locate the main electrical panel to access the main electric switch. However, some very large residences and many apartment buildings have a number of subpanels serving various parts of the building. Having one or more subpanels permits electricity to be shut off to some sections of the building while leaving electrical power on in other parts of the building. This may

Figure 10.22 Many electrical panels are located directly below the weather head.

be desirable or necessary so that the building's lighting, HVAC system, or fire pumps can continue to be used.

Historically, many fire departments trained their firefighters to secure the electrical service to a residential building by pulling the electrical meter. However, pulling an electrical meter can be dangerous to the firefighter pulling it, and it does not necessarily guarantee that electrical power to the building has been eliminated. Many departments also trained their firefighters to cut the drip loop at the weather head. Today, neither of these practices is recommended. If a building's electrical meter must be pulled or the drip loop needs to be cut, it should be done only by utility company personnel.

> ## WARNING!
> Pulling an electrical meter or cutting a drip loop or any other electrical wire can be hazardous to the firefighter performing the operation.

If their nonconductive tools and equipment have not been properly maintained and tested, and if the firefighters have not been trained in the proper use of the tools and equipment, fire departments should prohibit their firefighters from cutting electrical wires. Therefore, because of the difficulty involved in meeting the maintenance and training requirements, most fire departments now prohibit their firefighters from cutting any electrical wire that *might* be energized. And, as described in **Essentials**, firefighters should assume that all electrical wires are energized.

To secure electrical service to a burning residential building, firefighters in most departments are trained to locate the main electrical panel and to open the main switch or circuit breaker. Most agencies do not advocate removing the circuit breaker. Once the switch or breaker has been thrown, it should be locked in the open position and tagged (lockout/tagout). However, opening any electrical switch can create an arc or spark sufficient to ignite any flammable gases or vapors present.

As mentioned earlier, in high-rise and other large residential buildings, it may be desirable to maintain the electrical service to certain portions of the building so that elevators, HVAC systems, fire pumps, and other vital components can remain operational. Whenever possible, building maintenance personnel should operate all system controls, including those that control electrical power. Firefighters should rely on the building engineer or maintenance staff to open switches or circuit breakers that will eliminate power to selected portions of the building while maintaining electrical power to the remainder of the building.

Commercial

The same reasons for securing electrical utilities in residential buildings apply to commercial buildings. However, because there may be several subpanels, simply finding the right electrical switch in a commercial building can sometimes be extremely difficult. In some commercial occupancies, shutting off the main electrical switch activates a generator or other source of emergency power. In some occupancies, on-site battery banks or solar-electric panels may continue to provide power to areas that need to be shut down. The presence of generators and other emergency power sources should be identified during pre-incident planning inspections. Otherwise, the tools and techniques required for securing electrical power to commercial buildings is, in many cases, little different from securing power to large residential buildings.

In other cases, shutting off electrical power to commercial buildings can be much more hazardous than securing the power supply to residential occupancies. The hazards involved are related to the size of the electrical components installed in many commercial buildings, especially older buildings. The main electrical switches in many older commercial buildings are much larger than those in the typical residential building. Opening these large

switches often results in an electrical arc that (in addition to being a source of ignition if flammable vapors or gases are present) can damage the eyes of anyone looking at the switch. Therefore, when opening large main electrical switches, firefighters should turn their faces away from the switch as they operate the lever arm (**Figure 10.23**).

Figure 10.23 Firefighters should look away when opening large electrical switches.

Industrial

Unlike those in either residential or commercial buildings, the electrical utilities in industrial buildings or industrial facilities can be extraordinarily large and complex. Because of the tremendous power demands of some industrial processes, the on-site electrical utilities may be as large as those for some small communities. Some industrial facilities have fenced enclosures containing banks of high-voltage transformers (**Figure 10.24**). These transformers may contain polychlorinated biphenyls (PCBs), which are known carcinogens. Other

Figure 10.24 Some industrial facilities have their own transformer enclosures.

facilities may have their high-voltage electrical equipment housed in concrete utility vaults. Through pre-incident planning inspections conducted as often as necessary, firefighters must become as familiar as possible with the industrial electrical utilities in their response districts. However, during a major fire, the firefighters must rely upon plant personnel who know how to safely manipulate the system as needed (**Figure 10.25**). In these situations, plant personnel are responsible for working closely with the fire department to carry out the incident action plan.

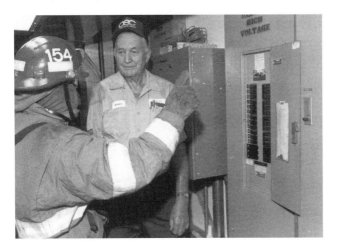

Figure 10.25 The building engineer should manipulate building system controls.

Wires Down Without Fire

The other major category of electrical emergencies to which firefighters are often called involves electrical wires that have fallen to the ground for some reason. Wires are sometimes blown down in storms, or they break under the weight of snow or ice. At other times they fall because the pole or tower supporting them is knocked down, often as a result of being hit by a vehicle. Regardless of why and how the wires fell, the priorities for the responding firefighters are still the same — life safety, incident stabilization, and property conservation.

NOTE: One of the most important actions that firefighters can take in these incidents is to contact the responsible utility company, describe the situation, and request its emergency response team.

> According to another NFPA report, in 1994 a vehicle struck a power pole beside a rural road, and the driver was thrown out. A paramedic and five firefighters strapped the victim to a backboard and attempted to slide the backboard under the uninsulated high-voltage power lines hanging close to the ground. When one of the firefighters holding the backboard brushed against one of the power lines, the paramedic, the victim on the backboard, and two firefighters were electrocuted. The other three firefighters holding the board were injured but somehow survived.

Unfortunately, this type of incident is not uncommon. Similar incidents occur even in newer residential neighborhoods with underground electrical service.

> In San Jose, California, an automobile jumped a curb and came to rest on a metal box that enclosed a distribution transformer. When the police officer investigating the incident touched the vehicle, he was electrocuted.

Handling these potentially lethal incidents is sometimes very similar to the procedures for handling the gas leak incidents discussed earlier in this chapter. In most cases involving downed electrical wires, firefighters should do nothing more than establish a perimeter and deny entry to all except utility company personnel (**Figure 10.26**). However, in some cases it is necessary for firefighters to do some basic hazard assessment in order to decide where the perimeter should be established.

Perimeter Control

Controlling the scene and denying unauthorized entry while waiting for utility company personnel to arrive is a very important and potentially lifesav-

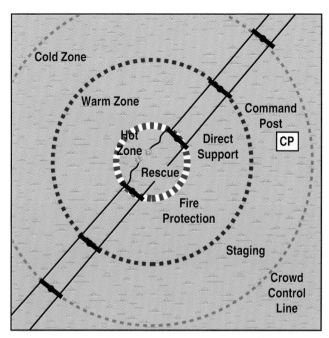

Figure 10.26 Firefighters should establish a perimeter and deny entry.

ing action. However, if a wire is down as a result of a storm, there may be many similar incidents in the area and that can tax the resources of the utility company. In areas with widespread storm damage, the response of local utility crews to any particular scene can be delayed — sometimes for hours. When there are many wires down in a fire department's response district, fire crews are unlikely to have enough resources to monitor every downed wire. In these cases, it may be necessary for individual companies to simply cordon off each hazard zone with barrier tape or mark it with traffic cones and move on to the next incident (**Figure 10.27**).

Figure 10.27 Traffic cones can be used to mark downed wires.

In some incidents involving downed electrical wires, establishing and controlling the perimeter is relatively easy. In others it can be quite difficult. For example, if a single strand of power line has parted for whatever reason, in many cases it is relatively easy to see where the break is and where the perimeter should be established to isolate the break. On the other hand, if an energized electrical wire falls across a metal fence (chain link, barbed wire, etc.), as described in **Essentials** the entire length of the fence can become energized. If the fence is enclosing a large institutional, industrial, or agricultural property, the fence may be miles (kilometers) in length. Anyone touching the fence may then complete the circuit to ground and suffer a severe electrical shock, or even electrocution. Similarly, if innocuous looking telephone wires or cable TV lines are down, even though these are normally low-voltage wires, they may be energized with the full electrical potential of the power lines if they are in contact with those lines at any point.

CAUTION
All downed wires should be treated as energized high-voltage lines until proven otherwise.

Establishing a perimeter around a downed electrical wire may be as simple as placing traffic cones around the hazard zone to direct motor vehicles around the scene. Or, it may be necessary to close a street at both ends of the block in which a wire has fallen. A common error is to establish a perimeter that is too small. As described in **Essentials**, the recommended isolation distance is that equal to one full span between the adjacent poles or towers in all directions from a break in a wire or the point of contact with the ground. If curious pedestrians are converging on the scene, it may be necessary to cordon it off with barrier tape or rope. In most cases, the method and degree of perimeter control established depends upon the nature and extent of the situation and on local protocols.

If the wire is down because a vehicle hit the pole or tower supporting it, and the driver and passengers are still inside, it is necessary to establish hot, warm, and cold zones as described in **Essentials**. The occupants of the vehicle should be advised not to attempt to exit the vehicle.

WARNING!

Do *not* attempt to remove a power line that is in direct contact with a vehicle unless you are properly trained and equipped to handle energized electrical wires. Avoid touching the vehicle — even if there are injured passengers still inside. Call the utility company and keep everyone away from the vehicle and the downed wire until utility company personnel have shut down the power.

Hazard Assessment

While the foregoing general rule for perimeter placement can be used in most downed wire incidents, in other situations, such as following an explosion or structural collapse, it may be necessary to more clearly define the hazard area. For example, if a downed wire is obscured by building debris or if it is obscured by smoke or darkness, it may be necessary for firefighters to use various forms of technology to identify the hazard area. There are a number of useful devices available to fire departments. Two of the most useful are *alternating current detectors* and *thermal imagers*.

Alternating current detectors. Alternating current detectors can detect unshielded AC current through snow, ice, and many solid objects. These battery-operated devices are handheld wands similar in size and shape to a police officer's baton **(Figure 10.28)**. In the presence of an alternating current, they emit an intermittent beep. The more rapid the beep, the closer the source is. The detection range (distance from the source at which the wand detects the current) varies with the situation. In general, the higher the voltage is, the greater the range will be. Under ideal conditions, these devices may be able to detect AC current in a single 120-volt line from as much as 15 feet (3 m). However, if the conductor is lying on wet soil, the range may be reduced to as little as 1 foot (30 cm). With higher potentials, such as those in distribution and transmission lines, the detection range can increase to

Figure 10.28 A typical AC power detector.

more than 500 feet (150 m). However, because power outages often result from very temporary causes, such as a tree limb being blown against a wire by high wind, most electrical distribution systems are programmed to automatically reenergize a few seconds after the circuit breaker in the substation trips. If the breaker trips again, many of these programs reenergize the system one more time before remaining off line. Therefore, even if a handheld detector fails to activate near a downed wire, it only means that the line is dead at that given moment but the line is not necessarily completely dead. In addition, when power from the normal utility source fails, some emergency generators may start automatically. If these units are not disconnected from the system, the power lines can be reenergized with 240 volts from the generators. Also, many overhead power lines are supplied from both directions; therefore, a single line break can still be energized on both sides of the break.

Thermal imagers. Thermal imagers can also be used to detect hidden wires. Electrical current creates heat whenever it encounters resistance in a circuit, and the heat is created at the point of resistance, not throughout the circuit. This phenomenon can be seen in the operation of an electric hot plate or an electric space heater. Resistance occurs when an uninsulated conductor (wire) is in contact with the ground or there is a kink in or damage to a conductor, insulated or not. This resistance creates heat and thermal imagers can detect that heat **(Figure 10.29)**.

Figure 10.29 Thermal imaging cameras can be used to locate hidden wires.

NOTE: Even though the technology just discussed allows firefighters to locate energized electrical conductors more safely and more reliably than in the past, most fire departments still do not allow their personnel to move or cut electrical wires under any circumstances. Most electric utility companies also support this practice. Therefore, unless directed otherwise by the IC or by local protocols, firefighters should locate and isolate downed electrical wires and wait for utility company personnel to shut down the power to those wires.

Water Control

The case history discussed in Chapter 1 involving the collapse of a hotel undergoing renovation also draws attention to the dangers associated with water accumulations during fire attack. While there were a number of factors that contributed to the collapse of that hotel, the weight of the water used to extinguish the fire was almost certainly one of them. This is easy to understand when the following hypothetical example is considered:

If extinguishing a fire on an upper floor of a 50- × 100-foot (15 m by 30 m) warehouse results in 6 inches (15 cm) of water accumulating on the floor, the total weight of that water exceeds 75 tons (68 *t*). This amount of water can be discharged from automatic sprinklers or hoselines (or both) in a very few minutes. In addition, the water may not have to be that deep if any of its volume were absorbed into the contents of the room.

Controlling the water supply in an emergency incident can be a lifesaving action. Uncontrolled water flow can contribute to structural instability and collapse, fill basements or cellars, and sometimes result in scalding injuries or steam burns to firefighters. When water fills a basement, it can short out the main electrical service and extinguish pilot lights in gas-fired appliances. In some cases, this can add a flammable gas leak to an already hazardous situation. However, just as there are variations in when and how other utilities are controlled, there are also situational differences with regard to controlling water supplies. The two most common situations relating to water control by firefighters are in structure fires and in buildings with major water supply leaks without fire.

Situational Differences

As with other utilities, water supplies often need to be controlled to prevent an incident from going from bad to worse. The two most common situations in which water supplies need to be controlled are in structure fires and where there are significant water leaks without fire.

Water Control in Structure Fires

Just as there are differences between structure fires and other types of emergencies in the need to control the water supply, there are differences between structure fire situations. The most prominent examples of these differences are between fires in sprinklered and unsprinklered buildings.

Sprinklered Buildings

Controlling the water supply to a sprinklered building on fire requires careful coordination between all aspects of the fireground operations. The primary need is to maintain and sometimes increase the water supply to sprinklers operating on the fire floor (**Figure 10.30**). Water may also be needed to supply hoselines operating from standpipes on the floor below the fire floor. Shutting off the building's water supply too soon could rob operating sprinklers and standpipes of the water needed to control the fire — and could place firefighters in serious jeopardy.

Figure 10.30 Supporting the sprinkler system is critically important.

As in the case history cited in Chapter 1, operating sprinklers can reduce the effectiveness of vertical ventilation efforts, and the runoff water can be heated to scalding temperatures by the fire. When this extremely hot water cascades down from above, it can deny firefighters and others on that floor access to perhaps the only available means of egress. Shutting off the building's water supply at the proper time can help reduce these effects, but timing is critically important. Shutting off the water too soon may allow the fire to overwhelm the on-scene fire fighting resources. Shutting it off too late can contribute to structural instability because of the weight of the water accumulating inside the building. Allowing sprinklers to continue discharging water after the fire has been controlled also adds to the live load of the building and may unnecessarily increase property damage.

In many cases, it may be prudent to shut down the sprinkler system water supply after the fire has been knocked down so that open sprinkler heads can be plugged or replaced (**Figure 10.31**). The water supply is then restored so that the standpipe system can be used during overhaul.

A growing number of single-family residences have full or partial sprinkler systems installed. As

Figure 10.31 The sprinkler system may need to be shut down.

in the larger commercial systems, a separate valve from the one that controls the domestic water supply controls the water supply to the sprinklers. But, unlike the commercial systems, the valve controlling the water supply to residential sprinklers may be either a small OS&Y valve or the same type of gate valve as is used to control the domestic water supply (**Figure 10.32**).

Figure 10.32 Typical controls on a residential sprinkler system. *Courtesy of Wes Kitchel.*

Unsprinklered Buildings

In most cases, the decision regarding when to shut off the water supply to an unsprinklered building that is on fire is relatively simple. Unless the water supply is contributing to the fire suppression effort, it should be shut down as soon as possible. The only reason to delay shutting off the water supply would be because of resource limitations and other, higher fireground priorities. But as soon as someone is available, the water supply should be shut down. On most small residential buildings, a single ordinary gate valve in the main line between the water meter and the building controls the water supply (**Figure 10.33**). When the water supply comes from a domestic well, there will be a gate valve somewhere between the well and the building. On larger, multiple residential and other large buildings, the water supply is controlled by a subsurface valve — often found in the sidewalk — between the water main and the building (**Figure 10.34**). In even larger

Figure 10.34 Some water service valves are located in the sidewalk.

buildings and complexes, the water supply is controlled by a large subsurface valve in the street adjacent to the front of the property. A large T-handle water key may be needed to operate this valve (**Figure 10.35**). Because municipal water systems can be damaged by street valves being closed too quickly, many agencies allow only water utility personnel to operate these valves. If local protocols permit firefighters to operate these valves, they must be trained in the proper valve-closing procedures.

Figure 10.33 A residential water service valve typical of some areas. *Courtesy of Francine DeLanty.*

Figure 10.35 The water may need to be shut off in the street.

Water Leaks Without Fire

Major water leaks can develop in buildings for a variety of reasons. Seismic activity can loosen pipe fittings or sever pipes completely. Water hammer caused by large valves being closed too quickly can also damage plumbing or cause numerous pressure relief valves to open simultaneously. And, of course, the effects of age, intermittent fluctuations in pressure, and the expansion and contraction due to changing temperatures (alternately freezing and thawing) can loosen pipe fittings over time or cause pipes to burst. All these causes, and any number of others, can produce water leaks within buildings that can have disastrous effects — especially if the leaks go undiscovered for an extended period of time.

Buildings With Basements or Cellars

The fact that a major water leak is not in the basement or cellar of a building does not necessarily mean that the space will not fill with water. Water is directly affected by gravity and will take the path of least resistance — usually downward. Therefore, a water leak anywhere from the basement or cellar to the top floor of the building may cause the basement or cellar to eventually fill with water (**Figure 10.36**). Because of insulation within the walls and high ambient noise levels inside and outside of many buildings — especially those in densely populated urban areas — water leaks can go undetected for long periods of time. Often, the first indication of a leak is when the lights suddenly fail or the furnace does not respond to commands from the thermostat. Water collecting in a seldom-used basement or cellar can short out the building's electrical system and/or extinguish the pilot lights in gas-fired furnaces and water heaters. If these gas-fired units are old enough, they may not have the thermocouple-controlled gas shutoff valves that have been required on similar units for decades. If not, the gas can continue to bubble up through the water and escape upward into the rest of the building. Should the gas reach another ignition source, a major explosion and fire could result. Anyone falling into the basement or cellar as the building collapses may drown in the water collected there, or they may be electrocuted because in many such buildings the main electrical panel is located there.

Summary

Some emergency incidents to which firefighters are called are initiated by one or more uncontrolled utilities. Accumulations of flammable gases may asphyxiate people by excluding the oxygen from the room in which they are sleeping, or the gases may reach an ignition source and explode violently. A malfunctioning electrical system may start a fire in an occupied building, or power lines may fall to the ground and electrocute anyone coming into contact with the downed wire. Leaking water can short out electrical systems, cause scald injuries and steam burns to firefighters and others in fires, and even drown anyone trapped in low areas following structural collapse.

Other incidents may not be caused by utilities but are made worse by them. Uncontrolled flammable gases can feed a structure fire and make it much more difficult to extinguish. Electrical wires that fall across a vehicle or other metal object can energize these objects and make rescues from them more difficult and much more dangerous for firefighters. Making rescues from collapsed buildings can be much more difficult if leaking water is rising in the areas where victims are trapped under the debris.

In all these situations and many other possible scenarios, firefighters must be aware of the dangers to themselves and others when utilities are uncontrolled. So that they know how to safely and quickly control the utilities in an incident when ordered to do so, firefighters must become familiar with the water utilities in their response districts through an ongoing program of pre-incident planning.

Figure 10.36 The basement should be checked for water accumulation.

Chapter 11
Controlling Building Systems

Chapter 11
Controlling Building Systems

Modern buildings have a number of systems for the comfort and convenience of those inside. Some systems are designed to control the interior environment by maintaining the temperature within a specified range. Some of these temperature control systems also control the interior humidity. Other building systems are designed to convey the building occupants from one part of the building to another. Still other systems are designed to detect fires or their byproducts, sound an alarm, and in some cases, control or suppress the fire. Finally, some building systems are designed to assist fire department personnel in extinguishing fires within the building. This chapter discusses various types of building systems and their hazards. Also discussed are common types of fire detection and suppression systems and how to control them.

Heating, Ventilating, and Air Conditioning Systems (HVAC)

Many types of structures, from single-family dwellings to huge industrial buildings, have some form of climate control system. These systems range from relatively small window-mounted units to huge commercial units that are themselves as large as some small buildings. While the potential hazards to firefighters associated with large commercial units are widely recognized, even the small window-mounted units can be hazardous under certain conditions. Therefore, firefighters must be familiar with the various types of HVAC systems in general and with the specific types of systems installed in buildings within their response districts.

HVAC Systems and Their Hazards

While there are different types of systems used to control the climate within buildings, the ones of greatest interest to firefighters are the HVAC systems. The equipment in this category includes everything from small built-in fans and gas-fired furnaces to heavy-duty combination units built into large residential, institutional, mercantile, and industrial structures (**Figure 11.1**). In general, the smaller the unit is, the smaller the potential risk is to firefighters. However, for their own safety and that of others, firefighters need to be familiar with all the various systems.

Figure 11.1 A typical large rooftop HVAC unit.

One reason that the acronym HVAC came into use was because the equipment needed to perform these three functions is often combined into a single system. This configuration produces significant savings because only one system of ducts is needed for all three functions. A common system of ductwork can have both positive and negative effects on structure fires. On the positive side, the HVAC ducts can be used to aid in ventilating a burning building by expelling smoke from within the building — both during the fire and after it has been extinguished. On the negative side, if the HVAC ducts are not controlled, smoke and fire can spread throughout a building through the ducts. Therefore controlling the HVAC ducts can be a critical element in successfully attacking and extinguishing a structure fire. Many HVAC ducts are equipped with fire/smoke detectors that automatically close dampers within the ducts during a fire.

Even the smallest gas-fired furnaces can be sources of ignition if combustibles are placed too close to them, and if these units leak they can also fill a compartment or an entire building with potentially explosive gas (**Figure 11.2**). Small electric blowers and heating elements can also be sources of ignition. Under the right conditions, they can be the source of electrical burns and even electrocution.

Window-mounted air conditioners are sometimes supported only by flimsy wooden or metal platforms that can fail during a fire. Others are held in place only by the window frame itself, and raising the windows as little as a few inches can cause the units to fall. Anyone working below them can be in danger of being struck by the falling units if their means of support fails (**Figure 11.3**).

Large built-in HVAC units can also be extremely hazardous to firefighters. Because HVAC units operate year round, they are subject to considerable wear and tear. Therefore, an increasing number of alarms can be associated with these units as they age. Calls reporting odors of smoke coming from HVAC ducts are common in older buildings. In many cases, the cause is defective worn-out V-belts or bearings on the drive shaft in HVAC units (**Figure 11.4**). In addition to all the potential hazards inherent in the smaller built-in units just discussed, large commercial units increase the potential for structural collapse because some extremely heavy rooftop units were installed on older buildings that were not originally designed for the additional dead load. Because of their sheer weight, the HVAC units can come crashing down onto the floor below if the roof assembly supporting these massive units is weakened by fire. This sometimes

Figure 11.2 Gas furnaces represent a variety of hazards. *Courtesy of Keith Flood.*

Figure 11.3 Window-mounted air conditioners can fall onto firefighters working below.

Figure 11.4 Worn-out V-belts cause many alarms.

sets off a chain reaction in multistory buildings — each floor fails when the one above collapses onto it (**Figure 11.5**). Lacking the support of the floor assemblies between them, the outer walls may then collapse inward onto the debris of the floors and roof (**Figure 11.6**). The outer walls can also suddenly collapse in an inward/outward pattern. In this type of wall collapse, a horizontal fissure forms across the middle of the wall and the top half falls inward as the bottom half falls outward (**Figure 11.7**). Firefighters working adjacent to the building would be in the collapse zone.

Control of HVAC Systems

As mentioned earlier, even the smallest climate control systems and equipment can be hazardous to firefighters and others. Larger commercial HVAC systems represent obvious potential hazards in fire

Figure 11.6 Without lateral support, sidewalls can collapse onto the debris.

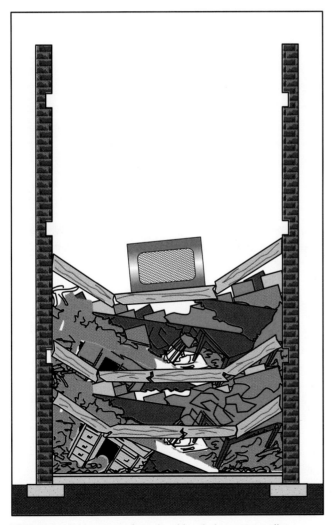

Figure 11. 5 Heavy rooftop dead loads increase collapse potential.

Figure 11.7 A typical in/out collapse.

situations. Therefore, controlling these systems during structure fires supports the three universal priorities — life safety, incident stabilization, and property conservation. Life safety is addressed when flammable gas explosions and structural collapse are prevented. Incident stabilization is facilitated when additional sources of ignition are eliminated, and the HVAC system is not allowed to spread the fire. Property is conserved when the fire is extinguished as soon as possible, and smoke is expelled from the building's interior.

Small gas-fired furnaces can usually be controlled by shutting off the fuel at the gas meter (**Figure 11.8**). Electric heaters can usually be controlled by unplugging them or shutting off the electrical service at the main panel (**Figure 11.9**). This is also true for the largest HVAC systems as well. The procedures for shutting down these utilities are as discussed in the previous chapter.

However, it is sometimes counterproductive to arbitrarily shut down the HVAC system in a large building. This is because the HVAC system can, under controlled conditions, be used as part of the ventilation effort by expelling smoke and hot gases from the building. This helps reduce smoke damage and may help limit the spread of the fire. Controlling the HVAC system is usually achieved by firefighters working closely with the building engineer or maintenance supervisor. The firefighters advise the engineer of what needs to be accomplished, and the engineer operates the system controls to make that happen (**Figure 11.10**). In most cases, firefighters should not attempt to operate the system controls themselves. Once again, pre-incident planning is critically important if firefighters are to become familiar with the systems installed in buildings in their districts and the capabilities and limitations of each system.

Figure 11.9 Many electric heating units can be controlled by unplugging them.

Figure 11.8 In most cases, gas can be controlled at the meter.

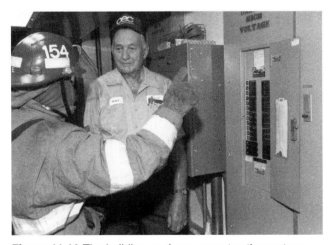

Figure 11.10 The building engineer operates the system controls under direction from fire fighting personnel.

Lighting Systems

While a wide variety of lighting systems are used in modern buildings, the two general types most critical during structure fires are *domestic* lighting systems and *emergency* lighting systems. To function both safely and efficiently at structure fires, firefighters need to be familiar with both of these lighting systems.

Lighting Systems and Their Hazards

As just described, there are two primary lighting systems with which firefighters must be concerned. For purposes of this manual, *domestic lighting* is defined as that normally used for interior and exterior illumination on a day-to-day basis. As the name implies, *emergency lighting* is that used to illuminate exit corridors and other means of egress when the domestic lighting fails for any reason.

Domestic Lighting Systems

These lighting systems use a variety of illuminating elements: incandescent bulbs, fluorescent tubes, neon tubing, and quartz bulbs. These systems normally operate on 110/120 AC. Some portable lighting fixtures use step-down transformers to reduce the operating voltage from 110/120 to 12 volts.

Regardless of how the lighting is used or how much or how little voltage it takes to operate, these systems and fixtures can all be hazardous under certain conditions. With the exception of those that are designated as *intrinsically safe*, all lighting units, both portable and fixed, are potential sources of ignition. In addition, electrically operated devices are potential sources of electric shock and even electrocution. Given the wet conditions that are often created by operating sprinklers or fire attack hoselines, the shock hazard for firefighters is greatly increased. Therefore, controlling these electrically operated systems and devices is critically important to firefighter safety.

Emergency Lighting Systems

As defined earlier, emergency lighting systems are those that are designed to provide sufficient light for occupants to be able to see their way out of a burning building (**Figure 11.11**). Most emergency lighting systems and units are designed to activate automatically when the domestic power to the building fails. Some of the automatic systems are battery operated; others are powered by an on-site emergency generator (**Figure 11.12**). Hard-wired emergency lighting units with battery backup represent as much of a hazard as the rest of the building's electrical wiring and components. In addition, those units with wet-cell batteries can cause acid burns if the shell breaks and the electrolyte solution gets on a firefighter's bare skin (**Figure 11.13**).

Control of Lighting Systems

Depending upon the nature of the incident, the IC may want some or all of the building's lighting left on during the incident. However, in the majority of structure fires, controlling both the domestic and emergency lighting is an important element in controlling the fire and increasing

Figure 11.11 Emergency lighting units provide illumination for exit passageways.

Figure 11.12 When public power fails, emergency generators take over.

Figure 11.13 A typical emergency lighting unit with a wet-cell battery.

firefighter safety during the incident. Therefore, it is important for firefighters to know the proper procedures for controlling these systems.

Controlling Domestic Lighting

In most cases, all domestic lighting can be shut down by opening the main electrical switch for the entire building or by switching the circuit breakers for specific areas to the "OFF" position (**Figure 11.14**). This allows the lights to stay on in areas not affected by the fire, while eliminating the power to the lights in areas near the fire. However, firefighters should be extremely careful when opening the main electrical switch on large control panels such as those in many commercial and industrial occupancies. Opening these large switches can produce an arc that is capable of damaging the eyes of anyone looking at the arc, and it can serve as a source of ignition if flammable vapors are present. Firefighters opening these large electrical switches should be in full PPE, and they should look away as they throw the switch (**Figure 11.15**).

Figure 11.14 Electrical power can be shut off at the main breaker.

Figure 11.15 Firefighters should look away from main electrical switches as they open them.

> # CAUTION
> **Opening the main electrical switch may automatically activate an emergency generator supplying power to areas that need to be shut down.**

Occupancies that have generators and/or other sources of emergency power should be identified during pre-incident planning inspections. In these occupancies, all electrical switches or breakers should be labeled to allow for selective shut down of the electrical power.

Controlling Emergency Lighting

In general, individual self-contained, battery-operated emergency lighting units are not a threat to firefighters or others. These units can be left on during a fire without adding to the hazards of the situation. However, as discussed earlier, if they are hard-wired units, they need to be controlled along with the rest of the building's electrical system.

Emergency lighting units supplied by the building's electrical system can be controlled by opening the main switch or circuit breaker at the main electrical panel. Those that are supplied by an emergency generator can only be controlled by shutting down the generator.

> # CAUTION
> **Shutting down an operating emergency generator in order to control the emergency lights may also eliminate power to fire pumps and other emergency systems. Therefore, an operating emergency generator should not be shut down arbitrarily — it should only be done on orders from the incident commander (IC).**

In some incidents, it may be necessary for fire department units to provide emergency power for lighting, ventilation, and other critical services when a building's own systems have been disabled by a fire. The specific techniques and equipment that are needed to establish this power supply should be identified during pre-incident planning.

Conveyance Systems

The most common conveyance systems that firefighters must control during structure fires are escalators and elevators. These "people movers" are found in many types of buildings from large single-family dwellings to high-rise residential and office buildings. These systems can both help and hinder firefighters during structure fires. If not properly controlled during structure fires, these systems can also be lethal to firefighters and others.

Conveyances and Their Hazards

According to an official investigative report, at about 7:30 p.m. on Wednesday November 18, 1987, a passenger leaving the London Underground noticed a small amount of smoke coming from beneath the treads of a wooden escalator in King's Cross Station. He reported the smoke to a ticket clerk who reported it to his supervisor. Due in part to the fact that the supervisor was mandated to personally investigate the report before passing it on to the London Fire Brigade, there was some delay in calling them. The fire was burning in accumulated grease and detritus (dust, fiber, and debris) on the track beneath the wooden escalator treads. The escalator continued to operate as the fire developed, and this helped spread the fire toward the top of the escalator tube. The railway personnel had not been trained in fire suppression, and they did not use any of the available fire extinguishers. Even though the station was filling with thick black smoke, trains continued to discharge passengers onto the platform at the bottom of the burning escalator. Shortly after the fire brigade arrived on scene, but before they could apply any water, the fire erupted up the escalator tube and engulfed the ticket hall. Thirty-one passengers were trapped and perished in the fire.

While this incident occurred in London, England, a number of wooden escalators are still in operation in North America (**Figure 11.16**). Regardless of the type of structure, there are a number of possible hazards related to fires in and around escalators. Unless protected by automatic fire shutters or sprinklers, one of the most significant hazards is that the

Figure 11.16 Wooden escalators are still in operation. *Courtesy of Peter Sells.*

openings through which an escalator passes from floor to floor can promote fire spread within the building. Another significant hazard associated with escalators is that a fire may cause a malfunction of the escalator controls allowing the conveyor to carry riders into the hazard area as happened in the King's Cross incident. In addition, if escalators continue to operate during a fire, there is the possibility that a firefighter's PPE may become entangled in the moving treads. If escalators are obscured by heavy smoke, firefighters and others can fall down the open passageway.

Likewise, numerous hazards are associated with elevators in structure fires — some of them quite deadly. For example, a number of case histories exist in which firefighters or other building occupants became fire victims when the elevators in which they were riding stopped at the fire floor and the doors opened automatically. At least one of these incidents occurred in a two-story building. Elevator shafts can become conduits for spreading fire, heat, and smoke throughout the building. This, too, can be deadly if the fire spread cuts off the egress for firefighters or building occupants. When visibility is obscured by heavy smoke, open elevator shafts represent a potentially fatal fall hazard for firefighters.

Control of Conveyance Systems

Obviously, both escalators and elevators can present firefighters with serious safety hazards during structure fires. By controlling these conveyance systems, firefighters can make an important contribution to their own safety and to implementing the Incident Action Plan. Therefore, firefighters need to know how to control these systems during a fire.

Controlling Escalators

As mentioned earlier, unless the passageway is sprinklered or protected by automatic fire shutters, there is little that firefighters can do to prevent fire spread through these openings (**Figure 11.17**). In sprinklered buildings, firefighters can make sure that the sprinkler system is adequately supplied, which increases the likelihood of the sprinkler system limiting fire spread from floor to floor (**Figure 11.18**). Beyond that, firefighters should shut down the electrical power to the escalator. This reduces the chances of any firefighter's PPE becoming entangled in the moving escalator treads. Firefighters should use pre-incident planning inspections to become familiar with the escalator design, emergency shut off locations, and the location of the escalator mechanical room.

Controlling Elevators

Because of the dangers associated with elevators and elevator shafts described earlier, many fire departments make elevator control one of their highest priorities and earliest assignments in high-rise fires. But as also mentioned earlier, this can be a lifesaving action even in two-story buildings. In many departments, one of the functions assigned to Lobby Control is to take charge of the building's elevators, bring them all to the lobby level, and lock them there (**Figure 11.19**). Building occupants are not allowed to use the elevators as a means of egress, and firefighters are not allowed to use them to reach the fire floor. Both occupants and firefighters must use interior or exterior stairs, aerial devices, or ground ladders to move up and down.

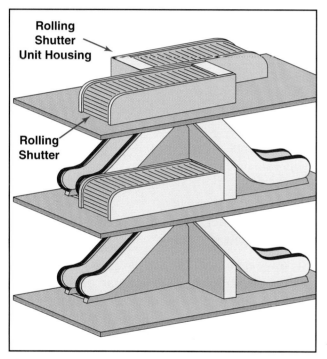

Figure 11.17 Some escalators are equipped with automatic fire shutters.

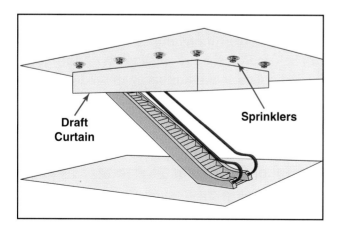

Figure 11.18 Sprinklers protecting escalators must be well supplied with water.

WARNING!

Firefighters must not be allowed to use any elevator that serves the fire floor or above until the officer in charge on the fire floor declares that it is safe for them to do so.

Figure 11.19 Elevators should be brought to the main elevator lobby.

Because it is less strenuous to walk down stairs than to walk up them, some departments allow their firefighters to use blind-shaft elevators to travel to a floor above the fire and then walk back down to the fire floor. It is a matter of department policy whether firefighters are allowed to use elevators that serve the fire floor or above. Some departments allow this, others do not.

Phase I operation. According to ASME A17.1, *Safety Code for Elevators*, published by the American Society of Mechanical Engineers, all modern passengers elevators must be equipped with what is called *Phase I Operation*. When the building's smoke detectors or a key-operated switch in the main elevator lobby activate the Phase I operation, all passenger elevator cars stop where they are and return to the *Designated Level*, usually the main elevator lobby (**Figure 11.20**). The car doors then open and remain open. If this mode of operation is initiated by a smoke detector on the Designated Level, the cars are programmed to divert to a preselected *Alternate Level*.

Phase II operation. During a fire, firefighters can take control of passenger elevators by inserting a special key into the required three-position switch in the main elevator lobby and turning the switch to the "ON" position. The elevators are then in the *Emergency Service* mode, also known as *Phase II Operation*. The key is then removed from the three-position switch and is used to initiate the *Firefighter's Control* (sometimes labeled *Firemen's Service*) inside the elevator car (**Figure 11.21**). In Phase II operation, the elevator cars can only be operated from inside the car, and the cars are programmed to ignore call signals from hallway landings. In addition, when an elevator car is operated in this mode, the car doors do not automatically open when the selected floor is reached. In most cases, the *door open* button must be used to open the door, and pressure must be maintained on the button until the door is fully open. If the button is released before the door is fully open, the door will automatically close.

Some departments allow their firefighters to use freight elevators — *when deemed safe to do so* — to travel to the floor below the fire floor. Freight elevators are usually bigger than passenger elevator cars and are more capable of carrying the weight of a fully equipped crew of firefighters (**Figure 11.22**). However, the same precautions listed for using passenger elevators during a fire also apply to freight elevators.

Figure 11.20 A firefighter activates Phase I operation.

Figure 11.21 Firefighter's Control is activated from inside the elevator car.

Figure 11.22 Freight elevators are designed to carry heavy loads.

Fire Detection and Suppression Systems

Most modern buildings and many older ones are equipped with some type of fire detection or suppression system. Some have more than one type of system. These systems range from simple battery-operated residential smoke detectors to highly sophisticated flame detection systems capable of actuating built-in fire suppression systems.

Types of Systems and Their Hazards

The principal types of systems within this category are smoke detection systems, heat/flame detection systems, flooding systems, sprinkler systems, and standpipe systems. With each of these systems there is at least one associated hazard to firefighters or building occupants. To protect themselves and others, firefighters must be familiar with the types of systems installed in buildings in their response districts.

Smoke Detection Systems

These systems range from individual, battery-operated detectors installed in single-family residences to hard-wired systems of multiple interconnected detectors in large residential, commercial, or industrial buildings. Because smoke detectors can be actuated by products of combustion generated early in the growth stage of a fire and do not have to wait for a specific level of heat to be produced, they can initiate an alarm much more quickly than most heat detector systems. Regardless of how the system is configured, there are two basic types of smoke detectors — *photoelectric* and *ionization*.

Photoelectric type detectors. A photoelectric smoke detector, sometimes called a *visible products-of-combustion detector*, uses a photoelectric cell and a light source. While there are other types, most photoelectric smoke detectors are of the *beam application* type (**Figure 11.23**). In this type of system, a beam of light from a source attached to the ceiling is focused horizontally onto a photoelectric cell on the other side of the compartment being monitored. The cell constantly converts the beam of light into electric current, which holds an electromagnetic switch open. When

smoke obscures the path of the light beam, the required amount of current is no longer produced and the switch closes initiating an alarm signal.

Ionization type detectors. An ionization smoke detector uses a tiny radioactive beta source (usually americium) to ionize air molecules as they enter a chamber within the detector. These ionized particles allow an electric current to flow between negative and positive plates within the chamber (**Figure 11.24**). When the particulate products of combustion (tiny particles and vapor droplets too small to be seen by the naked eye) enter the chamber, they attach themselves to the electrically

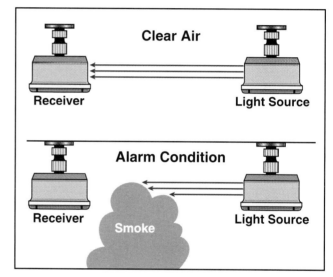

Figure 11.23 A typical *beam application* smoke detector.

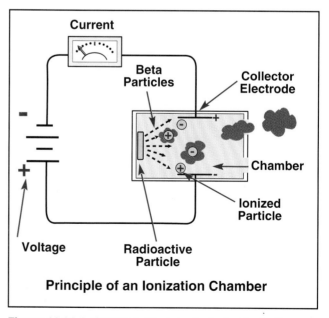

Figure 11.24 A simplified drawing of a typical ionization-type smoke detector.

charged air molecules (ions), making the air within the chamber less conductive. The decrease in current flow between the plates initiates an alarm signal.

Hazards Associated with Smoke Detection Systems

The major hazard with smoke detection systems is their susceptibility to initiating false alarms and the complacency that repeated false alarms produce in those who work and live in the protected buildings. Both types of smoke detection systems are vulnerable to being actuated inadvertently by steam and other opaque vapors, by solid objects (such as trapped birds) that interrupt the light beam in photoelectric systems, or by particulates unrelated to combustion that enter an ionization chamber. Some newer systems have microprocessor controls that allow the sensitivity of individual detectors to be adjusted to compensate for local conditions that produce false alarms.

Heat/Flame Detection Systems

These systems range from simple fixed-temperature heat detectors to those that can detect the light produced by flames. All these systems are electrically operated, and they consist of one or more detectors connected to an alarm panel by alarm circuit wiring.

Fixed-temperature thermostats. The most basic heat detection systems rely on tiny heat sensors (called *thermostats*) installed on the ceilings of the compartments to be protected (**Figure 11.25**). Most fixed-temperature thermostats operate by one of two means. They

Figure 11.25 A typical fixed-temperature heat detector.

either have a bimetallic contact that bends in response to heat, or they have a fusible element that melts and allows the switch to close. In the bimetal switch, the bend results from the different expansion ratios between two metals that are bonded together inside the thermostat. When the

temperature at the ceiling of the compartment reaches the designated temperature — usually around 135°F (57°C) in living spaces and 200°F (93°C) in attic spaces — the bimetallic switch bends and makes contact to initiate an alarm (**Figure 11.26**). In the fusible element type, when the designated temperature is reached, the solder holding the element in place melts and a spring-loaded plunger pushes the element out (**Figure 11.27**). This allows contact to be made in the internal switch and an alarm signal to be initiated.

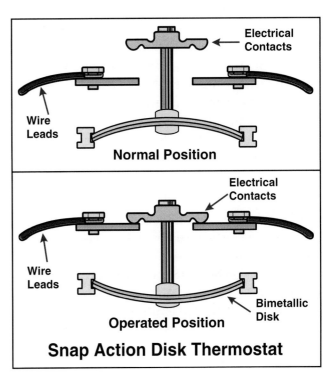

Figure 11.26 The operation of a bimetallic heat detector.

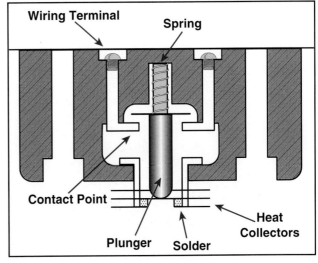

Figure 11.27 The operation of a fusible fixed-temperature heat detector.

Rate-of-rise thermostats. Other heat detectors are actuated by the rate at which the temperature in the compartment increases. In these *rate-of-rise* systems, the ceiling-mounted thermostats are small, dome-shaped air chambers, each with a tiny orifice of a specific diameter (**Figure 11.28**). Any increase in the ambient temperature causes the air within the chamber to expand. A slow increase in room temperature due to normal atmospheric heating allows the expanding air within the chambers to escape through the tiny orifices. However, if the rate of temperature rise is greater than about 12°F (7°C) in one minute — as would be the case in a developing fire — the air expands faster than it can escape from the chamber. This amount of expansion bends a thin metallic diaphragm within the detector to make contact and initiate an alarm. Because the alarm is initiated by a sudden rise in temperature, regardless of how low the initial temperature was, rate-of-rise thermostats can initiate an alarm at much lower temperatures than can fixed-temperature thermostats.

Hazards associated with heat detection systems. Since both types of heat detection systems operate at very low voltages, there is little or no danger of electric shock or as a source of ignition. The greatest hazard associated with these systems is their unreliability. While the vast majority of these systems are reliable and effective, some are prone to frequent false alarms. Therefore, the building occupants eventually begin to ignore the sound of the ringing bell. Therefore, if an alarm is initiated — especially late at night — by an actual fire in a building that has experienced numerous false alarms, occupants may be trapped inside because they ignored the alarm long enough for the fire to develop to major proportions.

Figure 11.28 A typical rate-of-rise heat detector.

Flame detectors. Sometimes called *light detectors*, flame detectors are among the most sensitive fire detection systems. There are three basic types of flame detectors:

- Those that detect light in the ultraviolet wave spectrum (UV detectors) (**Figure 11.29**)
- Those that detect light in the infrared wave spectrum (IR detectors) (**Figure 11.30**)
- Those that detect both types of light (**Figure 11.31**)

Flame detectors operate on a line-of-sight basis; therefore, they can be blocked by opaque objects. To reduce the likelihood of false alarms from sunlight and other steady light sources, IR detectors are designed to require the flickering motion of a flame to initiate an alarm.

Figure 11.29 One type of UV flame detector.

Figure 11.30 A typical infrared flame detector. *Courtesy of Detector Electronics Corp.*

Figure 11.31 A combination-type flame detector. *Courtesy of Detector Electronics Corp.*

Like heat detectors, flame detectors can also initiate false alarms. Flame detectors are susceptible to initiating false alarms from sunlight, welding, mercury-vapor lamps, and other bright light sources. Fewer false alarms are initiated by flame detection systems that have both UV and IR detectors protecting the same area. If both types of detectors must be activated to initiate an alarm, the likelihood of false alarms is greatly reduced.

Flooding Systems

As the name implies, these systems operate by flooding a closed compartment with a chemical agent intended to prevent, control, or extinguish a fire within the compartment. While there are other types of flooding systems, the three most common are those that use carbon dioxide (CO_2), Halon 1211, or Halon 1301. Even though the Montreal Protocol required that the production of halogenated hydrocarbons be stopped by the year 2000, the U.S. voluntarily stopped its production in 1993. However, there are still many Halon flooding systems in service.

Carbon dioxide. All CO_2 flooding systems must conform to the requirements of NFPA 12, *Standard on Carbon Dioxide Extinguishing Systems.* When

actuated, these flooding systems are designed to fill a compartment with CO_2 gas to displace or dilute the oxygen within the compartment and thereby smother the fire (**Figure 11.32**). These systems are most often installed to protect electrical systems and components, and processes that involve flammable liquids. Because the cold temperatures produced by the expanding gas can damage sensitive electronic devices and erase computer memory tapes, they are not usually installed in computer rooms.

Any level of oxygen that will not support combustion will also not support human life. Therefore, these systems are required to have a predischarge alarm (horn, bell, flashing light, or siren) to warn occupants that the system is about to flood the compartment with agent (**Figure 11.33**). Where these

Figure 11.32 A typical discharge horn on a CO_2 flooding system.

Figure 11.33 A typical predischarge alarm device.

systems are installed, the exit doors from the protected space are also required to be self-locking to prevent inappropriate reentry before the compartment is adequately ventilated. Obviously, the reduced oxygen level within a flooded compartment is a respiratory hazard to firefighters and any others not wearing SCBA.

Halon 1211. Systems that use Halon 1211 (bromochlorodifluoromethane) must conform to NFPA 12B, *Standard on Halon 1211 Fire Extinguishing Systems*. Because of its toxicity (hazardous above 40,000 ppm or 4 percent in air), Halon 1211 is not permitted to be used in occupied spaces such as computer rooms. As with CO_2 flooding systems, Halon 1211 systems must include a predischarge alarm because of the toxic decomposition products that may be generated in a fire.

Halon 1301. Systems that use Halon 1301 (bromotrifluoromethane) must conform to NFPA 12A, *Standard on Halon 1301 Fire Extinguishing Systems*. Halon 1301 is hazardous above 100,000 ppm or 10 percent in air. However, it is permitted to be used in occupied spaces because it is effective in such low concentrations that it poses little threat to occupants. Therefore, this is the agent most often used to protect computer rooms. Like Halon 1211, it can generate toxic decomposition products in a fire.

To protect themselves and others, firefighters must identify the types of fire detection and control systems in their response districts during pre-incident planning inspections. For more information on these systems, refer to the IFSTA **Fire Suppression and Detection Systems** manual.

Sprinkler Systems

In general, there are three types of automatic sprinkler systems — wet systems, dry systems, and those that incorporate characteristics of both wet and dry systems.

Wet systems. In most wet systems, water under pressure fills the entire system from the water source to each sprinkler head. These systems are installed in areas where freezing temperatures are unlikely. In areas subject to freezing, either due to weather or refrigeration, some wet systems have sections of distribution piping filled with an anti-freeze solution such as ethylene glycol, propylene glycol, or glycerine.

Dry systems. In occupancies that are subject to freezing temperatures, especially those where the volume of antifreeze would be excessive, dry systems are installed. In a dry sprinkler system, the distribution piping is filled with air under pressure, and water fills the piping only as the air escapes through one or more open sprinklers.

Other types of systems. There are other types of sprinkler systems, such as deluge systems and others, used to protect specialized occupancies. However, a discussion of these specialized systems is beyond the scope of this manual. For more information on automatic sprinkler systems, refer to the IFSTA **Fire Suppression and Detection Systems** manual.

Automatic sprinkler systems installed in residential buildings of more than four stories in height and other large buildings of any type must conform to the requirements of NFPA 13, *Standard for the Installation of Sprinkler Systems*. Sprinkler systems installed in smaller residential buildings must conform to either NFPA 13R, *Standard for the Installation of Sprinkler Systems in Residential Occupancies up to Four Stories in Height*, or NFPA 13D, *Standard for the Installation of Sprinkler Systems in One- and Two-Family Dwellings and Mobile Homes*. Statistically, sprinkler systems installed and maintained according to the requirements of the applicable NFPA standard are effective in controlling or extinguishing fires in well over 90 percent of cases. However, as was seen in some of the case histories cited in earlier chapters, properly operating sprinkler systems can also create hazards for firefighters.

Hazards associated with sprinkler systems. One of the hazards associated with operating sprinkler systems is that the water spray can sometimes keep smoke from being hot enough to melt the fusible links that keep smoke vents closed. Therefore, the smoke spreads laterally inside the building until firefighters open the roof vents. When heat and smoke cannot escape through ventilation openings, it can be trapped inside the building, subject interior fire crews to additional punishment, and increase property damage. Operating sprinklers can also prevent smoke and heat from escaping through vertical ventilation openings. Water discharged from sprinklers in attics can be heated by the fire to scalding temperatures. The water may collect atop the ceiling of a room, and if the soggy ceiling suddenly falls onto firefighters working in the room below, they can suffer traumatic injuries from being struck by the ceiling material and burn injuries from the extremely hot water. On the other hand, if the ambient temperature is below 32°F (0°C), run-off water from an operating sprinkler can freeze and make stairways and other areas treacherous for firefighters to walk on. In addition, if water from discharging sprinklers collects on the upper floors of a building, such as by being absorbed by bales of paper or cardboard boxes not on pallets, the weight of the water can threaten the building's structural integrity. If the water is not drained off it can contribute to the collapse of the fire-weakened building. However, even if firefighters create a sufficient number of openings to drain all standing water, the water that has been absorbed by the contents of the building will not drain.

To help prevent or reduce these hazards and others associated with automatic sprinkler systems, firefighters must know how to control these systems when necessary. However, just as there are potential hazards associated with leaving sprinkler systems in operation too long, there are also potential hazards with these systems being shut down too soon. Whenever a sprinkler system in a fire damaged building is shut down, a firefighter with a portable radio should be stationed at the main water supply valve so that it can be reopened quickly if the fire suddenly flares up (**Figure 11.34**).

Figure 11.34 If an OS&Y valve is shut down, a firefighter with a radio should remain at the valve in case it must be turned back on.

Standpipe Systems

According to NFPA 14, *Standard for the Installation of Standpipe, Private Hydrants and Hose Systems (2000 edition)* there are three *classes* of standpipes. These classes are as follows:

- Class I standpipe intended for use only by trained firefighters and equipped with a 2½-inch (65 mm) valve-controlled outlet (**Figure 11.35**)

- Class II system intended for use by untrained building occupants and equipped with a 1½-inch (38 mm) valve-controlled outlet, hose (usually unlined linen), and a nozzle (**Figure 11.36**)

- Class III system combining the features of both the Class I and Class II systems and equipped with a 2½-inch (65 mm) valve-controlled outlet and a 1½-inch (38 mm) valve-controlled outlet with hose and a nozzle (**Figure 11.37**)

There are also four different *types* of standpipes in buildings. The types of standpipes are as follows:

- Wet standpipe systems in which water pressure is always maintained, and water is immediately available when the outlet valve is opened

- Dry standpipe systems that supply water pressure only after a water supply valve (controlled by an electrical switch or other device in each hose station) is opened from the control device

- Dry standpipe systems in which the piping contains air under pressure and which admits water into the system piping when a outlet valve is opened

- Dry standpipe systems that have no permanent water supply and which must be supplied entirely from the fire department connection (FDC)

Hazards associated with standpipe systems. Unless properly maintained before a fire and properly controlled during a fire, each class and type of system has its potential hazards for firefighters or building occupants. For example, all classes and types of standpipe connections, valves, and other components are subject to vandalism, damage, or theft if they are accessible to the public — and most of them are. In many Class II hose cabinets, the brass nozzles have been stolen, and even the plastic replacement nozzles disappear. If the hose in Class II or Class III standpipes is not properly maintained, it can burst when pressurized for the first time dur-

Figure 11.35 A typical Class I standpipe.

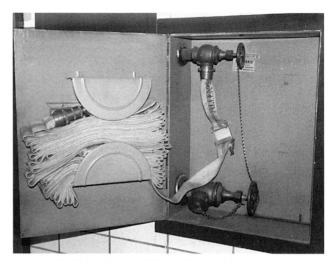

Figure 11.37 One form of Class III standpipe.

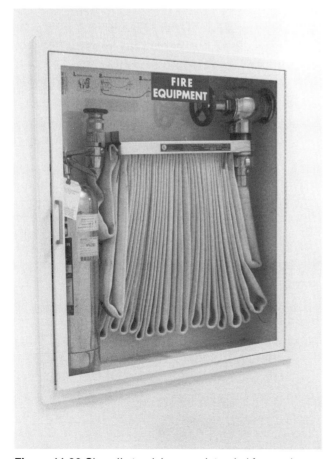

Figure 11.36 Class II standpipes are intended for use by the public.

ing a fire. If the occupant who charged the failed hose simply drops it and flees the area without closing the outlet valve, water is wasted, water damage may be increased, and the pressure to other hose connections may be reduced. If this scenario is repeated several times in the same building during a fire, the reduction in the standpipe's usefulness to firefighters may be significant. If firefighters connect an attack line to a dry standpipe outlet before the system is pressurized from the FDC, they can be in an extremely vulnerable position until the water arrives at their location. And, just as with sprinkler systems, the runoff water from standpipe hoselines can freeze and make walking in and around the building very dangerous for firefighters and others.

Control of Fire Detection and Suppression Systems

Pre-incident planning inspections can help firefighters become familiar with the types of systems installed in buildings in their response districts. These inspections can also make the firefighters aware of where the main control panels or valves and any subpanels are located, as well as how access to the panels or valves may be obtained.

Controlling Heat/Flame Detection Systems

When one of these systems initiates an alarm and the first-arriving firefighters find no sign of fire, it is helpful if the firefighters silence the alarm bell or other alerting device while completing their investigation into the source of the alarm (**Figure 11.38**).

Figure 11.38 It may be helpful to silence the alarm system while investigating the source of the alarm.

Figure 11.39 A firefighter with a radio should monitor the alarm panel during the investigation.

This reduces the level of noise at the scene and helps to calm any occupants who may be frightened by the commotion or agitated by the incessant ringing or other alarm signal. In most cases, the alerting device can be silenced with the push of a button or the flip of a switch at the main panel. However, the system should *not* be reset or turned off until the source of the alarm has been found. In addition, a firefighter with a radio should be assigned to monitor the alarm panel during the investigation in case a subsequent alarm is initiated (**Figure 11.39**). If a subsequent alarm is initiated — especially one from a different location than the first alarm — the IC should be notified immediately. Heat/flame detector actuation may also cause fire doors in some residential buildings to close automatically. In that case, the doors should remain closed until the source of the alarm has been located.

Once the source of the alarm has been located and determined either to be innocuous, such as a temporary system malfunction, or the source has been neutralized, the system can be reset. If the system was damaged in the incident, it may have to be turned off and placed out of service. In that case, all occupants of the building, the building owner or manager, and the fire department communications/dispatch center must be notified that the alarm system is inoperative.

Controlling Smoke Detection Systems

Except for those occupancies with individual smoke detectors that are not interconnected, the procedures for controlling these systems are essentially the same as those described for controlling heat/flame detection systems — with a few possible exceptions. In high-rise buildings, smoke detector actuation causes all elevators to automatically return to the designated level or an alternate level if one or more detectors were actuated on the designated level. Smoke detector actuation may also cause smoke vents on the roofs of some buildings to open automatically. After the source of the alarm has been located and neutralized, these vents should be checked to make sure they are closed before firefighters leave the scene.

Controlling Flooding Systems

Once a flooding system has actuated, the only control in which firefighters are likely to be involved is controlling entry into the flooded compartment. Flooding systems have a variety of actuating devices such as heat detectors, smoke detectors, and fusible links. And, for use by building occupants, both CO_2 and Halon flooding systems have manual system actuation.

CO_2 flooding systems have two forms of manual actuation. One is a manual pull handle that causes the system to flood the compartment after a delay for the pre-discharge alarm to sound (**Figure 11.40**). The other is an emergency system dump valve that causes the system to flood the compartment as soon as the valve is opened — there is no pre-discharge alarm (**Figure 11.41**).

Halon flooding systems also have manual actuation handles for use by building occupants. But, unlike the CO_2 systems, Halon flooding systems also have an "abort" switch (**Figure 11.42**). This switch can be used by building occupants to prevent the accidental discharge of a Halon flooding system — and the need for an extremely expensive system recharge.

Controlling Sprinkler Systems

Sprinkler systems are controlled by shutting down their water supply. In most cases, the OS&Y valve or PIV must be closed (**Figure 11.43**). Flow from an individual sprinkler can be temporarily controlled by installing a sprinkler stop as described in **Essentials**. In other systems, control is achieved by shutting down the fire pumps supplying water to the system.

> # CAUTION
> One of the most serious mistakes that firefighters can make is to shut down a sprinkler system too soon. Therefore, shutting down a sprinkler system must be done only on orders from the IC.

Some fire departments allow their personnel to replace fused sprinkler heads with new ones from the supply cabinet near the sprinkler riser; others do not. Likewise, some departments allow their personnel to restore a wet pipe sprinkler system to service after a fire; others do not. Most fire departments *do not* allow their personnel to attempt to restore any of the dry pipe systems to service as this can be a complex and time-consuming process. Regardless of the type of system involved, when it must be left in an inoperative condition after a fire or system malfunction, the building occupants, the owner or manager, and the fire department communica-

Figure 11.40 Flooding systems can be actuated manually.

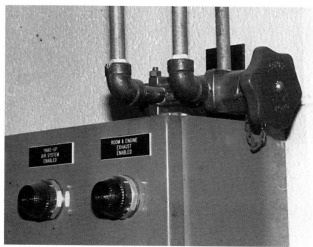

Figure 11.41 A typical flooding system dump valve.

Figure 11.42 A typical Halon system abort switch.

tions/dispatch center must be notified of the system's status. In addition, some departments leave one fire company on scene until the system is restored to service. Other departments assign a chief officer to revisit the scene at intervals until the system is back in service. Still other departments set up an electronic heat/smoke detector unit that operates either on battery or 110/120 volt AC power **(Figure 11.44)**. These units are designed to transmit an alarm to the department's communications/dispatch center in the event of a rekindle.

Figure 11.43 A sprinkler system can be shut down at the PIV.

Figure 11.44 An electronic rekindle detector. *Courtesy of Rick Montemorra.*

Controlling Standpipe Systems

As with sprinkler systems, standpipe systems are controlled by their water supply. In some dry pipe systems, the water supply is controlled simply by disconnecting the supply hose from the FDC. In other dry pipe systems and all wet pipe systems, the water supply must be shut off either at the pump or at the main water supply valve. In standpipe systems that share a water supply with a sprinkler system, the water supply must be shut down at the OS&Y valve or PIV. In some large buildings, the standpipe and sprinkler systems are subdivided into zones, and the water supply to individual zones can be shut down without compromising the protection in the rest of the building.

In most cases, all that is required of the fire department to restore a standpipe system to service is to remove their hoses and fittings from the system. Replacing the wet hose in Class II or Class III systems in usually not the fire department's responsibility. Nor is it the fire department's responsibility to repressurize a dry pipe system with air. However, in subfreezing temperatures, dry systems should be drained of water to prevent damage to the system piping. As with other types of fire detection and control systems, if a standpipe system must be left in an inoperative condition following an incident, the building occupants, the owner or manager, and the fire department communications/dispatch center must be notified of the system's status.

Summary

In addition to controlling a burning building's utilities — gas, electricity, and water — firefighters need to be able to control the building's systems. These are the building's HVAC system, fire detection system, and fire control systems such as flooding systems, sprinkler systems, and standpipes. In some buildings, firefighters will need to control conveyance systems such as escalators and elevators. To control these systems safely and efficiently, firefighters need to know what types of systems are installed in buildings within their response districts, where these systems are located, and how they can be controlled during a fire. This knowledge is best gained through an ongoing program of pre-incident planning inspections.

Chapter 12
Loss Control

Chapter 12
Loss Control

Historically, the work that has come to be known as "loss control" at structure fires was originally done by civilian salvage crews hired by fire insurance companies to save as much as possible of their policyholders' properties during a fire — and thereby reduce the amount of money the insurance companies would have to pay out. Eventually, public fire departments began to provide these services. But this function was still seen as less important than fighting the fire and in many departments was often performed almost as an afterthought. Today, salvage is recognized as a very important fire department function that is but one aspect of the broader category called *loss control*.

To paraphrase the IFSTA **Fire Service Loss Control** manual, the purpose of loss control is to reduce damage from fire, smoke, water, inclement weather, or other contingencies before, during, and after a fire. In other words, armed with knowledge about the involved occupancy gathered during pre-incident planning inspections, loss control operations consist of those actions that aid in reducing primary and secondary damage during and after the fire. *Primary damage* is that produced by the fire. *Secondary damage* is that resulting from fighting the fire and/or leaving the property inadequately protected.

Firefighters should consider loss control when conducting pre-incident planning inspections, during structure fire incidents, and in post-incident operations. Therefore, this chapter discusses those three phases of loss control at structure fires.

Pre-Incident Loss Control Operations

The purpose of all pre-incident planning, including that for loss control, is to increase incident safety, efficiency, and effectiveness. These ends are achieved by increasing the firefighter's familiarity with a particular building and its contents and by reducing the number of decisions that must be made during a fire in that building. Until acted upon by some outside intervention, all structure fires are uncontrolled emergencies. By definition, an emergency is an event that is *emerging* — it is a dynamic and changing phenomenon. Therefore, unless someone or something acts to stop the fire, it will continue to burn until all the available fuel and/or oxidizing agent have been consumed. For the firefighters assigned to control and extinguish a structure fire, pre-incident loss control information helps them make faster and more informed on-scene decisions and that lets them focus on protecting themselves and others, stabilizing the situation, and conserving property. Before a fire ever starts, pre-incident planning can answer many questions about the building, its contents, and any fire-related problems to be expected.

Using a systematic pre-incident planning process can increase the likelihood of a successful outcome on the fireground. As in all other aspects of fireground support operations, pre-incident planning helps firefighters prepare to perform loss control operations in a given building more safely and more effectively. By becoming familiar with a structure and its contents, firefighters can develop plans that help them reduce the overall loss resulting from a fire in that occupancy.

Typically, pre-incident loss control planning is not done separately from other pre-incident planning. Rather, loss control should be considered at each step in the process of developing an overall pre-incident plan — sometimes called an *operational plan* or *contingency plan*. Some departments use a very sophisticated risk management system as the basis for their loss control pre-incident planning. Other departments take a more traditional approach to assessing loss control risks and developing strategies for mitigating those risks. In this context, a *loss control risk* is any aspect of a building or its contents that has the potential for producing primary or secondary loss if there is a fire in that building. Regardless of what system is used to deal with loss control risks, all such systems involve the same basic steps — risk identification, risk evaluation, and plans development.

Risk Identification

Risk identification is usually accomplished through an ongoing program of pre-incident planning inspections. Some departments refer to these site visits as "surveys" to differentiate them from code enforcement inspections. Regardless of what these visits are called, they have three purposes:

- To allow firefighters to become familiar with the building and its contents
- To gather information for plans development
- To inform building owners/occupants of anything that they can do to reduce the risk of loss

During pre-incident planning inspections, firefighters should look for and document any condition that might result in a primary or secondary loss (**Figure 12.1**). Firefighters should note such items as the following:

- Life safety hazards
- Vital processes that should be shut down only as a last resort
- Repositories of vital information that *must* be protected, if possible
- Biohazards and highly flammable or reactive materials or processes

Figure 12.1 Potential loss control problems should be identified before a fire occurs.

- Structural designs that increase loss potential
- Highly absorbent contents that need to be protected from water

Firefighters should also identify the locations of Material Safety Data Sheets (MSDS), emergency contact lists, areas of restricted access, and items or areas of extremely high value. In addition, they should discuss with the owner/occupant the need to keep absorbent stock on pallets and not piled or stacked too high. They should also discuss the benefits of general good housekeeping (**Figure 12.2**).

In addition, firefighters should note any of the following features or systems that might reduce the risk of loss:

- Fire escapes, smoke towers, and areas of refuge
- Automatic fire doors
- Built-in fire detection/suppression systems
- Automatic smoke vents

Risk Evaluation

Once all the foregoing information has been gathered, it must be evaluated. This evaluation involves using judgment and experience to assess how any

Figure 12.2 Loss control potential should be pointed out to the occupant.

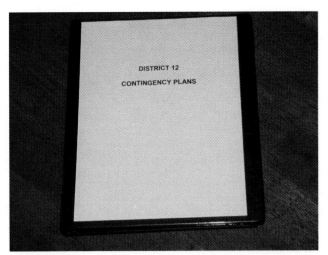

Figure 12.3 Survey information is translated into contingency plans.

particular item will increase or decrease the potential for primary or secondary loss. For example, automatic fire doors may help to reduce primary loss by limiting the spread of a fire, but they may also impede the occupants' ability to escape from the building. Automatic sprinklers may help to reduce primary loss by controlling a fire and allowing it to be extinguished while it is still relatively small. However, automatic sprinklers may also add to secondary loss by reducing the building's structural integrity because of the weight of a tremendous amount of water added to upper floors. The water discharged by automatic sprinklers may also damage or destroy building contents not involved in the fire. Therefore, every item of information must be evaluated for its positive and/or negative loss control potential.

Plans Development

Once a building has been inspected and the loss control risks identified and evaluated, the information and conclusions should be translated into contingency plans (**Figure 12.3**). In terms of structure fires, the initial response level should be determined and documented so that the appropriate number and types of resources are dispatched to that location whenever a fire is reported there. Mitigation plans should be devised for the most likely hazards to be encountered in a fire in that building. The mitigation plans may necessitate the acquisition of additional equipment and training on the implementation of the plans. In addition, any plans that are developed should include a loss control element. The loss control element of the plans may specify or indicate the following:

● Most effective and least destructive means of forcing entry into the building

● Most effective means of evacuating or protecting building occupants during a fire

● Where vital business records are stored and how best to protect them during a fire

● When and how the built-in fire suppression systems are to be supported and used

If the situation within the building is extraordinary in some way, the loss control element may also specify how building contents are to be protected from smoke and water damage.

A conscientiously applied program of pre-incident planning can contribute greatly to preventing or reducing primary and secondary loss when a fire occurs in a building. For more information on pre-incident loss control planning, refer to the IFSTA **Fire Service Loss Control** manual. Also see Appendix B for an example of a typical pre-incident planning form.

Incident Loss Control Operations

Once a fire has started within a building, the flames, heat, and smoke can cause an enormous amount of damage to the structure and its contents. This primary damage was once seen as outside the control of the firefighters. However, with advancements in fire detection technology and fire suppression tools and techniques, firefighters are more capable of rapid fire extinguishment than ever before.

During a structure fire, secondary damage can result from forcible entry, fire attack, ventilation and smoke removal, water use and removal, salvage, and overhaul. However, given the proper training and equipment, firefighters can minimize secondary damage. An important part of minimizing secondary damage is conducting an adequate size-up so that an accurate picture of the problem is developed. Actions taken by suppression forces based on inaccurate information can cause unnecessary damage.

Primary Loss Control

One of the most important ways that firefighters can limit primary damage in a structure fire is to extinguish the fire as quickly and as efficiently as possible. While others carry out search and rescue and direct fire attack operations, fireground support personnel can also have direct involvement in the rescue and fire control efforts by performing horizontal or vertical ventilation to improve the atmosphere inside the burning building and by overhauling the fire. In general, the most important factors in limiting primary damage are as follows:

- Adequate on-scene resources
- Effective method of attack
- Effective ventilation
- Thorough overhaul

Resources

Amassing a sufficient number of the right types of resources on-scene can greatly enhance the efficiency and effectiveness of the fire attack (**Figure 12.4**). Thorough pre-incident planning can help ensure that these resources are part of the initial alarm response. If they are not part of the initial re-

Figure 12.4 An effective fire attack may require a large commitment of resources. *Courtesy of Bill Tompkins.*

sponse, the IC may have to call for additional resources after sizing up the situation and developing an IAP. The delay involved in having to wait for additional resources to arrive at the scene may slow the fire attack and result in increased primary damage.

Attack

The method of attack can certainly affect the amount of primary damage from a fire. If the number and size of the attack lines are not sufficient to deliver enough water onto the fire to absorb the heat being generated, the fire will continue to grow and damage or destroy more of the building and/or its contents. Also, if water is applied to the outside of a building while the fire is burning inside, the fire is likely to destroy the entire building. To limit primary damage, there must be a sufficient number of firefighters properly trained and equipped to deliver the required amount of water directly onto the fire (**Figure 12.5**). And the sooner they can do this, the better the result will be.

Ventilation

As mentioned earlier, fireground support personnel can be involved in limiting primary damage by performing horizontal or vertical ventilation quickly and effectively. Until a working structure fire is ventilated, the dense smoke may prevent firefighters from finding trapped victims or the seat of the fire. In addition, the intense heat inside the structure may prevent firefighters from approaching the fire close enough to deliver their water effectively. The trapped heat and smoke can seriously damage

Figure 12.5 An aggressive fire attack can reduce primary fire loss.

Figure 12.6 Aggressive ventilation can also reduce primary fire loss.

building contents. Therefore, early and effective ventilation can reduce primary damage by limiting the spread of the fire and by helping hose crews to locate and extinguish the fire as quickly as possible (**Figure 12.6**).

Overhaul

Another way that fireground support personnel can help limit primary damage in a structure fire is by performing a thorough overhaul. Even though overhaul normally takes place after a fire has been knocked down, the damage done by hidden fire is still primary damage. Finding and extinguishing all remaining fire completes the fire suppression phase of the operation and can prevent a costly rekindle that could destroy all that remains of the building. Therefore, a thorough overhaul can be a very important part of primary loss control at structure fires. To reduce the chances of a rekindle and to eliminate the need to post a fire watch when fire crews leave the scene, some departments set up portable electronic rekindle detectors after a work-

ing structure fire (**Figure 12.7**). These units normally operate from battery power but can operate on AC power if it is available. When smoke or heat is detected, the unit automatically transmits an alarm by radio signal to the fire department communications/dispatch center.

Evidence preservation. Before the IC allows firefighters to begin the overhaul of any structure fire, the investigator or whoever is charged with determining the fire cause should be consulted. This

Figure 12.7 A typical rekindle detector. *Courtesy of Rick Montemorra.*

allows the investigator time to collect or protect critical evidence before overhaul begins and helps to ensure that the evidence is not disturbed or destroyed by the firefighters during overhaul (**Figure 12.8**).

Firefighter safety. Another major consideration during overhaul is firefighter safety. There are a number of factors that can make the overhaul process very hazardous for the firefighters assigned to this task. If the same firefighters who extinguished the fire and performed all the other associated tasks are the ones who will have to overhaul the fire, and this is frequently the case, then firefighter fatigue must be considered. When firefighters experience the physical and mental letdown that often follows the knockdown of a difficult and dangerous fire, their level of concentration may not be as acute as when they were fresh and rested. Mental exhaustion can make them more likely to miss subtle danger signs in the damaged structure such as creaking, cracking, or other sounds that might otherwise alert them to an impending structural collapse. Physical exhaustion reduces strength and coordination and slows reflexes — all of which increase the likelihood of injury while operating tools and equipment. Fatigue could also make the firefighters less capable of reacting to and escaping from any dangerous situation that might suddenly develop. In addition, if firefighters are allowed to work in areas with elevated levels of carbon monoxide (CO) and other toxic products of combustion without SCBA, their judgment can be seriously impaired. This can lead to poor decisions that could place them or others in jeopardy. Crews must be closely monitored by their supervisors. Setting up one or more Rehab stations will help to prevent accidents due to physical exhaustion (**Figure 12.9**).

Hidden fire. Obviously, finding all remaining fire can be a significant problem if the fire did major damage to the building and there are layers of debris in which glowing embers can remain hidden (**Figure 12.10**). But finding hidden fires can also be difficult where structural damage was less severe. For example, embers can smolder inside of walls and other structural voids that appear normal from the outside. Infrared heat detectors and the thermal imagers discussed in Chapter 5, Interior Operations, can make locating these and other hidden fires much easier and can reduce the chances of missing a hot spot. Some departments use blowers to help locate hot spots. The increased airflow through the damaged portion of the structure will sometimes fan glowing embers enough for them to start producing smoke, and this helps firefighters

Figure 12.9 Firefighter fatigue must be monitored during overhaul.

Figure 12.8 Overhaul may have to be delayed until evidence is collected. *Courtesy of Bill Lellis.*

Figure 12.10 Layers of debris can hide glowing embers.

to locate them. In addition, the increased airflow helps to reduce the level of CO and other toxic products of combustion in the areas where firefighters must work during overhaul. However, the time-tested methods of looking for wisps of smoke, feeling for hot spots, and listening for the crackle of fire can still be used effectively.

Toxic products of combustion. Even after all visible smoke has been cleared from a compartment in which a fire has been burning, invisible but very toxic products of combustion can continue to be present in dangerous concentrations. In addition to the CO that is always present after a fire, any of several other toxic gases may be present, depending upon the types of materials that were involved and the conditions under which they burned. If a broad-spectrum gas analyzer is available, the atmosphere within the damaged area should be checked for all known or suspected gases that may be present (**Figure 12.11**).

If only a CO meter is available, CO can be used as an *index gas*. In order for CO to be used as an index gas, the meter must be capable of measuring the CO *level* — not just detecting the presence of CO. When using CO as an index gas, the basic assumption is that if CO has been reduced to safe levels by ventilation, any other gases present will also have been similarly reduced. Local protocols must be followed, but many departments require a CO reading of less than 35 parts per million before firefighters are allowed to work inside the compartment without SCBA.

Figure 12.11 The atmosphere should be sampled continually during overhaul.

As previously mentioned, structure fires can produce or release a variety of toxic gases in addition to CO, depending upon the types of materials that are involved. Other common fire gases and their sources are as follows:

- *Acrolein* (CH_2CHCHO) is a strong respiratory irritant that is produced when polyethylene is heated and when items containing cellulose, such as wood and other natural materials, smolder. It is used in the manufacture of pharmaceuticals, herbicides, and tear gas.

- *Hydrogen chloride* (HCl) is a colorless but very pungent and irritating gas given off in the thermal decomposition of materials containing chlorine such as polyvinyl chloride (PVC) and other plastics.

- *Hydrogen cyanide* (HCN) is a colorless gas with a characteristic almond odor. Twenty times more toxic than CO, it is an asphyxiant and can be absorbed through the skin. HCN is produced in the combustion of natural materials, such as wool and silk, which contain nitrogen. It is also produced when polyurethane foam and other materials that contain urea burn. The concentrated bulk chemical is also used in electroplating.

- *Carbon dioxide* (CO_2) is a colorless, odorless, and nonflammable gas produced in free-burning fires. While it is nontoxic, CO_2 can asphyxiate by excluding the oxygen from a confined space. It is also a respiratory accelerant that can increase the intake of other toxic gases.

- *Nitrogen oxides* (NO and NO_2) are two toxic and dangerous gases liberated in the combustion of pyroxylin plastics. Because nitric oxide (NO) readily converts to nitrogen dioxide (NO_2) in the presence of oxygen and moisture, nitrogen dioxide is the substance of most concern to firefighters. Nitrogen dioxide is a pulmonary irritant that can also have a delayed systemic effect. The vapors and smoke from the oxides of nitrogen have a reddish brown or copper color.

- *Phosgene* ($COCl_2$) is a highly toxic, colorless gas with a disagreeable odor of musty hay. It may be produced when refrigerants, such as Freon, contact flame. It can be expected in fires in cold-storage facilities. It may also be present in fires involving heavy-duty HVAC systems. It is a strong pulmonary irritant, the full deleterious effect of which is not evident for several hours after exposure.

Secondary Loss Control

While other firefighters are limiting primary loss by attacking a structure fire, fireground support personnel can make significant contributions to the secondary loss control effort. Secondary loss control considerations may involve forcible entry, ventilation, water control, and salvage.

Forcible Entry

One of the most effective means of secondary loss control is by performing careful forcible entry. While quick and efficient access into the building can significantly reduce primary damage by allowing the direct interior fire attack to begin sooner, it can also reduce secondary loss if unnecessary damage is avoided by using the least destructive tools and techniques. For example, if a lockbox can be accessed instead of forcing entry, if a door can be removed instead of being forced open or if a window can be opened instead of being broken out, property damage is minimized without impeding the fire suppression operation (**Figure 12.12**).

Ventilation

Like forcible entry, careful ventilation can contribute to both primary and secondary loss control. As mentioned earlier, quick and effective ventilation can limit the spread of fire, heat, and smoke within a building, and this can reduce primary damage. However, careless or inept ventilation can increase secondary loss significantly. For example, if the initial ventilation opening cut in a roof is too small or is in the wrong location, having to cut additional holes can delay fire extinguishment and greatly in-

Figure 12.12 Secondary loss can be minimized if doors do not have to be forced. *Courtesy of Wes Kitchel.*

crease the costs of post-fire repairs. Also, if rafters, joists, or trusses are cut unnecessarily, the costs of repairs will be increased. As in forcible entry, if windows are broken out for horizontal ventilation instead of being opened, the cost of replacing the broken glass increases the secondary loss.

Water Control

Another means of reducing secondary loss is by training hose crews to apply water judiciously. In other words, to use as much water as necessary to extinguish the fire — but only that much — and no more. And, as mentioned earlier, stopping the flow of water from open sprinklers as soon as the fire is controlled also reduces secondary damage. In addition, some departments use only 100-foot (30 m) lengths of hose inside of buildings to reduce the number of couplings from which water may leak. After a fire has been knocked down, placing a leaking nozzle out a window can also reduce water damage (**Figure 12.13**).

Salvage

Perhaps the most effective means of reducing secondary loss in a structure fire is by performing rapid and effective salvage operations. Firefighters help

Figure 12.13 Water damage can be reduced if leaking nozzles are placed outside.

to limit secondary loss whenever they initiate any salvage effort — simple or complex. For example, simply keeping their protective clothing and equipment clean helps to limit secondary loss because it reduces the likelihood of firefighters soiling upholstered furniture, draperies, and similar items that they handle in or remove from the occupant's home or business.

In general, firefighters should start salvage operations on the floor below the fire as soon as the fire attack is ready to begin. But, in some cases, it may be prudent to delay the fire attack briefly to allow a certain amount of salvage work to be done first. For example, if there is an attic fire above an office containing files, drawings, or other papers vital to the survival of the business, it may be cost effective to delay the attack long enough for salvage covers to be spread over desks, drafting tables, computer workstations, or filing cabinets. The value of the contents in the room below can easily exceed the cost of repairing or replacing the ceiling and roof assembly. In this case, delaying the fire attack while covering the high-value contents may slightly increase the primary damage, but it can *greatly* decrease the secondary damage. However, in the same scenario, if the initial attack were made with penetrating nozzles pushed up through the ceiling, the fire attack and salvage operations could be performed simultaneously. However, if this tactic were

used from the exterior — down through the roof — the suppression effort could drive smoke and flame downward onto the firefighters performing salvage operations below. Therefore, such tactics must be used with discretion.

In structure fires, a variety of salvage operations may be required to meet secondary loss control objectives. Some of the more common loss control objectives are the following:

- Protecting floors and floor coverings
- Protecting building contents
- Expelling smoke
- Removing heat
- Controlling water
- Removing water

Protecting floors. Whenever possible, firefighters should protect the floors and floor coverings between their point of entry into the structure and the fire-involved area. They can do so by using narrow canvas or plastic floor runners — sometimes called *hall runners* — in hallways and other high traffic areas (**Figure 12.14**). In rooms where firefighters are likely to pull the ceilings, the floors should be protected with salvage covers or plastic sheeting.

Protecting contents. Within the limits of the on-scene resources, firefighters should move valuable building contents from the hazard area to a protected area inside or outside of the building. Items that cannot be moved should be protected with salvage covers or plastic sheeting and elevated off the floor if possible (**Figure 12.15**).

Figure 12.14 Protecting the building's floors can reduce secondary loss.

Figure 12.15 Contents that cannot be removed should be protected.

Expelling smoke. In any way that is consistent with the IAP, firefighters should confine smoke to the smallest area possible. For example, ventilating as close as possible to the seat of the fire limits the spread of smoke within the building and channels it to the outside (**Figure 12.16**). Also, if a hallway is to be used to channel smoke to a window, the doors to the rooms that open onto the hallway should be closed first, if possible. Archways and other large wall openings without doors can be sealed with salvage covers or plastic sheeting.

Figure 12.16 Ventilating helps reduce fire spread.

Removing heat. In general, the same techniques used to remove smoke from a building can also be used to remove heat. But, in addition to using ventilation techniques to limit the spread of heat within a building, the appropriate application of water to the burning material is an obvious and very direct way of reducing the amount of heat within the building.

Controlling water. The indiscriminate use of water in the fire attack, such as by spraying water into smoke or flames and not onto the material that is burning or by allowing an open sprinkler to continue discharging water after the fire has been controlled, can result in an excessive amount of water accumulating within the building. In extreme cases, the weight of the accumulated water can contribute to structural instability and even structural collapse.

In addition to absorbing water from the floor, some materials can absorb moisture from the air in the humid environment created when the heat of a fire turns the water from hoselines or sprinklers to steam. Absorbing water from the floor or the air can cause some materials to expand enough to crack the walls of the room in which they are confined. If bearing walls are damaged by this expansion, this can also lead to structural collapse. In other situations, water absorbed by materials at the bottom of a tall stack can cause the entire stack to lose stability and topple over. If the stacked materials happen to be rolls of newsprint that can weigh more than 2,500 pounds (1.58 t) each, such a collapse can be lethal (**Figure 12.17**).

Removing water. In the scenarios just described, venting the humid atmosphere from the building and removing accumulated water may prevent loss of life as well as reduce property damage. In general, the tools and techniques described in the IFSTA **Essentials** and **Fire Service Loss Control** manuals can be used to remove water accumulations from buildings. The techniques used may involve the following:

• Wiping water from horizontal surfaces

• Constructing water chutes and catch basins

• Using mops, squeegees, water shovels, or water vacuums to remove water from floors

Figure 12.17 Firefighters or others could be killed if stacked newsprint were to fall on them.

- Using portable pumps to evacuate water from basements and other low areas

- Breaching exterior walls to create improvised scuppers

- Removing toilets to allow water to drain into the sewer system

However, firefighters must be careful not to discharge water that is contaminated with any toxins or other hazardous materials into public sewers or storm drains. Contaminated water must be contained until it can be decontaminated or removed for proper disposal. Contaminated water can be temporarily contained in catch basins, ditches, or other low areas that have been properly dammed or diked. The potential for contaminated runoff from a fire in a particular occupancy should be determined during pre-incident planning inspections, and appropriate mitigation plans developed.

Post-Incident Loss Control Operations

Loss control operations should continue after a structure fire has been extinguished. These operations may take two forms — *economic* loss control and *psychological* loss control. It is important for firefighters to deal with both forms of loss.

Economic Loss Control

To reduce economic losses from fires, firefighters should salvage as much of the victim's property as possible while overhauling the fire. Before they leave the scene, firefighters should properly secure the building to prevent possible looting, vandalism, or damage from inclement weather.

During overhaul, any valuables such as cash, bank books, credit cards, stock certificates, or professional licenses or certificates that are found should be turned over to the Occupant Services Sector (if one has been established) or to its equivalent, the IC, or law enforcement (**Figure 12.18**). Firefighters should place photo albums, videotapes, personal collections, trophies, awards, and other items that may have tremendous sentimental value to the owner/occupant in a protected area. Some departments provide the owner/occupant with cardboard boxes and packing material to make protecting salvaged items easier. Some also make a videotape of the scene after overhaul is completed to record damage to the building's contents, which can greatly assist the owner/occupant in filing insurance claims.

Figure 12.18 Valuables found in a fire must be turned in.

After salvage and overhaul operations have been completed, but before firefighters leave the scene, the fire-damaged building should be properly secured. As described in the IFSTA **Fire Service Loss Control** manual, this may involve covering ventilation holes in the roof with plywood, salvage covers, or plastic sheeting to prevent additional damage due to weather. Securing the building may also involve boarding up open doorways and window openings to discourage trespassers (**Figure 12.19**). Finally, firefighters may set up a rekindle detector as described earlier or post a fire watch. The building owner/occupant may be required to secure the entire property if there are potential hazards in or around the building, such as downed electrical wires, fire-weakened structural members that could collapse, or holes in floors into which someone could fall. Securing the property may involve installing a temporary chain-link fence, posting a security guard, or both. If hazardous conditions exist, firefighters should acquaint the owner/occupant with them by conducting a tour of the property, if safety allows, or by providing the owner/occupant with a written description of the hazardous conditions. This process should also include recommendations on what the owner/occupant needs to do to secure the property.

Figure 12.19 Fire-damaged structures must be properly secured.

Psychological Loss Control

As a result of the fire, the property owner/occupant may have lost irreplaceable mementos, important records and documents, a family pet, or — worst of all — a family member, friend, or employee. Firefighters need to be sensitive to the psychological trauma that the property owner/occupant may have suffered, even if it is not apparent from his demeanor. With a departmental commitment to support customer service and loss control, firefighters can reduce the psychological impact of the fire on the occupant.

To reduce psychological fire losses, firefighters can often refer the victims to individuals and agencies that are equipped to assist victims in getting their lives back to normal. Recognizing the importance of these services, some departments have formalized them in various ways. For example, a number of fire departments have developed booklets that serve as after-the-fire guides for those who have experienced a structure fire. These guides contain the telephone numbers of local relief agencies and a brief description of the types of services each provides. The guides can help the owner/occupants arrange for temporary housing, if that is needed, or any of a wide variety of other services. While the guides contain local information, most are based upon the FEMA booklet entitled *After the Fire! Returning to Normal*, published by the U.S. Fire Administration (**Figure 12.20**).

Figure 12.20 This booklet can help survivors get their lives back to normal.

Fire departments can also reduce the victims' psychological losses by taking an active role in helping them cope with this significant disruption of their lives and/or livelihoods. This assistance can be as basic as providing shelter and security at the scene. It can also involve notifying friends or family of the situation, providing a cell phone with which the victims can contact sources of support, and/or transporting the victims to temporary housing. Some departments have on-call chaplains who can come to the scene and assist fire victims in coping with their losses (**Figure 12.21**).

Figure 12.21 A public safety chaplain consoles victims of a fire.

Summary

For both humanitarian and political reasons, anything that a fire department can reasonably do to reduce the amount of loss suffered by the victims of a fire should be done. Publicly funded fire departments have a moral and legal responsibility to protect their citizens from preventable fire losses. This dictates that departments develop pre-incident plans for fireground loss control and train and equip their members to conduct fireground operations in the most efficient and least destructive ways possible. Forcible entry, fire attack, ventilation, salvage, and overhaul operations should all be performed with loss control in mind. Politically, reducing both primary and secondary losses from structure fires can result in a substantial increase in public support for the fire department. Regardless of what form of loss control and victim support the department provides, the reductions in economic and psychological losses and the resulting increase in public goodwill toward the department make these efforts worthwhile.

Chapter 13
Coordinated Fireground Support Operations

Chapter 13
Coordinated Fireground Support Operations

The case history cited in Chapter 4, Access Into Structures, calls attention to what can happen on the fireground when various operations are not adequately coordinated. In that incident, vertical ventilation was performed before the entry doors could be forced open to allow fire attack crews inside. This caused the fire to be drawn toward the ventilation opening, which could have put the vent crew and adjacent exposures in jeopardy. If ventilation is performed before fire attack crews can enter a burning structure because the forcible entry crews are having difficulty gaining access, the fire can continue to burn unchecked and greatly increase primary damage. However, if a fire that has been burning for some time in a closed compartment is not properly ventilated first, firefighters can be injured or killed by a violent backdraft when they open a door or window into the structure. If a burning building's utilities are not properly controlled, a natural gas explosion could result, firefighters could be electrocuted, or they could be caught in a building collapse caused by excessive water accumulation on upper floors. All of these scenarios — and countless others — can result from lack of fireground coordination.

On the other hand, if firefighters have done adequate pre-incident planning on the building that is burning, they know what forcible entry and ventilation tools and techniques are needed to quickly and efficiently perform those functions on that building. They also know how that building is constructed, how old it is, and how a fire is likely to behave in it. Armed with this knowledge, their safety and effectiveness can both be greatly increased. Familiarity with the burning building and its contents can assist fireground support personnel in doing their main job — helping to implement the IAP.

Safely and efficiently implementing the IAP requires the coordination of a variety of fireground resources and functions. The majority of the resources that must be coordinated on the fireground are personnel and equipment. The major functions that must be coordinated are search and rescue, the fire attack, and support activities. Therefore, this chapter discusses the coordination of all these resources and functions.

Fireground Priorities

As discussed in earlier chapters, the universal priorities for all emergency incidents, including structure fires, are life safety, incident stabilization, and property conservation. How these priorities are translated into incident goals and objectives varies from incident to incident depending upon a number of factors. The most important of these variables are the *incident* and the available *resources*.

Incident

The nature and scope of an emergency incident dictate the resource needs. Fires in large, fully occupied residential, institutional, or public assembly buildings compound the life-safety problem because to the lives of numerous occupants (who may or may not be capable of escaping the fire without assistance) must be added the lives of the firefighters who are assigned to rescue the victims and extinguish the fire. This can translate into the need for a large number of personnel (firefighters and others) to evacuate the building or move the occupants from the hazard zone to an area of safe refuge within the building (**Figure 13.1**). This extraordinary life safety hazard may dictate that the fire attack be delayed temporarily, or even abandoned, and that the firefighters operate in the *rescue mode*, also called an *all-hands rescue*. An all-hands rescue is an *extremely rare* mode of operation in which all on-scene personnel temporarily focus on the life-safety priority to the exclusion of the other two priorities. The rescue mode of operation is explained in more detail later in this chapter.

In the majority of structure fire incidents, sufficient resources are on scene to pursue all of the universal priorities simultaneously (**Figure 13.2**). An aggressive fire attack, supported by timely and effective forcible entry and ventilation operations, helps to stabilize the incident while conserving property and facilitating search and rescue. But the

key is having sufficient resources immediately available. Occupancies that will require more resources than are normally dispatched on the first alarm should be identified during pre-incident planning inspections, and the first alarm assignment upgraded accordingly.

Resources

As defined earlier, fireground resources are personnel (firefighters and others), apparatus, tools, equipment, and the supplies needed to keep them functioning. Firefighters need adequate PPE, clean breathing air — and on protracted incidents — food and water. Apparatus and equipment need fuel and proper maintenance, and engines need an adequate water supply. The two major considerations related to fireground resources are their *availability* and their *capability*.

Resource Availability

Having the most sophisticated and effective resources in the world is of little tactical value if these resources are not readily available when and where they are needed. If the IC must request additional resources and wait for them to respond to the scene, by the time they arrive the fire may have grown to the point where these additional resources are insufficient and even more resources will have to be requested. If pre-incident planning has not resulted in an adequate first-alarm assignment being dispatched to this incident, the IC must use his training and experience to anticipate the number and types of resources that will be needed to handle the situation and request them as soon as the initial size-up is completed (**Figure 13.3**).

Figure 13.1 Firefighters must have specific assignments if rescue efforts are to be successful.

Figure 13.2 Pursuing all fireground priorities often requires a massive commitment of resources. *Courtesy of Tom McCarthy.*

Figure 13.3 The IC needs to order additional resources immediately.

Resource Capability

On the other hand, having a vast amount of resources immediately available is also of little tactical value if these resources are not up to the job for any reason. For example, if the responding apparatus is not designed for the type of fire that must be handled, it may make the process more difficult and more time consuming than if more appropriate types had been dispatched initially. If firefighters lack the physical strength to safely and efficiently perform all aspects of the required operations and lack the stamina to perform them for as long as they are required, these firefighters will not only be ineffective but may also be a danger to themselves and others. If they are poorly equipped or they lack the necessary training and experience to safely and effectively use the apparatus, tools, and equipment with which they have been supplied, their ability to achieve any of the universal priorities will be greatly impaired (**Figure 13.4**).

Operational Modes

In general, the on-scene resources can be used in any of three operational modes. These modes are *offensive*, *defensive*, and *rescue*. The operational mode used at any given time in a structure fire incident depends upon the situation and the capabilities of the on-scene resources.

Offensive Mode

The offensive mode is the classic fire attack because it involves taking direct action to extinguish the fire. This also is the mode in which firefighters are most comfortable. The offensive mode is used when the IC decides that the situation is such that the on-scene resources can overwhelm the fire with an aggressive interior attack (**Figure 13.5**). Even though this mode of operation appears to focus exclusively on the property conservation priority, a quick and efficient extinguishment of the fire also stabilizes the incident by limiting fire spread and may virtually eliminate any life-safety hazard.

Figure 13.4 To be safe and effective, all resources must be fully capable.

Figure 13.5 The offensive mode requires aggressive action by firefighters.

Defensive Mode

In most cases, a defensive mode is chosen because there are not enough resources available on-scene to conduct a safe and effective offensive attack or because there is no reasonable expectation of saving lives. For example, if a fire is burning in an abandoned derelict building, the IC may decide that it is not worth the risk to firefighters to order an aggressive interior attack. Or, if a building is so heavily involved in fire that it is not reasonable to expect that anyone inside could still be alive, the IC may decide that the risk/benefit would make it imprudent to put firefighters in mortal jeopardy by ordering them inside to conduct a search (**Figure 13.6**).

Defensive operations necessarily sacrifice property that is already lost to save that which is not. A defensive fire attack is one in which a strategic decision has been made to use the on-scene resources to protect exposures instead of fighting a fire in a building that may already be lost. Operating in this mode is intended to confine or isolate a fire until additional resources can be brought in to safely stabilize the incident by extinguishing the fire. Isolating a structure fire in a defensive mode means limiting the fire to the room or building of origin and protecting exposures. This means sacrificing that which is burning to save that which is not.

A defensive mode is usually (but not always) an exterior operation. Traditionally, many fire fighting texts have suggested that if a fire attack was conducted inside a burning building, it was necessarily an offensive attack. Likewise, an attack that was conducted from the exterior was necessarily defensive. Current concepts differ from this view in that the mode of operation is defined more by the purpose of the attack and less by the location from which it is conducted.

Inside a burning building, a defensive mode can be used in two ways. First, if there are insufficient resources inside the building to be able to extinguish the fire, a defensive mode can be used to merely contain the fire within a room or area until additional hoselines can be deployed. Once additional hoselines are brought in, the mode can be switched from defensive to offensive and the fire extinguished. On the other hand, if additional hoselines are not available, a defensive mode can be used to contain the fire while search and rescue operations are being conducted. Once search and rescue operations have been completed, all interior attack crews can be withdrawn.

Rescue Mode

As mentioned earlier, when there is a rapidly spreading fire in a residential building (especially late at night or in the early morning hours), it may be necessary to use all on-scene personnel to locate and evacuate the occupants of the building while waiting for more resources to arrive on scene. Once the additional resources arrive and all occupants have been removed from the hazard zone, the mode can be switched to offensive to deal with the fire.

> One of the most important requirements of an all-hands rescue is that it be declared over the radio to alert the communications/dispatch center and other incoming units of the situation and the tactical decision.

To initiate a rescue mode, the IC must transmit an *emergency traffic* message. This alerts all units to cease transmitting because critical information is to follow.

In an all-hands rescue, each search and rescue team may or may not take a charged line with them and if they do, the line is only for their protection and that of those being rescued — not for fire extinguishment (**Figure 13.7**). Obviously, the rescue mode is a drastic and infrequently used tactic that

Figure 13.6 Firefighters should not be put at risk to save that which is already lost.

invokes the exception provided in the two-in/two-out rule — but with lives clearly in jeopardy, invoking the exception is fully justified.

NOTE: The NFA course entitled *Managing Company Tactical Operations* does not include the rescue mode and instead describes what is called a *transitional* mode. The transitional mode is used when firefighters switch from one mode of operation to another. One example of the transitional mode described in the NFA course is "when efforts are directed at confining the fire until rescue can be accomplished (offensive), after which personnel are withdrawn to protect exposures (defensive)." Another example is when there are insufficient resources on scene to mount an offensive attack, the resources are used to protect exposures (defensive). When more resources arrive on scene, they are switched (transitioned) to an interior (offensive) attack.

Regardless of whether it is seen as a separate mode of operation, unless the transition from one mode of operation to another is clearly communicated and carefully coordinated, individual firefighters or even entire companies can be put in jeopardy. For example, if fire attack crews have been working inside a burning building for some time without making significant progress toward extinguishing the fire, the IC may decide that it is unsafe to continue the offensive interior operation and order all companies to withdraw from the building and switch to an exterior defensive mode. Unless the withdrawal of the interior crews is closely coordinated and clearly communicated to all companies by a prearranged evacuation signal, some firefighters can be left in positions where the fire could suddenly surround them and cut off their means of egress. In addition, a personnel accountability report (PAR) of each company and all personnel should be requested at the time of withdrawal (**Figure 13.8**).

Figure 13.7 In the rescue mode, a charged line is for personal protection and not for fighting the fire.

Figure 13.8 An Accountability Officer records a PAR.

Coordinated Fireground Operations

Even when the appropriate number and types of resources are immediately available to handle an incident of the nature and scope presented by the building that is burning, the use of those resources must be coordinated to make them most effective. Effective coordination translates into the quickest and least costly means of achieving all three of the universal priorities in structure fires. However, the amount and type of coordination needed will vary with the situation. While all structure fires require the coordination of fire attack and support operations, some structure fires require more coordination than others (**Figure 13.9**).

If the on-scene personnel required to handle even a relatively small structure fire were allowed to freelance; that is, operate independently and not according to a single incident action plan, the resulting chaos and confusion could be disastrous. Needless damage could be done by firefighters attempting to force entry at several locations simultaneously. Ventilation efforts could be frustrated by openings being made indiscriminately at various locations. Firefighters could be injured if hoselines were simultaneously introduced from opposite sides of the fire, blowing the fire *toward* each other. Firefighters could be injured or the fire made worse if the building's utilities were not shut off. And, worst of all, occupants could become victims if a primary search of the building were omitted or even just delayed. Obviously, this sort of pandemonium is inefficient and unprofessional, and it could be fatal.

To effectively control the on-scene resources and implement a logical incident action plan, most departments use some form of organized command/control system. The Fire Service Incident Management System Consortium has developed an Incident Management System (IMS) that combines elements of and is compatible with both the Fireground Command (FGC) system developed by the Phoenix (AZ) fire department and the National Interagency Incident Management System (NIIMS) Incident Command System (ICS) that is based on

the FIRESCOPE model developed in Southern California (**Figure 13.10**). Firefighters must use the incident command/management system that their department has adopted, but IMS is the system that is discussed in this manual.

Figure 13.9 Some fireground operations require close coordination.

Figure 13.10 IMS is compatible with both fireground command systems.

Command Options

As described in Chapter 1, Size-Up, to formulate an effective IAP, the IC must first size up the fire. Because fires vary in size and complexity, the IMS allows the initial IC some flexibility in how to operate immediately after arrival at the scene. When assuming initial command of the incident, the first-arriving officer can use either of three possible command modes: *investigation, fast attack,* or *command.*

Investigation Mode

When the nature and extent of a structure fire are not obvious on arrival, the first-in officer will need to investigate as part of his size-up. In these cases,

IMS allows the officer to assume initial command of the incident while conducting the investigation. The IC transmits "nothing showing" or "investigating" over the radio, and in many departments, the IC advises other incoming units to "stage at Level I." In Level I staging, other incoming units stop (stage) at the last intersection in their normal route of travel before reaching the reported incident location (**Figure 13.11**). Staging in this way allows for maximum deployment flexibility. Once the investigation (size-up) has been completed, the IC can deploy the other units as needed or release them to return to quarters.

Fast Attack Mode

In situations that require immediate action by the first-arriving company, the IMS allows the officer in charge of that company to simultaneously take command, direct the actions of the company, and participate in those actions as needed (**Figure 13.12**). Some examples of situations in which a fast attack command might be needed are as follows:

● Critical rescues in which immediate action could save lives

● Relatively small fires with potential for spread

● When adjacent structures are uninvolved but seriously threatened

In the fast attack mode, the officer maintains command by communicating over a portable radio. The fast attack mode should not last for more than a few minutes, and it ends with any of the following:

● The incident is stabilized.

● The incident has not been stabilized, but the officer must withdraw to the exterior to establish a Command Post. The officer must decide whether to withdraw the remainder of the crew. This decision is based on the crew's capabilities and experience, their safety, and the likelihood of their being able to stabilize the incident. The crew must not be left inside without radio communications capability.

● Command is transferred to another officer. The new IC must decide whether to have the first officer rejoin his crew or be reassigned to a subordinate command role.

Figure 13.12 IMS allows for a "fast attack" mode of command when necessary.

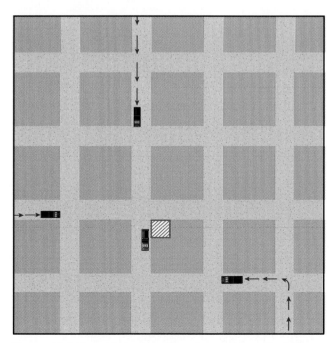

Figure 13.11 Level I staging allows for maximum flexibility.

Command Mode

If a structure fire is of such size and complexity or has such spread potential that it is unlikely that the on-scene crew can bring it under control, the first-arriving officer should assume command of the incident (**Figure 13.13**). The IC assumes command by announcing the following over the radio:

- Incident name
- A brief report on conditions (including actions taken)
- Location of command post
- Additional resources needed
- Location of Staging or Base

In addition, the IC must decide how to use the balance of the crew. There are normally three options:

- Appoint one of the crew members as the acting officer and give him a tactical objective.
- Assign the crew to work under the supervision of another company officer.
- Use the crew members to perform staff functions in support of command.

Transfer of command. When there is a need for the IC to transfer command of the incident to another officer, the transfer must be done correctly. Otherwise, there can be confusion about who is really in command of the incident. The officer relinquishing command must communicate directly with the officer assuming command by radio or face-to-face — with face-to-face being strongly preferred (**Figure 13.14**). *Command cannot be trans-ferred to someone who is not on the scene.* When transferring command, the officer relinquishing command should brief the new IC on the following:

- Name of the incident
- Incident status (fire conditions, number of victims, etc.)
- Safety considerations
- Action plan for the incident
- Progress toward completion of tactical objectives
- Deployment of assigned resources
- The need for additional resources

Structure Fire Scenarios

The coordination of typical fireground resources in three common structure fire scenarios is discussed in the following section. These scenarios are initial attack, sustained attack, and extended attack fires.

Figure 13.14 A face-to-face transfer of command is preferred.

Figure 13.13 A company officer assumes command of an incident.

Initial Attack

In this context, an initial attack fire is defined as one that can be handled by the resources in the initial (first alarm) response. Unless requested by the IC, no additional resources will be dispatched to this incident. Depending upon the size, age, construction, and configuration of the building and the nature of its contents, the number and types of resources included in the initial alarm may vary considerably. In general, an initial attack structure fire is probably not beyond what is commonly called a *room-and-contents* fire. In other words, the fire is confined to a single room or other small portion of the building.

A typical initial attack fire in a single-family dwelling may be confined to the following:

● Wastebasket

● Clothes dryer

● Oven or range top

● Car in the garage

● Contents of a room

● Attic

Typically, at least two engines (perhaps more if there is no truck company), a truck company (if one exists), and one or more chief officers are initially dispatched to such a fire (**Figure 13.15**). Some departments have increased the number of engines included in the first-alarm response to reported structure fires to provide enough firefighters to comply with the two-in/two-out rule. Other departments include a rescue unit, especially if they do not have a truck company. In some departments, every engine is a *quint* (pump, water tank, hose, ground ladders, and an aerial device), thereby reducing the need for a separate ladder company

except on fires in high-rise buildings (**Figure 13.16**). In areas with a minimal public water supply system, or none at all, a mobile water supply unit (tanker/tender) may also be included in the initial alarm assignment. Assuming that there is an officer and two or more firefighters on each unit, there may be from fifteen to twenty personnel in the initial alarm assignment.

If the fire is in a large residential, commercial, institutional, or other structure with a potentially heavy occupant load, the number of units and firefighters in the initial alarm assignment may be higher — in some cases, a lot higher. Even though there may be several more units and dozens more firefighters than on an initial alarm response to a single-family residence, it remains an initial attack fire unless and until the IC begins to request additional resources.

On every emergency incident, including structure fires, the first and most important consideration is life safety. On relatively small initial attack fires, the IC may also fulfill the role of Incident Safety Officer (ISO). On larger initial attack fires, the IC is likely to delegate this authority by appointing an ISO. The ISO is responsible for enforcing departmental safety-related SOPs regarding the use of PPE (including SCBA), personnel accountability, search and rescue (including two-in/two-out), fire attack, firefighter rehabilitation (Rehab), and all other fireground operations (**Figure 13.17**). The ISO is also responsible for ensuring that all fireground operations are conducted according to the requirements of any applicable state, provincial, or federal safety regulations such as those from OSHA and/or NFPA.

Figure 13.15 A typical first-alarm assignment in many departments.

Figure 13.16 A typical quint.

Figure 13.17 A safety officer is a critical component of a fireground organization. *Courtesy of Ron Jeffers.*

Figure 13.18 Additional resources are held in Staging until needed.

Once life safety has been provided for, the IC must make one of the most critical initial decisions — are the resources at the scene and en route sufficient to handle this incident? If the answer to that question is "no," or even "maybe," the IC should *immediately* request any additional resources that may be needed. The sooner these additional resources are requested, the sooner they will arrive on scene where they are needed. If there is doubt about the need for any specific resources, they should be requested so that they can be started toward the scene as soon as possible. Any of these additional resources that prove to be unnecessary can be released to return to district while still en route or after arriving at the scene. Additional resources that arrive, but for which there is no immediate assignment, are directed to specified locations (Level II Staging) where they are held in reserve until needed (**Figure 13.18**).

The next critical decision that the IC must make is which operational mode is most appropriate at this point in the incident. As discussed earlier, the options are offensive, defensive, or rescue modes. This decision is based upon the current situation, what is likely to happen in the next few minutes, and the capabilities and limitations of the on-scene resources. The initial mode chosen may or may not be used throughout the incident. As the situation changes — for better or worse — the IC may find it necessary or desirable to switch from one mode of operation to another. As also mentioned earlier, any change in the operational mode must be clearly communicated (using an *emergency traffic* declaration) and closely coordinated.

Once the initial operational mode has been chosen, the IC must do a quick risk/benefit analysis of the available deployment options. This and all the other considerations previously discussed are then combined into the initial IAP. Based on this plan, the on-scene resources must then be deployed in the safest and most effective way possible (**Figure 13.19**). Initially, resources must be assigned to the following:

- Building access (forcible entry)
- Search and rescue
- Fire attack
- Utilities control
- Ventilation

As soon as the fire situation and the available resources allow, salvage operations must be conducted. However, everyone in the fireground

Figure 13.19 Resources are deployed according to the IAP.

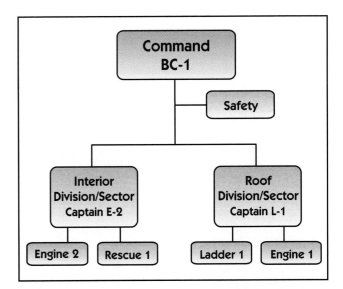

Figure 13.20 A typical initial-attack organization.

Figure 13.21 Firefighter stress and fatigue must be managed carefully.

organization should keep loss control in mind as they carry out their assigned duties. After fire control has been achieved, the fire cause has been investigated, and any critical evidence has been protected, overhaul must also be conducted. A typical initial attack fireground organization is shown in **Figure 13.20.**

Sustained Attack

There are no universally accepted timelines that differentiate an initial attack fire from a more sustained one. However, for purposes of this discussion, once a structure fire has progressed to the point where the IC decides that the first alarm resources need to be supplemented, the incident moves into the category of a sustained attack fire. When this happens, a number of additional concerns are added to the coordination of fireground operations. For example, if a Rehab unit has not been established, one should be because firefighter fatigue needs to be managed **(Figure 13.21).** Managing firefighter fatigue may also necessitate calling in additional companies for crew rotation and/or relief.

In fires of this size, the IC will more than likely appoint an Operations Section Chief (Ops) in addition to an ISO. Under IMS, the Ops Chief is responsible for designating the locations for staging areas, in addition to his other fireground responsibilities. The Ops Chief also appoints a manager for each staging area **(Figure 13.22)**. This allows the additional resources to be managed efficiently as they arrive in the area of the fire and helps to avoid the congestion that could otherwise result. Companies in Staging must be ready to respond within three minutes of being called. In high-rise fires, additional companies and spare equipment are usually staged two floors below the fire floor and their apparatus parked about a block away in Base. A typical sustained attack fireground organization is shown in **Figure 13.23.**

Figure 13.22 Each Level II staging area has a manager.

Extended Attack

When a structure fire is such that it continues burning beyond the original operational period, it is considered to be an extended attack fire. An operational period may be 12 hours from the time of alarm, the point at which the on-duty crews are scheduled to be relieved, or some other arbitrary point in time. A new IAP is created for each operational period and disseminated to all units.

Extended attack fires frequently involve mutual aid companies, strike teams, task forces, or other outside assistance. These outside resources may be used to staff vacated fire stations within the district, provide technical assistance at the scene, or play a tactical role on the fireground. Personnel from outside the district may not be familiar with the district's layout and topography. If they are to be used to respond to emergency calls in place of local units that are assigned to the fire, they may require detailed maps or a member of the host department

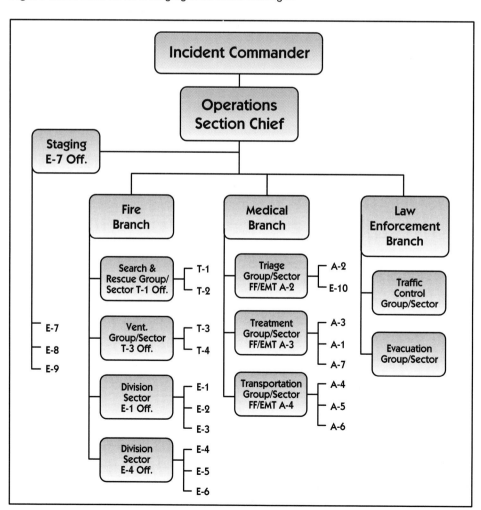

Figure 13.23 A typical sustained attack fireground organization.

to help them find their way around. If personnel from outside the district are responding to the scene, they may need to rendezvous with a local representative at some well-known landmark and be escorted to the scene from that point. When mutual aid personnel are to be used on the fireground, they must be briefed on the current IAP, and their operational capabilities and limitations must be determined. Unless they are capable of communicating on the assigned fireground radio frequencies, they must be supplied with portable radios that will allow them to do so **(Figure 13.24)**.

If outside resources are to be used on the fireground, they must be used selectively and with discretion. Before any outside resource can be relied upon for a tactical assignment, that resource must be carefully evaluated. The capabilities and limitations of the apparatus, equipment, and personnel must be verified. Outmoded or poorly maintained apparatus and equipment may not meet the minimum requirements for safe and effective operation. If the apparatus, equipment, or outside personnel do not meet the minimum requirements, they should be used either in support functions or not at all.

Just because someone holds a particular rank or title within his own organization does not mean that he has the necessary training, experience, and physical capabilities to function safely and effectively in this fire situation. Giving a critical assignment to someone who is incapable (for any reason) of carrying out that assignment safely and

Figure 13.24 Mutual-aid companies may have to be issued incident-compatible radios.

effectively may place that person and others in serious jeopardy. Those with questionable fireground qualifications can be assigned to support functions and thereby free up others with proven ability who can be reassigned to more critical roles on the fireground.

Extended attack fires may also involve other considerations that fires of shorter duration do not. Some of these considerations are as follows:

● Apparatus need to be refueled and perhaps repaired.

● On-scene personnel and outside agency personnel staffing fire stations may need to be supplied with food. A nearby restaurant or fast-food outlet may be contracted to fill this need.

● Sanitary facilities for on-scene personnel must be provided in addition to the services provided by one or more rehab units. Portable toilets may have to be brought to the scene if facilities in nearby buildings are insufficient or unavailable.

● Sleeping bags or other bedding and folding cots may be needed. Gymnasiums or other large buildings may be used as improvised dormitories when outside resources are to be committed beyond their initial operational period.

● Large spaces may also be needed as improvised morgues.

Supplying the resources just described may require the establishment of a Logistics Section. Obviously, the fireground organization must expand if the fire continues to grow in size and complexity.

Finally, fires of this magnitude may require different strategy and tactics than those used in smaller fires. For example, in large strip malls and other commercial or industrial complexes, there may be more reliance on trench or strip ventilation to help contain the fire. Also, there may be a need to apply massive quantities of Class A foam, Class B foam, or other chemical agents to extinguish the fire. The vast majority of extended attack fires are controlled and extinguished by conventional fire attack methods. However, extraordinary control measures may be necessary in *group fires* (those involving large-scale building-to-building spread) that may involve an entire city block, and *conflagrations* (huge fires

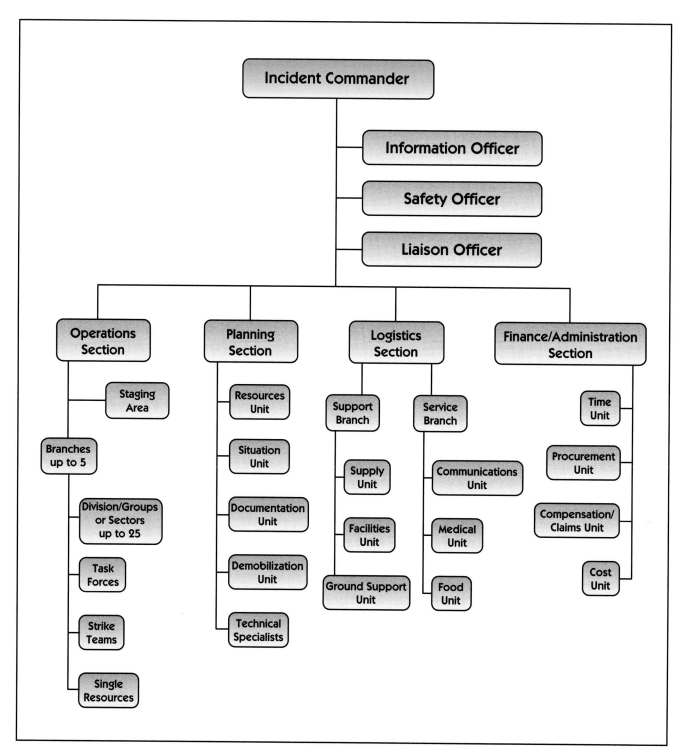

Figure 13.25 A fully expanded fireground organization.

that cross streets, highways, rivers, or other natural fire breaks) that may engulf entire neighborhoods. For example, in these extremely rare situations, it may be necessary to demolish buildings in the path of the fire to deny it more fuel. A typical extended attack fireground organization is shown in **Figure 13.25**

Summary

To be most effective, fireground support operations must be coordinated with the other operations being conducted. Because fire attack crews need to get in and occupants need to get out of a burning building, forcible entry must be done as soon as possible. But if the building is opened up before the fire attack and search crews are ready to enter, the additional combustion air may cause the fire to intensify. Ventilation must be done at the time and in the form that is most conducive to a safe and effective fire attack. Loss control must be considered as each and every fireground operation is conducted.

Regardless of the size of the fire, the universal priorities must always be considered when fireground decisions are made and implemented. This involves assessing the hazards to firefighters and others and taking appropriate steps to mitigate those hazards. It also involves doing a risk/benefit assessment of each tactical option before any action is ordered. One of the most important considerations is selecting the most appropriate mode of operation based upon the situation and the capabilities and limitations of the available resources.

Finally, the most appropriate command mode — investigation, fast attack, or command — must be selected and implemented. Implementation of the correct command mode sets the tone for the rest of the incident, whether it is an initial attack fire, a sustained attack fire, or an extended attack fire that may last for many hours or several days.

Appendices

	PHOENIX REGIONAL STANDARD OPERATING PROCEDURES
ACCOUNTABILITY	M.P. 201.03 02/94-R Page 1 of 8

Purpose

This procedure identifies a system of incident site firefighter accountability. The purpose is to account for all firefighters, at any given time, within a small geographic area, within the "hot zone" of an incident. Use of the system will provide enhanced personal safety for the individual firefighter, and will provide the Incident Command Organization staff an improved means to track and account for all personnel working in the hot zone.

The hot zone will be defined as any area that requires an SCBA charged hose line and special protective clothing or in which a firefighter is at risk of becoming lost, trapped, or injured by the environment or structure. This would include entering a structure reported to be on fire, operating in close proximity to the structure during exterior operations, confined space or trench rescue, etc.

Accountability

Accountability involves a personal commitment to work within the safety system at an incident.

o   Command will always maintain an accurate tracking and awareness of where resources are committed at an incident.
o   Command will always be responsible for including accountability as a major element in strategy and attack planning, and must consider and react to any barriers to effective accountability.
o   Sector Officers will always maintain an accurate tracking and awareness of crews assigned to them. This will require the Sector Officer to be in his/her assigned area and maintaining close supervision of crews assigned to them.
o   All crews will work for Command or Sectors -- no free-lancing.
o   Crews arriving on the scene should remain intact for all intents and purposes. A minimum crew size will be considered two or more members and a radio will be required.
o   All crews entering a hot zone must be supervised by a designated supervisor or other ranking individual.
o   All crews will go in together, stay together, and come out together. Reduced visibility and increased risk will require very tight togetherness.
o   If a radio fails while in the hot zone, the crew will exit unless there is another working radio with the crew.

PASSPORTS

To enhance accountability and to improve tracking of firefighters in the hot zone, the "PASSPORT" system will be used. PASSPORTS involve a plastic card with the crew members names affixed that is turned into an Accountability Officer. The Accountability Officer may be a pump engineer, a Sector Officer, or a designated Accountability Officer, depending on the nature, type, and complexity of the incident.

The first arriving company will announce their accountability location in a follow-up report after the "on-scene report and assumption of Command". This report should include the accountability unit identification, their geographic side (i.e., north, south, etc.), and initiating the accountability system.

20551

For Example: <u>Engine Two on the scene of a two-story frame residential</u> occupancy smoke showing. <u>Engine Two attacking with a 1-1/2" going in for</u> search and rescue. <u>Engine Two will be Command.</u>

(Alarm repeats)
--no radio traffic--

<u>Command to Alarm. Engine Two will be north side accountability.</u>
(Alarm repeats)

Alarm Copy -- Engine Two north side accountability.

As staged units are assigned, Command will give their respective accountability unit and the geographic locations along with any other instructions.

Alarm will repeat initial assignment of accountability locations.

PASSPORT Equipment

The PASSPORT system equipment involves a 2" x 4" plastic card with the company's ID etched on it. The PASSPORT should contain the names of all personnel <u>presently</u> assigned to that company.

The PASSPORT will always be located on the dash of the apparatus at the Company Officer position or passenger side. A velcro strip will allow the PASSPORT to be affixed on the dash and easily removed.

Each firefighter will be issued five individual name tags. These will be affixed to velcro strips on the underside of their helmet.

All engines, and ladders, and specialized equipment will be equipped with an 8"x11" status board. This will be used to affix PASSPORTS on and will always be located on the inside door of the Engineer's/driver's position. The status board will be attached with velcro to permit easy removal.

The Company Officer will be responsible for ensuring that the PASSPORT always reflects only currently assigned personnel. When entering a hazard zone with a partial crew (i.e., engineer remains at the engine to pump lines), the Company Officer must remove name tags of those members not entering the hazard zone. The name tags of these members may be returned to the member, placed on the Company Officer's helmet velcro strip or placed in his/her coat pocket.

Company Identification Designation - Helmets

Firefighter helmets will be equipped with magnetic strips permanently attached to each side of the helmet. Another set of magnetic tapes, each affixed with company ID's, will be attached to the helmet by laying them over the permanently attached magnetic tape. The helmet shall always reflect the ID of the company the firefighter is presently assigned. Each company will be equipped with an extra supply of helmet ID's.

20551

All PASSPORTS and helmet ID's equipment will be considered as safety equipment and will be inspected quarterly as other safety equipment and will be repaired or replaced as soon as possible on a priority request.

Tactical Benchmarks

Several accountability benchmarks are included in tactical operations. The Personnel Accountability Report (or "PAR") involves a roll call of personnel assigned. For the Company Officer, a "PAR" is a confirmation that members assigned to his/her crew are visually accounted for. For the Sector Officer, a "PAR" is an accounting for all crew members of all companies assigned to his/her sector. Reports of PAR's should be conducted face-to-face within the company or with the sector whenever possible.

Example: "Engine 17 to East Sector, I have a PAR" (all members accounted for).

A personnel accountability report will be required for the following situations:

o   The second arriving unit (engine, ladder, rescue) after reporting on-scene or staged will request a PAR from Command.
o   Any report of a missing or trapped firefighter (Command initiates a PAR of all crews on the scene).
o   Any change from offensive to defensive (Command initiates a PAR of all crews on the scene).
o   Any sudden hazardous event at the incident - flash over, backdraft, collapse, etc. (a PAR is initiated by Command).
o   By all crew(s) reporting an "all clear" (Company Officers of crews responsible for search and rescue will ensure they have a PAR for their crews at the time they report an all clear).
o   At every 30 minutes of elapsed time.
o   At a report of fire under control.

Accountability Officers

Accountability Officers may be Engineers, Sector Officers, or personnel specifically assigned to sectors to serve as Accountability Officers for the Sector Officer.

The first engine to each geographic side of the incident will serve as the initial accountability location. The engineer will serve as the initial Accountability Officer. All crews entering the incident will deliver their PASSPORTS to the accountability location closest to their "point of entry" prior to entering the hot zone. As sectors are implemented, Sector Officers will manage PASSPORTS only if he/she is not entering the hot zone (i.e., defensive operation). PASSPORTS will remain on the first engine (accountability location). As staff officers arrive on the scene and stage, they will be assigned accountability responsibilities for given sectors. These officers will report to their assigned Sector Officer to manage accountability for that sector (i.e., mini lobby sector).

20551

As the incident escalates and staff officers fill accountability positions for each sector, these Accountability Officers will be assigned to a radio channel designated by Command. Depending on the situation, Accountability Officers will report to either Command or Logistics.

At incidents with a critical need for Accountability Officers to assist Sector Officers, Command may chose to split up a company and distribute the crew members to different sectors to act as Accountability Officers.

Accountability Sector

As the incident escalates to the level that Accountability Officers are assigned, Command should implement an Accountability Sector to coordinate Accountability Officers.

The Accountability Sector Officer will be assigned to Logistics and will operate on the assigned logistics radio channel. The Accountability Sector Officer should be located in the Command Post.

The Accountability Sector Officer's responsibilities include:
1. Develop and implement a plan designed to track and account for all personnel working in the hot zone.

2. Ensure that Accountability Officers are implemented in each sector as necessary.

3. Request and manage sector resources as needed.

4. Provide progress reports to Command.

5. Initiate PAR's upon benchmarks or as needed

Shift Change, AWR, CM, Transfer
Arriving crew members will be responsible for immediately updating the company PASSPORT as they arrive to duty - including any constant man duty, AWR's or following transfer from another station.

Arriving crew members will remove the name tag from the PASSPORT of the crew member they are replacing. For permanently assigned members, the name tag may be placed on an adjacent strip of Velcro on the dash of the apparatus.

For those crew members not permanently assigned, the name tag should be placed on velcro strip of their helmet on the underside of the rear brim.

Arriving crew members will also ensure that their helmets reflect the company ID that they are assigned to. Company Officers are responsible for ensuring that the PASSPORTS and helmet ID's always remain current. PASSPORTS must reflect only those members presently assigned to the company and only those crew members about to enter the hazard zone.

20551

Rules of Thumb

PASSPORT implementation should consider the following basic rules of thumb:

o   PASSPORTS never enter the hot zone.

o   PASSPORTS must be maintained at the point of entry to the hot zone.

o   PASSPORTS must reflect only those personnel _presently_ in the hot zone.

o   Crews must turn in their PASSPORTS upon entering and must _retrieve_ their PASSPORTS upon exit from the hot zone.

PASSPORT Implementation - The Incident

Implementation of the PASSPORT system will occur at any incident that requires the use of SCBA.

The objective of the PASSPORT system is always to have the crew members PASSPORTS near the point of entry and that they be accurate, reflecting only those members entering the hot zone. For those situations where it is not clear-cut as to when and where to turn in PASSPORT, crews should consider the above-cited objective for their decision.

For single company incidents, the PASSPORT remains on the apparatus dash. The Engineer will assume accountability sector responsibilities.

For 2-1 assignments and greater, the PASSPORT system will function as follows:

o   The first engine to each geographic side of the incident becomes the initial accountability location for all later arriving companies to that side of the incident.

o   PASSPORT of the first engine to each geographic side of the incident will remain attached to the dash.

o   The Engineer becomes the initial Accountability Officer until PASSPORTS are collected later in the incident by the Sector or Accountability Officer who assumes accountability responsibilities.

o   Crews of the initial assignment that have apparatus parked in _very_ close proximity (i.e., 50 feet or less) of the initial engine (accountability location) may leave their PASSPORTS on the dash of their apparatus or take them to the first engine (accountability location).

o   The Engineer of the first engine (accountability location) will collect the PASSPORTS from these additional companies, time permitting, and mount them on the status board at the accountability location.

o   Any crew whose apparatus is more than 50 feet away must deliver their PASSPORTS to the accountability engine and place the PASSPORTS on the status board. The status board will always be located on the inside panel of the engineer's/driver's door.

20551

o   Ladder companies on the initial assignment (first alarm) may leave their PASSPORTS on the dash of the apparatus if they are parked at a position that would not permit easy delivery of the PASSPORTS to the accountability engine.

o   Any ladder company assigned to a sector will deliver the PASSPORT to the Sector Officer, or a designated Accountability Officer (designated by the Sector Officer or Command).

o   As the incident escalates, and Sector Officers and/or Accountability Officers are assigned, all PASSPORTS will be delivered to these officers prior to entry into the hot zone.

o   Where the Sector Officer is operating within the hot zone, PASSPORTS must remain outside the zone with a designated Accountability Officer (i.e., initial engineer or staff officer) serving as an Accountability Officer. A Sector Officer operating within the hot zone will not have PASSPORT accountability responsibilities.

o   Command must maintain an awareness of which engine companies are serving as accountability locations, and provide this information to companies being assigned to each geographic side of the incident (sector).

Point of Entry Control

PASSPORTS will remain with the designated Accountability Officer near the "point of entry" to the hot zone. Upon entry, crews will turn in their PASSPORT. Upon exit, the crew must retrieve their PASSPORTS. The accountability status board will contain only the PASSPORTS of those crews in the hot zone.

Crews exiting at a different location than the original point of entry, must immediately notify their original Sector Officer and/or Accountability Officer of their changed status. The PASSPORT must be retrieved.

Where physical distance/barriers prevent easy retrieval of the PASSPORT, and where the crew is being re-assigned to another sector, a "make-up" PASSPORT must be assembled. Crew members will provide the new Sector Officer another name tag. Where another "make-up" PASSPORT is not available, the individual name tags will be placed on the accountability status board.

The original Sector Officer and/or Accountability Officer must be made aware of the change.

Multi-Story/High-rise

Multi-story or high-rise incidents present only a minor modification in the standard approach to PASSPORT accountability.

o   The first engine to each geographic side of the incident remains the accountability location.

o   First-in crews that are parked in very close proximity (50 feet) of the first engine may leave their PASSPORTS on the apparatus

20551

o   Companies parking a greater distance away will deliver their PASSPORTS to the initial engine and place the PASSPORTS on the status board of the accountability engine.

o   Once a lobby sector is established all crews reporting to the building will deliver their PASSPORTS to the lobby sector.

o   The lobby sector will be responsible for collecting the PASSPORTS of the initial companies as soon as possible (may use incoming crews reporting to the building to pick them up).

o   Once the Resource Sector is established, the Resource Sector Officer will collect the PASSPORTS of all crews assigned to fire combat positions. The Resource Sector will assign Accountability Officers at each point of entry to stairwells, etc.

o   PASSPORTS for crews assigned to the lobby sector or any support sectors within the building (non-hot zone crews) will be maintained by the Sector Officers.

Terminating The PASSPORT System

PASSPORT accountability will be maintained through a report of "fire under control," at which time a PAR for all crews must be obtained. Command will determine at that time, based on the situation and risk, as to whether to continue with the PASSPORT system. If visibility is still impaired or a significant hazardous condition still exists, Command may choose to extend the PASSPORT system further.

Upon termination and release from the incident, Company Officers and crew members will ensure that the PASSPORT is returned to the dash of their apparatus and that the PASSPORT is up-to-date.

Rapid Intervention Crews (RIC)

Command must assure that a RIC unit has been dispatched for all working fire situations and/or operations that pose a special hazard (i.e., confined space rescue).

Lost/Missing Firefighter

An absent member of any crew will automatically be assumed lost or trapped in the hazard zone until otherwise determined safe. Company Officers must immediately report any absent members to Sector Officers or Command. For any reports of missing firefighters, Command must request the next greater assignment or alarm (i.e., 2-1 goes to a first alarm or a second alarm goes to a third alarm). Command must next initiate an immediate roll call (PAR) of all companies assigned to duty in the hazard zone. Command must also send the Rapid Intervention Crew (RIC) to the last reported working area of the lost firefighter to begin a search. Simultaneously with these actions, Command must adjust on-scene strategies to a priority search and rescue effort.

20551

Summary of Accountability Responsibilities

Accountability will work only with a strong personal commitment to the safety system. This commitment involves the following responsibilities:

FIREFIGHTER - Responsible for staying with his/her crew at all times and ensuring that his/her name tag is on the PASSPORT at all times.

ENGINEER - The Engineer of the first engine to each geographic side of the incident becomes the initial Accountability Officer. The Engineer must collect PASSPORTS from crews and apparatus assigned to his/her side of the incident (sector) and manage accountability until relieved by a Sector Officer or Accountability Officer.

COMPANY OFFICER - Responsible for keeping his/her crew intact at all times and that the PASSPORT is current and accurate. The PASSPORT must reflect only those personnel entering the hazard zone. The PASSPORT must be turned in at the point of entry and retrieved upon exit.

SECTOR OFFICER - Responsible for accounting for all crews in his/her assigned sector, maintaining an awareness of their exact location, and maintaining accurate PASSPORTS of those crews in the hazard zone.

In those situations where the Sector Officer must enter the hazard zone, PASSPORTS will continue to be managed by the Engineer of the first engine to each side of the incident or a designated Accountability Officer for his/her sector.

ACCOUNTABILITY OFFICER - Responsible for teaming up with the assigned Sector Officer and to manage all accountability for that sector. The Accountability Officer must collect all PASSPORTS from engineers, apparatus, or the Sector Officer. The Accountability Officer must maintain close coordination with other Accountability Officers.

ACCOUNTABILITY SECTOR OFFICER - Responsible for managing Accountability Officers and system. Causes PAR's to be initiated at tactical benchmarks or as needed.

COMMAND - Responsible for tracking the location of all crews. Must advise later assigned crews of which engine is serving as the accountability location for PASSPORTS or that the Sector or Accountability Officer will be accepting PASSPORTS at the point of entry.

20551

The fire department often responds to incidents that present a high risk to fire fighter safety. This procedure identifies the requirements and operation of Rapid Intervention Crews (RICs). Other related procedures are Lost/Trapped Fire fighters Basic Self Survival and Rescue-Lost Fire fighters Command Responsibilities.

This procedure increases fire fighter safety at emergency incidents by providing for fire fighter rescue at the outset of an event before a team enters an unknown atmosphere, potential or actual IDLH (immediately dangerous to life and health). It should integrate with procedures that are already in effect, such as the requirement for a back-up rescue team for hazardous materials entry. The objective of a RIC crew is to have a fully equipped rescue team on-site, in a ready state, to immediately react and respond to rescue injured or trapped fire fighters or civilians.

Required Use of RICs
This procedure shall be implemented at all "working" interior structural fires beyond the incipient stage and other incidents where fire department members are subject to hazards that would be immediately dangerous to life and/or health in the event of an equipment failure, sudden change of conditions, or mishap.

Examples of special hazards include, but are not limited to:
- Offensive Fire Operations (assumed to be IDLH)
- Hazardous Materials Incidents (IDLH, potential IDLH, or unknown atmosphere)
- Trench Rescue
- Confined Space Rescue (assumed to be IDLH)
- Any other incident having significant risk

IRIC (Initial RIC)
- Temporary two person RIC team assigned at the outset of an incident to allow teams to enter an IDLH, potential IDLH, or unknown atmosphere.
- Priority of Command to upgrade IRIC to a full RIC crew as soon as practically possible.

One IRIC member must be solely dedicated to tracking interior personnel. Their function is to account for location of interior crews and initiate a fire fighter rescue. This position requires an attack line, radio, PPE, and SCBA.

The other member of the two-person IRIC is permitted to take on other roles, such as incident commander, safety officer, or equipment operator. This position requires a radio with PPE and SCBA nearby to be donned as soon as possible.

Standard Implementation IRIC Four-Person Crew
IRIC can be used when a mobile Command mode is utilized by the first arriving company officer making an interior attack on a working fire with the nozzle person. The plug person assumes the primary IRIC position and the engineer assumes the secondary IRIC position. This would allow for an interior attack when the second due company has a delayed response.

Standard Exceptions to the IRIC Requirement at Structure Fires
1. When there is a life hazard where immediate action could prevent the loss of life.

20564

2. When the fire is in an incipient stage that could be controlled by a portable fire extinguisher.

Dispatch and Implementation

Upon declaration of working fire, an additional engine company will be dispatched. Declaration of a working first alarm, an additional engine and ladder will be dispatched to satisfy RIC assignments. The assigned unit will acknowledge response via radio (Unit ID responding). The unit should stage on-scene in a location to maximize their options and await instruction from Command. This company should be prepared for a RIC assignment if an IRIC has not been upgraded to a full RIC on their arrival. During major operations, RICs will normally be assigned a standby position near the Command Post or the rehab operation. A minimum of one company will be required.

Command may assign more than one company as a RIC if necessary. Operations of a large or more complex nature may call for multiple RIC units to standby at different entry points. After dispatch of a company, Command has the following options for use:

1. Assign the company to RIC duties and be designated Rescue Sector.
2. Cancel the company en-route after the declaration of fire under control AND PAR's have been obtained from **all** crews and the IDLH atmosphere no longer exists.
3. Assign other duties, such as heat relief for working crews overhaul duties, etc.
4. If assigned anything other than RIC duties Command must request an additional company as a RIC unit to be available for emergencies affecting fire fighters.

En-route potential RICs should monitor the tactical radio channel and initiate a tactical worksheet noting location of operating companies. Upon assignment of RIC responsibilities, the RIC company officer should obtain a detailed briefing from Command or the IRIC they're relieving on the status and location of all assigned companies. The tactical worksheet should be continually updated.

All RIC crew members will assume a ready state, including full protective clothing and SCBA. For other types of incidents the protective clothing and equipment will be appropriate for the hazards. The RIC team company officer will closely monitor the assigned tactical radio channel at all times.

In some cases the RIC may need to conduct a recon to maintain awareness of working companies and conditions. The team must be able to react immediately to sudden emergency events at the incident site. In all cases, the RIC must have the ability to rapidly deploy.

In some situations, protective hoselines may need to be pre-deployed. RIC companies should assess the need for other access points to provide for egress, rescue, and ventilation. Forcible entry may be necessary. When companies are operating on floors above ground, the RIC should consider pre-positioning ground ladders to allow for emergency egress and rescue.

If a fire fighter gets in trouble or an emergency occurs, Dispatch should immediately be contacted with a declaration of "May Day". Dispatch will sound emergency traffic and declare the "May Day" and advise responding units. Whenever a RIC is deployed it should be replaced as soon as possible to back up the crews involved in a rescue operation.

20564

If RIC crew units are needed to respond to a sudden emergency, in which the Sector Officer is incapacitated (physically or emotionally), the RIC Company Officer will assume sector responsibilities for the area in which the emergency exists. Rescue sector should coordinate their activities with the involved sector to maximize the rescue operation.

If not deployed as a RIC unit, Command may assign this company as a relief unit and rotate them with interior companies. RICs can be used for any appropriate assignments after all crews are out of danger, PAR's have been obtained, and an IDLH atmosphere no longer exists.

High-rise Fires
For high-rise fires, RICs will be assigned to standby positions in the Resource Sector location, stairwell, or other appropriate location(s). A secondary standby location may be in the Lobby Sector location. RIC company must take RIC bag to the Resource or Lobby Sector and standby.

RIC - S.C.B.A. Rescue Kits
Once assigned to RIC standby duties, the assigned company must obtain the RIC S.C.B.A. Rescue Kits from any Battalion or Command vehicle. Each kit should be checked for air supply and tools (See Appendix A). Upon a report of a lost or trapped fire fighter, the kit (or more than one kit) must be taken to the rescue area.

Commitment to Rescue of a Lost or Trapped Fire Fighter
Upon a report of a lost or trapped fire fighter, Command should deploy the RICs to the last reported location of the lost/trapped fire fighter(s). The RIC-- S.C.B.A. kit(s) must be taken. The Company Officer of the RIC may be assigned a Rescue Sector designation. Appropriate rescue equipment and crews must be quickly assembled and organized.

APPENDIX A

RIC - S.C.B.A. RESCUE KIT

The items to be included in each RIC--S.C.B.A. Kit are as follows:

4   Flashlights
4   Packstraps
4   Door straps
4   Sprinkler wedges
4   Life lines with deployment bags
1   Bolt cutter (small 12")
1   Channel Lock (multi-adjustable pliers 12")
1   Phillips head screwdriver (6")
1   Folding knife (3-4" blade)
1   Wire cutter (snub nose pliers with side cutter 7-10")
1   Straight blade screwdriver (6")
1   S.C.B.A. bottle supply pigtail
1   S.C.B.A. bottle

20564

PROVIDENCE FIRE DEPARTMENT PRE-FIRE DATA CARD

ADDRESS: _____

BLDG.

NAME: _____

BOX #: _____ LOCATION: _____

PANEL LOCATION: _____

KNOX BOX LOCATION: _____

CONSTRUCTION: _____ DIMENSIONS: _____

OCCUPANCY: _____ STORIES: _____

SPECIAL HAZARDS

SPRINKLERS		**STANDPIPES**

SPRINKLERS	STANDPIPES
TYPE: _____	CLASS: _____ TYPE: _____
FDC: _____	FDC: _____
PIV: _____	PRV: _____
OS&Y: _____	FIRE PUMP: _____

ELEVATORS	STAIRS
LOCATION: _____	LOCATION: _____
FF SERVICE: _____	TYPE: _____
EMER. POWER: _____	VENTABLE: _____
MACHINE ROOM: _____	ROOF ACCESS: _____
FREIGHT: _____	BASEMENT ACCESS: _____

BLDG. OWNER: _____ PHONE: _____

BLDG. OCCUPANT: _____ PHONE: _____

MAINT. SUPER: _____ PHONE: _____

IN EMERGENCY: _____ PHONE: _____

ALARM COMPANY: _____ PHONE: _____

LOCATION OF SHUTOFFS

GAS: _____

ELECTRIC: _____

WATER: _____

HVAC: _____

FIRE PUMP: _____

BOILER ROOM: _____

TYPE OF HEAT: _____ FUEL: _____

TRASH CHUTES: _____

MSDS LOCATION: _____

INSPECTED BY: _____ DATE: _____

Glossary and Index

Glossary

A

Aerial Device — Any piece of mobile fire apparatus having the means to reach at least 65 feet (20 m) above grade, with many being capable of reaching more than 100 feet (30 m). Aerial devices are usually either aerial ladders or telescoping or articulating booms.

Air-Handling System — *See* HVAC.

Arched Roof — Any of several different types of roofs of which all are curved or arch shaped, resembling the top half of a horizontal cylinder. Typical applications are on supermarkets, auditoriums, bowling centers, sports arenas, and aircraft hangars.

Area of Refuge — Two-hour-rated compartment containing one elevator to the ground floor and at least one enclosed exit stairway.

Assembly — All component parts necessary to form a complete unit or system joined or fitted together.

Atrium — Open area in the center of a building, similar to a courtyard but usually covered by a skylight, to allow natural light and ventilation into interior rooms.

Attic — Concealed and often unfinished space between the ceiling of the top floor and the roof of a building. Also called Cockloft or Interstitial Space.

Autoexposure — *See* Lapping.

Awning Window — Window that is hinged at the top and swings outward at the bottom.

B

Backdraft — Instantaneous explosion or rapid burning of superheated gases in a confined space. It may occur because of inadequate or improper ventilation procedures.

Balloon-Frame Construction — Type of framing used in some single-story and multistory buildings where the studs are continuous from the foundation to the roof. There may be no fire stops between the studs.

Bar Joist — Open web truss constructed entirely of steel, with steel tubes used as the web members.

Base — At a high-rise fire, the location where reserve companies are staged until needed, also called Level II Staging. Base may be collocated with the incident command post. There is only one Base per incident.

Beam — Structural member in a roof or floor assembly that is subjected to vertical loads perpendicular to its length.

Bearing Wall — Wall that supports itself and the weight of the roof and/or other structural components above it.

BLEVE — Acronym for *boiling liquid expanding vapor explosion*.

Blower — Large-volume fan used to blow fresh air into a building or other confined space in positive-pressure ventilation (PPV).

Breach — To make an opening (usually in a masonry wall) to allow access into or out of a structure.

Brick Veneer — Single layer of bricks applied to the inside or outside surface of a wall for aesthetic and/or insulation purposes.

Bridge Truss — Heavy-duty truss, usually made of heavy wooden members with steel tie rods, that has horizontal top and bottom chords and steeply sloped ends.

Building Engineer — Person who is responsible for and familiar with the operation of a building's heating, ventilating, and air-conditioning (HVAC) system and other essential equipment.

Built-Up Roof — Roof covering made of several alternate layers of roofing paper and tar, with the final layer of tar being covered with pea gravel or crushed slag. Also called Tar and Gravel Roof.

Bulkhead — Structure on the roof of a building through which the interior stairway opens onto the roof. Sometimes called a Penthouse.

Butterfly Roof — V-shaped roof style resembling two opposing shed roofs joined along their lower edges.

C

Casement Window — Window hinged along one side, usually designed to swing outward by means of a small crank, with the screen on the inside.

Ceiling — Nonbearing structural component separating a living/working space from the underside of the floor or roof immediately above.

Cement — Any adhesive material. In construction, a fine clay powder called portland cement is combined with sand and/or other aggregates and water to produce mortar or concrete.

Center Rafter Cut — *See* Louver Vent.

Chase — *See* Pipe Chase.

Chimney Effect — *See* Stack Effect.

Chord — Top or bottom longitudinal member of a truss.

Churning — Movement of smoke being blown out of a ventilation opening only to be drawn back inside by the negative pressure created by the ejector because the open area around the ejector has not been sealed. Also called Recirculation.

Cockloft — *See* Attic.

Compression — Those vertical or horizontal forces that tend to press objects together; for example, the force exerted on the top chord of a truss.

Command Post (CP) — Designated location at which the IC and other members of the Command Staff function during an incident. CP may be collocated with Base.

Command Staff — In a fully developed fireground organization, the Information Officer (PIO), Safety (ISO), and Liaison Officer report directly to the IC.

Communications/Dispatch Center — Telecommunications facility at which fire calls are received from the public and from which fire/rescue units are dispatched to emergencies.

Concealed Space — Any structural void that is not readily visible from a living/working space within a building.

Concrete — Mixture of portland cement and an aggregate filler/binder to which water is added to form a wet, moldable slurry that sets into a rigid building material. In structural concrete, the filler/ binder is usually sand and/or gravel; in lightweight concrete, such as soundproofing material, the filler/ binder may be sand and/or vermiculite.

Crawl Space — Space between the ground and the floor, a space between the ceiling and the roof, or any other structural void with a vertical dimension that does not allow a person to stand erect within the space. These spaces often contain ductwork, plumbing, wiring, etc.

Curtain Boards — Fire-resistive half walls, intended to limit the spread of smoke and fire gases, which extend down from the underside of the roof of some commercial buildings. Also called Draft Stop.

D

Dead Load — Weight of the structure, structural members, and any other object that is permanently attached to the building.

Decking — *See* Sheathing.

Dicing — Ventilation exit opening created by making multiple cuts in the sheathing perpendicular to the ridge beam.

Dome Roof — Hemispherical roof assembly, usually supported only at the outer walls of a circular or many-sided structure.

Double-Hung Window — Window having two vertically moving sashes.

Draft Stop — *See* Curtain Boards.

Drywall — *See* Wallboard.

E

Elevating Platform — Work platform attached to the end of an articulating or telescoping aerial device.

Entry Point (Entry Opening) — In ventilation, the opening through which replacement air enters; usually the same opening through which rescue/attack crews enter the structure.

Exit Opening — In ventilation, the opening that is made or used to release heat, smoke, and other contaminants to the atmosphere.

Extended Attack Incident — An incident that was not controlled within the initial operational period.

Exterior Exposure — Building or other combustible object located close to the fire building that is in danger of becoming involved due to heat transfer from the fire building.

F

Facade — Fascia added to some buildings with flat roofs to create the appearance of a mansard roof.

Fan — Generic term used interchangeably for both blowers and smoke ejectors.

Fiberboard — Lightweight insulation board made of compressed cellulose fibers and often used as panels in suspended ceilings.

Fire Door — Rated assembly designed to automatically close and cover a doorway in a firewall during a fire.

Fire Escape — Means of escaping from a building in case of fire; usually an interior or exterior stairway or slide independently supported and made of fire-resistive materials.

Fire Stop — Solid material, such as a wooden block, placed within a wall void to retard or prevent the spread of fire through the void.

Fire Wall — Rated separation wall, usually extending from the foundation up to and through the roof of a building, to limit the spread of a fire.

Fixed Window — Window designed not to be opened.

Flashover — Stage of a fire at which all surfaces and objects within a space have been heated to their ignition temperature and flame breaks out almost at once over the surface of all objects in the space.

Flat Roof — Roof with little or no pitch or slope. Flat roofs generally have a slight pitch to facilitate runoff.

Forced Ventilation — Any means of ventilation other than natural. This type of ventilation may involve the use of blowers, smoke ejectors, or fog streams. Also called mechanical ventilation.

G

Gabled Roof — Style of pitched roof with square ends in which the end walls of the building form triangular areas beneath the roof.

Gambrel Roof — Style of gabled roof on which each side slopes at two different angles; often used on barns and similar structures.

Gang Nail — Form of gusset plate. Thin steel plates are punched with acutely V-shaped holes that form sharp prongs on one side that penetrate wooden members to fasten them together.

Girder — Large, horizontal structural member used to support joists and beams at isolated points along their length.

Grade — Surface level of pavement or stable earth.

Gusset Plate — Metal or wooden plates used to connect and strengthen the intersections of metal or wooden truss components.

H

Hatch — A square or rectangular access opening on a roof, usually locked on the inside. Also called a Scuttle.

High Rise — Uniform Building Code (UBC) definition: Any building of more than 75 feet (23 m) in height. Practical definition: any building with a roof that is beyond the reach of the fire department's longest ladder.

Hip Roof — Pitched roof that has no gables. All facets of the roof slope down from the peak to an outside wall.

Hopper Window — Window hinged along the bottom edge and usually designed to open inward.

Horizontal Ventilation — Any technique by which heat, smoke, and other products of combustion are channeled horizontally out of a structure by way of existing or created openings.

HVAC — Heating, ventilating, and air-conditioning. Air-handling system within a building consisting of fans, ducts, dampers, and other equipment necessary to make it function. Also called Air-Handling System.

I

I-Beam — Steel or wooden structural member with a cross section resembling a capital I.

Incident Action Plan (IAP) — Strategic goals, tactical objectives, and support requirements specified for the current operational period during an incident. All incidents require an IAP. On relatively small incidents, the IAP is usually not in writing. On larger, more complex incidents, a written IAP is created for each operational period, and is disseminated to units assigned to the incident.

Incident Commander (IC) — Individual responsible for the management of all incident operations.

Incident Safety Officer (ISO) — Member of the Command Staff responsible for monitoring and assessing safety hazards and unsafe conditions during an incident, and developing measures for ensuring personnel safety. The ISO is responsible for the enforcement of all mandated safety laws and regulations and departmental safety-related SOPs. On very small incidents, the IC may act as the ISO.

Index Gas — Any commonly encountered gas, such as carbon monoxide (CO), whose concentration can be measured. In the absence of devices capable of measuring the concentrations of other gases present, the CO measurement may be assumed to indicate their concentrations as well.

Initial Attack Incident — An incident that can be handled by the resources in the first-alarm assignment.

Interior Exposure — Any area of a fire building that is not involved in fire, but is connected to the fire area in such a manner that may allow fire spread through any available opening.

Interstitial Space — *See* Attic.

Inversion — Atmospheric phenomenon that allows smoke to rise until its temperature equals the surrounding air temperature, and then it spreads laterally in a horizontal layer. Also called Night Inversion.

J

Jalousie Window — Window consisting of narrow, frameless glass panes set in metal brackets at each end that allow the panes a limited amount of axial rotation for ventilation.

Joist — Horizontal supporting member in a roof, ceiling, or floor assembly.

K-L

Labeled Assembly — *See* Rated Assembly.

Lantern Roof — Roof style consisting of a high, gabled roof with a vertical wall above a downward-pitched shed roof section on either side.

Lapping — Means by which fire spreads vertically from floor to floor in a multistory building. Fire issuing from a window laps up the outside of the building and enters the floor(s) above, usually through the windows. Also called Autoexposure.

Lee (Leeward) — Direction opposite that from which the wind is blowing; the protected side.

Level I Staging — The point at which incoming units stop (stage) while the first-due company investigates the incident. Units usually stage at the last intersection on their route of travel before reaching the reported incident location.

Level II Staging — *See* Base.

Light Well (Light Shaft) — Vertical shaft at or near the center of a building to provide natural light and/or ventilation to offices or apartments not located on an outside wall.

Live Load — Loads within a building that are movable. Merchandise, stock, furnishings, occupants, firefighters, and the water used for fire suppression are examples of live loads.

Lobby Control — In high-rise fire fighting, the individual responsible for taking and maintaining control of the lobby and the elevators, setting up internal communications, coordinating the flow of personnel and equipment up the interior stairway(s), and coordinating with the building engineer.

Louver Vent — Rectangular exit opening cut in a roof, allowing a section of roof deck (still nailed to a center rafter) to be tilted, thus creating an opening similar to a louver. Also called center rafter cut.

Low-Rise Elevator — Elevator that serves only the lower floors of a high-rise building.

M

Mansard Roof — Roof style with characteristics similar to both gambrel and hip roofs. Mansard roofs have slopes of two different angles, and all sides slope down to an outside wall.

Mechanical Ventilation — *See* Forced Ventilation.

Membrane Roof — Roof covering consisting of a single layer of waterproof synthetic membrane over one or more layers of insulation on a roof deck. Also called single-ply roof.

Modern Mansard Roof — Roof style having sides that slope at only one angle up to meet a flat deck in the center section.

Monitor Appliance (Monitor) — Master stream appliance whose stream direction can be changed while water is being discharged. Monitors may be fixed, portable, or a combination.

Monitor Roof — Roof style similar to an exaggerated lantern roof having a raised section along the ridgeline, providing additional natural light and ventilation.

Monitor Vent — Structure, usually rectangular in shape, which penetrates the highest point of a roof to provide additional natural light and/or ventilation. They may have metal, glass, wired glass, or louvered sides.

Mushrooming — Tendency of heat, smoke, and other products of combustion to rise until they encounter a horizontal obstruction. At that point they will spread laterally until they encounter vertical obstructions and will begin to bank downward.

N

Natural Ventilation — Ventilation techniques that use the wind, convection currents, and other natural phenomena to ventilate a structure without using fans, blowers, or other mechanical devices.

Negative-Pressure Ventilation — Technique using smoke ejectors to develop artificial circulation and to pull smoke out of a structure. Smoke ejectors are placed in windows, doors, or roof vent openings to pull the smoke, heat, and gases from inside the building and eject them to the exterior.

Neutral Pressure Plane — That point within a building, especially a high-rise, where the interior pressure equals the atmospheric pressure outside. This plane will move up or down, depending on variables of temperature and wind.

Night Inversion — *See* Inversion.

Nonbearing Wall — Wall, usually interior, that supports only its own weight. These walls can be breached or removed without compromising the structural integrity of the building.

O

Occupancy — Building Code classification of the use to which owners or tenants put buildings or portions of buildings.

Occupant Services Unit — Sector/Group designated to provide information and support services to the victims of a fire. Among the services provided may be assistance in contacting relatives, public agencies, and/or charitable institutions for transportation, temporary shelter, and other basic needs.

Open Up — To ventilate a building or other confined space.

Open Web Truss — Structural assembly consisting of a top chord and a bottom chord connected by a triangulated series of web components such as bars or tubes.

Operational Period — Period of time during which a specified set of operational goals and objectives, as identified in the IAP, are to be achieved. An operational period may be 12 hours, 24 hours, or any other arbitrary amount of time. A new IAP is created for each operational period.

Oriented Strand Board (OSB) — Construction material made of many small wooden pieces (strands) bonded together to form sheets, similar to plywood.

P

PAR — *See* Personnel Accountability Report.

Parapet Wall — Vertical extension of an exterior wall, and sometimes an interior fire wall, above the roofline of a building.

Party Wall — Wall that stands on the property line between two adjoining buildings and is common to both buildings. Almost always a load-bearing wall and usually serves as a fire wall.

Penthouse — Structure on the roof of a building that may be used as a living space, to enclose mechanical equipment, or to provide roof access from an interior stairway. Also called a Bulkhead.

Personnel Accountability Report (PAR) — A roll call of all units (crews, teams, groups, companies, sectors) assigned to an incident. Usually by radio, the supervisor of each unit reports the status of the personnel within the unit at that time. A PAR may be required by SOP at specific intervals during an incident, or may be requested at any time by the IC or the ISO.

Pipe Chase — Concealed channel in which pipes and other utility conduits are housed. Pipe chases that are not properly protected can be major contributors to the spread of smoke and fire in a building. Also called Chase.

Pitch — The slope of a roof expressed as a ratio of rise to span.

Pitched Roof — Roof, other than a flat or arched roof, having one or more pitched or sloping surfaces.

Plasterboard — *See* Wallboard.

Plate — Horizontal construction member at the bottom (sole plate) or top (top plate) of a framed wall.

Platform Frame Construction — Type of framing in which each floor is built as a separate platform, and the studs are not continuous from floor to floor. Also called Western Frame Construction.

Poke-Through — Opening in a floor, ceiling, or wall through which ductwork, plumbing, or electrical conduits pass. If these openings are not properly caulked or sealed, they can contribute significantly to the spread of smoke and fire in a building.

Positive-Pressure Ventilation (PPV) — Method of ventilating a confined space by mechanically blowing fresh air into the space in sufficient volume to create a slight positive pressure within, thereby forcing the contaminated atmosphere out the exit opening.

Pre-Incident Inspection — Thorough and systematic inspection of a building for the purpose of identifying significant structural and/or occupancy characteristics to assist in the development of a pre-incident plan for that building.

Pre-Incident Plan — Operational plan for the safe and efficient handling of emergency situations within a specific building or occupancy.

Pressure Differential — Effect of altering the atmospheric pressure within a confined space by mechanical means. When air is exhausted from within the space, a low-pressure environment is created and replacement air will be drawn in. When air is blown into the space, a high-pressure environment is created, and air within will move to the outside.

Q-R

Rafter — Structural member to which the roof decking is attached.

Rapid Intervention Crew (RIC) — Two or more fully equipped and immediately available firefighters designated to stand by outside the hazard zone to enter and affect rescue of firefighters inside, if necessary.

Rated Assembly — Doors, walls, roofs, and other structural features that may be, because of the occupancy, required by code to have a minimum fire-resistance rating from an independent testing agency. Also called Labeled Assembly.

Razor Ribbon — Coil of lightweight, flexible metallic ribbon with extremely sharp edges; often installed on parapet walls and on fence tops to discourage trespassers.

Reading a Roof — Observing the surface and other features of a roof from a position of safety in order to assess the roof's condition before stepping onto it.

Refuse Chute — Vertical shaft with a self-closing access door on every floor, usually extending from the basement or ground floor to the top floor in multistory buildings.

Rehab — Incident Management System (IMS) term for a rehabilitation station at a fire or other incident where personnel can rest, rehydrate, and recover from the stresses of the incident.

Resources — Personnel and equipment available, or potentially available, for assignment on an incident.

RIC — *See* Rapid Intervention Crew.

Ridge Beam — Highest horizontal member in a pitched roof to which the upper ends of the rafters attach. Also called Ridge Board or Ridgepole.

Rollover — Condition common to the Development Stage of a fire in a confined space. When additional oxygen is supplied by opening doors and/or applying fog streams, superheated unburned gases that have accumulated at the ceiling ignite and roll across the ceiling of the space.

Roof Decking — *See* Sheathing.

S

Safety Officer — *See* Incident Safety Officer (ISO).

Sawtooth Roof — Roof style characterized by a series of alternating vertical walls and sloping roofs, resembling the teeth of a saw, most often found on industrial buildings.

Scuttle — Openings in ceilings or roofs, fitted with removable covers, which may be used for access or ventilation.

Shaft — Any vertical enclosure within a building; such as a stairwell, an elevator hoistway, etc.

Shear Strength — Ability of a building component or assembly to resist lateral or shear forces.

Sheathing — Refers to the first layer of roofing material laid directly over the rafters or other roof supports. Sheathing may be plywood or OSB sheets, or planks that are butted together or spaced about 1 inch (25 mm) apart. Also called Decking or Roof Decking.

Shed Roof — Pitched roof with a single, sloping aspect, resembling half of a gabled roof.

Sheetrock® — Brand name often used to describe any gypsum wallboard. See Wallboard.

Single-Ply Roof — *See* Membrane Roof.

Size-Up — Continuous and ongoing evaluation of an emergency situation. Initial size-up is used as the basis for the incident action plan (IAP), which may be adjusted as the situation changes.

Skylight — Any of a variety of roof structures or devices intended to increase natural illumination within buildings.

Smoke Ejector — Ducted fan used primarily to expel (eject) smoke from a building, but it may be used to blow in fresh air. Most are driven by electric motors, but some are driven by gasoline engines or by water pressure. They may be used in conjunction with a flexible duct.

Smoke Tower — Fully enclosed escape stairway that exits directly onto a public way. These enclosures are either mechanically pressurized or require the user to exit the building onto an outside balcony before entering the stairway. Also called Smokeproof Stairway or Smokeproof Enclosure.

Sounding — Process of testing the structural integrity of a roof or floor of a building, or of locating underlying supporting members, by striking the surface of the assembly with the blunt end of a hand tool.

Stack Effect — Tendency of any vertical shaft within a tall building to act as a chimney or "smokestack" by channeling heat, smoke, and other products of combustion upward due to convection. Also called Chimney Effect.

Staging — In high-rise fire fighting, the Incident Management System (IMS) term for the area within the building where relief crews are assembled and spare equipment is stockpiled, usually established two floors below the fire floor. Staging may also include a first-aid station and Rehab.

Stem Wall — In platform frame construction, the exterior wall between the foundation and the first floor of a building.

Stratification — Settling at various vertical levels of accumulations or layers of smoke according to density and temperature, the heaviest on the bottom.

Strip Vent — *See* Trench Ventilation.

Stud — Vertical structural member within a wall; most often made of wood, but some are made of light-gauge metal.

Substrate — Layer of material between a roof deck and the roof covering that may or may not be bonded to the roof covering. The most common substrate is roofing felt or tar paper.

Suspended Ceiling — Very common ceiling system composed of a metal framework suspended by wires from the underside of the roof or the floor above. The framework supports fiberboard panels that constitute the finish of the ceiling. Common applications are in office buildings and in common areas of apartment buildings and hotels.

T

Tar And Gravel Roof — *See* Built-Up Roof.

Tension — Those vertical or horizontal stresses that tend to pull objects apart; for example, the force exerted on the bottom chord of a truss.

Tepee Cut — *See* Triangular Cut.

Tilt-Slab Construction — Type of construction in which concrete wall sections (slabs) are cast on the concrete floor of the building, and are then tilted up into the vertical position.

Top Ventilation — *See* Vertical Ventilation.

Trench Ventilation — Defensive tactic that involves cutting an exit opening in the roof of a burning building, extending from one outside wall to the other, to create an opening at which a spreading fire may be cut off. Also called Strip Vent.

Triangular Cut — Triangular opening cut in a roll-up or tilt-slab door to provide access into the building or a means of egress for those inside. Also called Tepee Cut.

Truss — Structural assembly consisting of a top chord and a bottom chord that are separated by some triangulated configuration of web members, often found in lightweight roof construction.

U

UBC — Uniform Building Code published by the International Conference of Building Officials.

Universal Priorities — Operational priorities that apply to all emergency incidents. In order of importance (priority) they are: *life safety*, *incident stabilization*, and *property conservation*.

V

Vent Group/Sector — Firefighters assigned to ventilate a structure.

Ventilation — Systematic removal of heated air, smoke, or other airborne contaminants from a structure, and their replacement with a supply of fresher air.

Venturi Principle — Physical law stating that when a fluid, such as water or air, is forced under pressure through a restricted orifice, there is an increase in the velocity of the fluid passing through the orifice and a corresponding decrease in the pressure exerted against the sides of the constriction. Because the surrounding fluid is under greater pressure (atmospheric), it is forced into the area of lower pressure. Also called Venturi Effect.

Vertical Ventilation — Ventilating at the highest point of a building through existing or created openings and channeling the contaminated atmosphere vertically within the structure and out the top. Also called Top Ventilation.

W

Wallboard — Fire-resistive building material consisting of a layer of highly compacted gypsum material sandwiched between two layers of paper. Also called Drywall, Plasterboard, or Sheetrock®.

Western Frame Construction — *See* Platform Frame Construction.

Windward — Direction from which the wind is blowing; the unprotected side.

Wired Glass — Glass in which a wire mesh is embedded during manufacture. Either transparent or translucent, wired glass is installed in exterior doors, windows, and skylights to increase interior illumination without compromising fire resistance and security.

A

access into structures. *See also* forcible entry
  basements and underground areas, 209
  case histories involving, 47–48, 275
  doors used for, 49–62
  overview, 47–48
  roofs used for, 150, 170–171, 199–200
  size-up and, 47
  walls used for, 66–67
  windows used for, 62–66
access to structures
  fences affecting, 38–42
  gates affecting, 36–38
  perimeter control, establishing, 24, 221–222, 229–231
  pre-incident planning inspections, 34, 38
  security measures affecting, 42–44
  topography and landscaping affecting, 33–35
accountability systems, 23–24
After the Fire! Returning to Normal, 270
air conditioners. *See* heating, ventilating, and air conditioning (HVAC) systems
Americans with Disabilities Act, 80
apparatus, 283, 287. *See also* resources
approaching scenes. *See* access to structures; size-up
area of rescue assistance, 80
areas of refuge, 80
Arizona case history, 215–216
ASME A17.1, 245
assessment of incidents. *See* hazard assessment; size-up
atmospheric pressure, 94, 201–203
attacks. *See also* coordinated operations; interior operations
  in attics, 83–84, 108, 191
  in high-rise buildings, 195–197
  loss control considerations, 262
attics
  attack tactics, 83–84, 108, 191
  fire behavior and fire spread, 14, 15, 95
  roofs indicating presence of, 161
  salvage operations, 82–84
  size-up, 14, 15
  ventilation, 108, 153–154, 191
autoexposure, 110
axes
  breaching walls, 70, 122
  breaking windows, 66, 134, 135
  foothold during ventilation, 163
  opening roofs, 183, 185, 186
  PPE worn during forcible entry, 63
  sounding roofs, 171
  ventilation using, 145–146

B

backdrafts
  overview, 10
  roofing materials affecting, 183, 186
  size-up, 17, 93–94
  ventilation affecting, 93, 94
basements and underground structures
  size-up, 14–15
  ventilation, 116, 119, 208–209
  water leaks, 234
below grade (low) areas. *See* basements and underground structures; topography and landscaping
blowers. *See* fans (blowers and ejectors)
breaching. *See* forcible entry
building construction

features helpful to firefighters, 101–103, 104–106, 260
fire spread affected by, 95
occupancy-related features, 106–107
pre-incident planning and loss control potential, 260
remodels
  case history involving, 9, 13
  collapse potential affected by, 105
  fire behavior and size-up, 100–101
  pre-incident planning, 3
  during pre-incident planning, 103
  ventilation of remodeled buildings, 210–211
size-up. *See* size-up, building construction
ventilation and, 119–127, 131

C

California case histories
commercial building (1998), 47–48, 275
  garage fire, roof collapse (1978), 89
  vehicle striking transformer, 228
ceilings. *See* attics; roofs
cellars. *See* basements and underground structures
chemicals released during fires. *See* gases as products of fires
churning, 137
civilians and perimeter control, 24, 222, 229. *See also* victims
climate control systems. *See* heating, ventilating, and air conditioning (HVAC) systems
collapse potential
  building features affecting, 102, 105–106
  case history involving, 9, 11, 13
  fire behavior and, 10–11
  HVAC systems and, 238–239
  indicators of, 24–25
  newer buildings, 101
  older buildings, 100
  of roofs
    age of buildings, 12
    bowstring arch roofs, 174, 175
    building type affecting, 75
    case histories involving, 11, 48, 89
    flat roofs, 170
    light-gauge metal/fiberglass roofs, 186
    multiple roofing layers and, 182
    pitched roofs, 160–161, 166
    pitched roof trusses, 180
    tile/slate roofs, 185
    trussed roofs, 178
    water tanks affecting, 105
  SOPs, 25, 293–303
  veneer walls, 122
  warehouses, 16
  water supply affecting, 231
collapse zones, 24–25
combustible materials
  age of buildings, 12
  insulation, 158
  roof construction, 184
  ventilation exposing adjacent structures, 110–111
combustion, 93
command options at coordinated operations, 280–282. *See also* operational modes
commercial structures
  building construction
    doors, 50–54
    windows, 64
  case history involving, 47–48, 275
  electrical service, controlling, 227

occupant loads, 76
communication
    about alarm systems, 253
    about evacuation or rescue attempts, 81
    about interior operations, 75
    about operational mode changes, 278, 279, 284
    about primary search operations, 78
    about sprinkler systems, 254–255
    about unstable roofs, 151
    firefighter safety, 23
    with trapped firefighters, 26
    with utility companies, 228
    with victims, 81
concealed spaces, 175. *See also* confined spaces; hidden fires
confined spaces, 116. *See also* concealed spaces; hidden fires
conflagrations, 287–288
contents. *See* property contents
contingency plans, 261. *See also* pre-incident planning
    inspections
controlling scenes. *See* perimeter control, establishing
controlling utilities. *See* utilities, controlling
convection, 95
conveyance systems, 243–245. *See also* elevators and
    elevator shafts
coordinated operations
    case history involving, 47-48, 275
    command options, 280-282
    heat removal and, 81
    incident scene priorities, 275–276
    opening windows, 82
    overview, 280
    pre-incident planning and, 275
    salvage and, 267
    size-up and ventilation, 107–110
    at structure fires, 282–288
    utilities control, 242
    with utility companies, 228
    ventilation, 82, 90, 107–110
cordoning scenes. *See* perimeter control, establishing
correctional facilities
    building construction
        doors, 60–61
        fences, 39
        roofs, 170, 171
    ventilation, 210

D

detection systems
    controlling, 252–253
    hazards of, 247, 248–249
    types of, 246–247, 247–248, 263
detention facilities. *See* correctional facilities
doors
    blocking open, 126, 132
    emergency egress through, 28
    firefighter safety and, 52, 58
    fire spread affected by, 102, 105
    forcible entry through, 51–54, 57–61
    industrial/institutional structures, 54–61
    locks on, 36–37, 51, 125
    lost firefighters locating, 27
    pre-incident planning identification, 50, 57, 261
    residential/commercial structures, 50–54
    security systems, 61–62
    ventilation, 124–127, 132, 136
ducing, 190–191

E

egress
    emergency, 26–29
    means of

case history involving, 3, 9
    elevators, 244
    in high-rise buildings, 205
    remodels affecting, 14
    from roofs, 150, 187
    when searching floors above fires, 77
ejectors. *See* fans (blowers and ejectors)
electrical systems. *See also* utilities, controlling
    case histories involving, 54, 225, 228
    controlling
        before breaching walls, 68
        coordinating with attacks, 242
        procedures for, 225–231
        at structure fires, 225–228
        wires down without fire, 228–231
    flooding systems protecting, 249
    lighting systems and, 241, 242–243
    water leaks affecting, 231, 234
    wiring, 99–100, 101, 122
electrocution
    HVAC systems and, 238
    perimeter control around hazards, 229–230
    wires down without fire, 228, 229
elevators and elevator shafts
    controlling, 244–245
    fire spread affected by, 95, 103, 104
    hazards of, 243
    roof access using, 200
    using during incidents, 196–197
    ventilation, 103, 199
emergency response decision model (Phoenix Fire
    Department), 22
Emergency Services Incident Management System (NFPA
    1561), 24
England case history, 243
entrainment, 90
entry. *See* forcible entry
equipment. *See* tools and equipment
escalators, 243, 244
escape routes. *See* egress
exit openings, 128, 129–130, 148, 188
exits. *See* egress, means of
exposures and ventilation, 110–111, 115
extended attacks, 286–288

F

fans (blowers and ejectors)
    in basements and underground areas, 209
    defined, 116
    heat removal operations using, 82
    overhaul operations using, 264–265
    ventilation using
        with ducts, 117, 118–119, 131
        horizontal, 90, 116, 117, 136–138
        wind affecting, 131
Federal Emergency Management Agency (FEMA),
    After the Fire! Returning to Normal, 270
fences
    access affected by, 38–42, 42–43
    electrocution hazards when wires are down, 229
fire behavior. *See also* fire spread
    backdrafts, 10, 17, 93–94, 183, 186
    building construction affecting, 11–17, 98–101
    in high-rise buildings, 197–198
    mushrooming, 197–198
    overview, 7
    remodels and, 100–101
    rollovers, 10, 92
    routine fires, 7–9
    self-vented fires, 9–10

size-up and, 3, 7–11
stack effect, 197
stages of progression, 91–94, 97
stratification, 197–198
structural collapse and, 10–11
ventilation affecting, 89
Fire Department Occupational Safety and Health Program
    (NFPA 1500), 24, 25, 66
firefighter safety. *See also* hazardous conditions
    accountability systems, 23–24
    atmospheric temperatures affecting, 111–112
    backdrafts, 94
    barbed wire, 42
    collapse zones, 24–25
    communication, 23
    cutting tools and, 143
    electrical systems, securing, 226, 227, 242
    electrocution, 228, 229, 230
    emergency egress, 26–29
    escalators, 243, 244
    fatigue, 264
    fire doors, 126
    fuel oil, 220
    in growth stage of fire development, 92
    incident scene priorities, 21–23
    light and ventilation shafts, 155
    "look up, look down, look around", 9
    LPG tanks, 218
    mental exhaustion, 264
    overhaul operations, 264
    oxygen deprivation (carboxyhemoglobin), 9, 79
    rapid intervention and, 25–26
    rollovers, 10, 92
    roll-up doors, 58
    on roofs, 149, 185, 187
    size-up and, 4–5, 6–7
    skylights and, 154, 173
    smoke and, 96
    SOPs, 22–23
    in stairways, 201
    training including, 22–23
    two-in/two-out rule, 23, 75
    utilities, securing, 68, 215
    ventilation and, 89, 90, 152
    ventilation shafts, 155
    walls, breaching, 68
    weather and size-up, 6–7
    when lost, 26–27, 293–300
    when trapped, 26
    white ghosts, 220
    windows, breaking, 63, 66, 134, 135, 205
fire spread. *See also* fire behavior
    in basements and underground areas, 15, 209
    building features affecting, 102–103, 104
    overview, 95–96
    parallel chord trusses and, 177
    size-up, 15, 16
    ventilation affecting, 128
    in Victorian-style residences, 16
fire streams and ventilation. *See also* hoselines
    horizontal ventilation, 138–139
    improperly directed, 130
    vertical ventilation, 153
    visibility affected by, 107
flameovers (rollovers), 10, 92
flashovers
    roof construction affecting, 183, 186
    self-vented fires and, 9–10
    as stage of fire development, 92–93
floors

collapse potential, 9, 106
    salvage operations and, 267, 268
forced ventilation
    defined, 90
    in high-rise buildings, 203, 205
    horizontal, 91, 135–139
    natural ventilation compared to, 110
    situations requiring, 110
forcible entry. *See also* access into structures
    building features affecting, 104
    case history involving, 47–48
    doors, overcoming, 51–54, 57–61
    fences, overcoming, 39, 40, 41, 42
    loss control considerations, 266
    roofs, opening, 169
    walls, breaching, 29, 41–42, 66–70
    windows, breaking, 62–66, 205
    wiring and piping exposed, 122
fuel, smoke indicating type of, 96–97
fuel oil, 21, 219–220. *See also* liquefied petroleum gas
    (LPG); natural gas

G
garages, case histories involving, 54, 89, 225
gases as products of fires. *See also* toxic products of
    combustion
    backdrafts and, 93–94
    in decay stage of fire development, 93
    fire walls and, 120
    in growth stage of fire development, 91, 92
    index gases during overhaul, 265
    neutral pressure plane, 202
    pressure transfer, 97–98, 201
    removing, 93, 118, 119
    rollovers (flameovers), 92
    types released during fires, 265–266
gas leaks without fires, 220–225, 234
geography (landscaping) affecting access, 33–35, 104
government buildings, ventilation, 210
group fires, 287
Guide for Smoke and Heat Venting (NFPA 204), 207
Guidelines on Roof Coverings and Roof Deck Construction
    (NFPA 203), 181

H
hazard assessment, 222–223, 230–231. *See also* size-up
hazardous conditions. *See also* firefighter safety
    air conditioners, 238
    conveyance systems, 243
    detection systems, 247, 248–249
    electrocution, 228, 229, 230
    elevators and escalators, 243, 244
    fences, 229
    gas leaks without fires, 223–225
    HVAC systems, 237–239
    lighting systems, 241
    during overhaul, 264
    on roofs, 162–163, 169–171, 175
    searching floors above fires, 77
    securing property during post-incident operations, 270
    suppression systems, 249–252
    during ventilation, 129–131, 148–153
hazard zones, 24, 25–26, 222, 223
heat. *See also* temperatures
    convection, 95
    in decay stage of fire development, 93
    electrical currents creating, 230
    in flashover stage of fire development, 92
    in growth stage of fire development, 91
    heat removal operations, 81–82, 268
    radiation, 95

sliding doors activated by, 126
thermal imagers detecting, 78–80
ventilation affecting, 90, 107
heating, ventilating, and air conditioning (HVAC) systems
controlling, 239–240
hazards of, 237–239
overview, 237
ventilation, 116, 206, 240
heating oil. *See* fuel oil
hidden fires, 11, 13, 84, 264–265
high-rise buildings. *See also* multistory buildings
attack tactics, 195–197
fire behavior in, 197–198
HVAC and smoke-control systems, 206
overview, 195
utilities, controlling, 206, 215, 218
ventilation, 198–206
horizontal ventilation
backdrafts affected by, 94
building construction and, 119–127
doors used for, 124–127
establishing and supporting, 128–131
exposures, 110–111
fire spread affected by, 115, 128
forced, 91, 135–139
hazardous conditions, 129–131
in high-rise buildings, 199, 204–205
in multistory buildings, 109
natural, 91, 132–135
structures and situations appropriate for, 109, 115
tools and equipment used for, 115–119, 121, 122, 134, 135
vertical ventilation compared to, 109
walls used for, 119–122
windows used for, 100, 122–124
hoselines. *See also* fire streams and ventilation
fans powered using, 137
finding exits when lost, 27
in rescue mode, 278
rollovers (flameovers) and, 92
ventilation and, 107, 152–153
HVAC systems. *See* heating, ventilating, and air conditioning (HVAC) systems
hydraulic ventilation, 138–139

I

IAP. *See* Incident Action Plans (IAP)
ICs. *See* Incident Commanders (ICs)
ignition
firewalls affecting, 120
sources of
actuating electrical switches, 226, 227
construction materials in older buildings, 12
eliminating at natural gas leak situations, 223–224
sparks from cutting metal, 49
ventilation exposing adjacent structures, 110–111
wooden shingles and shakes, 181
in stages of fire development, 91, 92–93
IMS (Incident Management System), 280, 285
Incident Action Plans (IAP)
coordinated operations, 108, 275
forcible entry in, 54
interior operations affecting, 75
resources called to scenes, 262
size-up affecting, 4, 5
water supply factors, 6
Incident Commanders (ICs)
command options at coordinated attacks, 280–282
communication during interior operations, 75
resources requested by, 276
size-up responsibilities, 5

Incident Management System (IMS), 280, 285
Incident Safety Officers (ISOs), 283
incident scene priorities
coordinated operations, 275–276
overview, 21–23
utilities, controlling
fuel oil, 219–220
gas leaks without fires, 220–225
LPG, 218–219
natural gas, 216–218
industrial/institutional structures. *See also* correctional facilities
building construction
doors, 54–61
roofs, 161–162
windows, 64
electrical service, controlling, 227–228
features affecting fireground operations, 106–107
occupant loads, 76
initial attacks, 283–285
institutional structures. *See* industrial/institutional structures
interior operations. *See also* access into structures; attacks
communication with IC, 75
coordinating with ventilation, 107–110
defensive mode, 278
heat removal, 81–82
search and rescue operations, 75–81
two-in/two-out rule, 23, 75, 77
ISOs (Incident Safety Officers), 283, *284*

J

jails. *See* correctional facilities

L

ladders
built onto buildings (fire escapes), 170
egress through windows using, 28, 77–78
forcible entry through windows using, 63
overcoming access obstacles using, 35
roof access using, 150
ventilation using, 152, 163
landscaping and topography affecting access, 33–35, 104
lapping, 110
life safety
building type and occupancy affecting, 76, 77
HVAC systems and, 240
Incident Safety Officers (ISOs), 283
incident scene priority, 21, 22, 23
ventilation affecting, 89
Life Safety Code (NFPA 101), 80
lighting systems, 241–243
lightweight construction, 176–181
liquefied petroleum gas (LPG), 218–219, 223, 224–225
London case history, 243
"look up, look down, look around", 9
loss control. *See also* salvage
defensive mode, 278
HVAC systems and, 240
overview, 259
post-incident, 269–271
pre-incident planning and, 259–261
primary, 259, 262–266
salvage operations, 82–85
secondary, 259, 266–269
slate/tile roofs, 185
ventilation considerations for, 89, 90
LPG (liquefied petroleum gas), 218–219, 223, 224–225

M

Massachusetts case history, 13
means of egress. *See* egress, means of
mechanical ventilation. *See* forced ventilation
mitigation plans, 261. *See also* pre-incident planning inspections
mule kick, 52
multistory buildings. *See also* high-rise buildings
　fire spread in, 95–96
　sprinkler systems in, 250
　ventilation, 109, 115
mushrooming, 197–198
mutual aid companies. *See* coordinated operations

N

NAERG2000, 218, 221
National Institute for Occupational Safety and Health (NIOSH), 5–7
National Interagency Incident Management System (NIIMS), 280
natural gas, 68, 215–218, 223–224
natural ventilation, 90, 91, 110, 132–135, 198–199
negative pressure, 90
negative-pressure ventilation (NPV), 117, 118–119
New York case histories
　candle starting apartment fire (April, 1978), 3
　propane tank explosion (1983), 21, 220
New York (FDNY) SOPs, 49
NFPA 12, *Standard on Carbon Dioxide Extinguishing Systems*, 249
NFPA 12A, *Standard on Halon 1301 Fire Extinguishing Systems*, 249
NFPA 12B, *Standard on Halon 1211 Fire Extinguishing*, 250
NFPA 13, *Standard for the Installation of Sprinkler Systems*, 250
NFPA 13D, *Standard for the Installation of Sprinkler Systems in One- and Two-Family Dwellings and Mobile Homes*, 250
NFPA 13R, *Standard for the Installation of Sprinkler Systems in Residential Occupancies up to Four Stories in Height*, 250
NFPA 14, *Standard for the Installation of Standpipe, Private Hydrants and Hose Systems*, 251
NFPA 101, *Life Safety Code*®, 80
NFPA 203, *Guidelines on Roof Coverings and Roof Deck Construction*, 181
NFPA 204, *Guide for Smoke and Heat Venting*, 207
NFPA 1500, *Fire Department Occupational Safety and Health Program*, 24, 25, 66
NFPA 1561, *Emergency Services Incident Management System*, 24
NFPA 1620, *Recommended Practice for Pre-Incident Planning*, 76
NIIMS (National Interagency Incident Management System), 280
NIOSH (National Institute for Occupational Safety and Health), 5–7
North American Emergency Response Guide (NAERG2000), 218, 221
NPV (negative-pressure ventilation), 117, 118–119

O

occupancy and occupancy loads
　building features related to, 106–107
　initial alarm assignment affected by, 283
　as life safety factor, 76
　as size-up factor, 6
occupants. *See* civilians and perimeter control; victims
Occupational Safety and Health Administration (OSHA) CFR 1910.134, 25
office buildings
　access considerations, 34

fire behavior in, 17
fire spread in, 95
oil. *See* fuel oil
operational modes, 277–279, 284. *See also* command options at coordinated operations
overhaul, 13, 263–266
owners. *See* victims
oxidation, 93–94
oxygen
　holes in firewalls providing, 120
　oxidation, 93–94
　smoke indicating levels of, 96–97
　in stages of fire development, 92, 93, 97

P

PARs (personnel accountability reports), 24, 279
pedestrians. *See* civilians and perimeter control; victims
perimeter control, establishing, 24, 221–222, 229–231
personal protective equipment (PPE)
　case histories involving, 9, 243
　escalator hazards, 243, 244
　eye protection, 65, 66–67, 68, 69
　gloves, 58
　hearing protection, 69
　respiratory protection, 66–67, 68
　worn during forcible entry
　　through doors, 58, 61
　　through walls, 66–67, 68, 69
　　through windows, 63, 65
　worn during gas leaks, 221, 224
　worn during primary searches, 78
　worn while on roofs, 149
　worn while using rotary saws, 143
personnel. *See also* resources
　in extended attacks, 286–287
　high-rise building incidents affecting, 195
　incidents dictating need for, 275–276
　from outside the district, 286–287
　physical abilities of, 277
　services provided for, 287
personnel accountability reports (PARs), 24, 279
Phoenix Fire Department (PFD), 22
piping exposed during forcible entry, 122
positive pressure, 90
positive-pressure ventilation (PPV)
　in basements and underground areas, 209
　ducts used in, 117
　establishing, 138
　in high-rise buildings, 198, 199, 203, 204
power. *See* electrical systems; utilities, controlling
PPE. *See* personal protective equipment (PPE)
PPV. *See* positive-pressure ventilation (PPV)
pre-incident planning inspections
　access obstacles identified, 34, 38
　building codes and, 12
　building type identified, 76
　coordinated operations, 275
　doors and security systems identified, 50, 61
　emergency power sources identified, 242
　flooding systems identified, 250
　gas meter shutoff valves identified, 217, 218
　high-rise buildings, 199, 206
　HVAC and smoke-control systems identified, 206
　loss control considerations during, 259–261
　new construction observations, 103
　occupant loads identified, 80
　power sources identified, 227, 228, 242
　remodels and, 3, 103
　roof construction identified, 82–83, 84, 165, 169, 171
　roof features identified, 148, 186

salvage operations considerations, 82
sample form for, 305
of secure buildings, 210
size-up and, 3
stairways identified, 200
walls identified, 66, 67, 119
windows identified, 64
prisons. *See* correctional facilities
products of combustion, 90, 265. *See also* toxic products of combustion
property contents. *See also* loss control
impeding ventilation, 130
protecting, 267
returned to occupants, 269
securing during post-incident operations, 270
public assembly structures, 76
pyrolysis, 93

R
radiation, 95, 110
rapid intervention and firefighter safety, 25–26
rapid intervention crews (RICs)
communication with, 23
establishing, 78
requirements for, 77
SOPs for, 301–303
rapid intervention teams (RITs). *See* rapid intervention crews (RICs)
recirculation, 137
remodels. *See* building construction, remodels
"report on conditions", 5. *See also* Incident Action Plans (IAP)
rescue and search operations, 75–81
rescue saws. *See* saws, rotary saws
residential structures
access considerations, 33
building construction. See also specific parts of structures (e.g. attics)
doors, 50–54
overview, 12, 13
roofs, 180
size-up factors, 6
windows, 64
electrical service, controlling, 226–227
fences, 41–42
fire situation as interior operation variable, 77
forcible entry, 51–54, 64
lighting systems, 241, 242
occupant loads, 76
sprinkler systems in, 232, 250
water supply, controlling, 232
resources
additional, calling for, 5, 6, 284
apparatus, 283, 287
availability of, 276
capability of, 277
deployment of, 284
incidents dictating need for, 275–276
loss control requiring, 262
from outside the district, 287
retail structures. *See* commercial structures
RICs. *See* rapid intervention crews (RICs)
risk/benefit analysis, 77, 78, 84, 284
rollovers (flameovers), 10, 92
roofs
accessing, 149–150, 157–158, 199–200
assemblies
collapse potential affected by, 106
failure, 89
pre-incident planning identification, 82–83, 84, 186
size-up, 100, 101

collapse potential. *See* collapse potential
construction
arched roofs, 173–176
flat roofs, 164–173
lightweight construction, 176–181
pitched roofs, 156–163, 166
pre-incident planning identification, 165, 169, 171
coverings, 181–186
firefighter safety while on, 149, 162–163, 169–171, 185, 187
supports located using thermal imagers, 79
testing condition of
reading roofs, 150–151, 165, 169–170, 187
sounding roofs, 151–152, 171, 185, 187
ventilation through
arched roofs, 175–176
existing openings, 153–156, 171, 173
features affecting, 148
firefighter safety during, 152, 153
flat roofs, 171–173
pitched roofs, 162–163
procedures for opening, 186–192
vents on, 103, 154–155, 207

S
Safety Code for Elevators (ASME A17.1), 245
salvage, 82–85, 266–269. *See also* loss control; property contents
salvage covers, 42, 43, 84
saws
chain saws, 62, 70, 144–145, 187–188
rotary saws
forcible entry using
blades used for, 48, 49, 58
described, 48–49
SOPs and, 49
through doors, 51–52, 53–54, 57–60, 61–62
through walls, 68, 69, 70
through windows, 64, 65
maintenance of, 49
ventilation using
horizontal, 115, 134
vertical, 143–144, 169, 171
SCBA. *See* self-contained breathing apparatus (SCBA)
scenes
collapse zones established, 24
operational modes, 277–279, 284
priorities. *See* incident scene priorities
securing. *See* perimeter control, establishing
schools, occupant loads, 76
search and rescue operations, 75–81
seats of fires
locating, 79, 108
ventilation exit openings placement above, 128, 148
securing utilities. *See* utilities, controlling
security measures
access affected by, 42–44, 170–171
means of egress affected by, 14
ventilation affected by, 124
self-contained breathing apparatus (SCBA)
accountability systems, 23–24
breathing techniques, 26
EEBSS, 26
in growth stage of fire development, 92
removing before dropping from heights, 27
worn during forcible entry, 61, 67
worn during overhaul, 265
worn during ventilation, 183, 184
worn in hazard zones, 26
worn while on roofs, 149, 183, 184
worn while working below grade, 208

self-rescue (emergency egress), 26–29
self-vented fires, 9–10
sheltering in place, 80–81
site access. *See* access to structures; interior operations
size-up. *See also* hazard assessment
    access into structures based on, 47
    backdraft potential, 94
    building construction
        age of building affecting, 11–12, 98–101
        collapse potential, 12, 13
        features helping firefighters, 101–103
        features hindering firefighters, 103–106
        fire spread and, 96
        part of building, 14–15. *See also specific parts*
        remodels, 13–14
        type of building, 15–17, 98–99. *See also specific types*
    case histories involving, 3, 7–9, 9, 13
    collapse potential, 13
    fire behavior knowledge and, 3, 94
    IAP affected by, 4, 5
    IC command options, 280–282
    IC responsibilities, 5
    NIOSH model, 5–7
    overview, 3–5
    pre-incident planning and, 3
    resources called to scenes, 262, 276
    smoke and, 15, 96–98
    structure familiarity and, 3
    ventilation. *See* ventilation, size-up
smoke
    adjacent structures exposure to, 110–111
    as backdraft indicator, 94
    behavior of, 96–98
    channeling, 90, 118, 200–204, 268
    in decay stage of fire development, 93
    HVAC and smoke-control systems, 206
    size-up and, 15, 96–98
smoke blowers and ejectors. *See* fans (blowers and ejectors)
stack effect, 197, 202–203, 203–204
staffing. *See* personnel
stages of fire development, 91–94, 97
stairways
    accessing roofs using, 200
    firefighter safety in, 201
    size-up, 15
standard operating procedures (SOPs)
    firefighter safety, 22–23
    lost firefighters, 293–300
    PPV establishment, 138
    RICs, 301–303
    rotary saw blades, 49
    structural collapse, 25, 293–303
stratification of smoke and fire gases, 197–198
streams. *See* fire streams and ventilation
structural collapse. *See* collapse potential
structure interiors. *See* interior operations; *specific interior areas*
structures. *See* building construction; *specific types of structures*
substrate, 181
suppression systems
    controlling, 254–255
    hazards of, 249–252
    reducing fire spread, 102–103
    types of
        flooding systems, 249–250, 254
        sprinkler systems
            case history involving, 3
            collapse potential affected by, 105
            controlling, 231–232, 254–255

        escalators and, 244
        fire spread affected by, 95, 102
        hazards of, 250–251
        pre-incident planning identifying, 261
        remodels affecting, 14
        types of, 250
        ventilation and, 250–251
    standpipe systems, 251–252, 255
surveys. *See* pre-incident planning inspections

T

temperature control systems. *See* heating, ventilating, and air conditioning (HVAC) systems
temperatures. *See also* heat
    fire streams cooling, 153
    mushrooming, 197
    stack effect, 197
    in stages of fire development, 91, 92, 93
    ventilation size-up, 111–112
thermal imagers and thermal imaging cameras (TIC)
    locating rafters and roof supports using, 187
    locating seat of fire using, 94
    overview, 78–80
    reading roofs using, 150, 170
    when wires are down without fires, 230
TIC (thermal imaging cameras). *See* thermal imagers and thermal imaging cameras (TIC)
tools and equipment. *See also specific tools*
    for breaching fences, 39
    for opening gates, 36–37
    for overcoming walls, 66, 68, 69–70
    for overcoming window security systems, 66
    primary search operations including, 78
    for securing electrical service, 226
    for ventilation
        horizontal, 115–119, 121, 122, 134, 135
        vertical, 143–148, 163, 171, 172, 182
topography and landscaping
    access affected by, 33–35, 104
    low areas affected by ventilation, 119
townhouses and size-up, 15
toxic products of combustion. *See also* products of combustion
    overhaul operations and, 265
    released from interior finishes and furniture, 101, 104
    released from roofing materials, 183, 184
    released in new buildings, 12
"try before you pry", 49
tunnels. *See* basements and underground structures
two-in/two-out rule, 23, 75, 77

U

underground structures. *See* basements and underground structures
utilities, controlling
    before breaching walls, 68
    case history involving, 215–216
    electrical service, 225–231
    firefighter safety and, 215
    fuel oil, 219–220
    gas leaks without fires, 220–225
    in high-rise buildings, 206, 215, 218
    LPG, 218–219
    natural gas, 216–218
    scene priorities, 216–220
    water service, 231–234

V

vaults. *See* basements and underground structures
ventilation
    atrium vents used for, 207–208

backdrafts affected by, 94
basements and underground structures, 208–209
building construction affecting, 96, 98–101
building features affecting, 103
case histories involving, 3, 8, 9, 47–48, 89, 275
coordinated with attacks, 82, 90, 107–110
elevator shafts used for, 103, 199
exit openings, 128, 129–130, 148, 188
fire behavior and, 91, 93, 96
forced ventilation. *See* forced ventilation
heat removal compared to, 81
in high-rise buildings, 198–206
horizontal. *See* horizontal ventilation
HVAC systems and, 116, 206, 240
location of openings
 coordinated with attacks, 108–109
 horizontal ventilation, 128
 vertical ventilation, 148, 186–187, 188
loss control and salvage operations, 262–263, 266, 268
natural, 90, 91, 110, 132–135, 198–199
negative-pressure ventilation (NPV), 117, 118–119
overview, 89–91
positive pressure. *See* positive-pressure ventilation (PPV)
of remodeled buildings, 210–211
roof vents used for, 207
in secure buildings, 210
self-vented fires, 9-10
size-up
 building construction affecting, 98–107
 coordinated with attacks, 107–110
 exposures, 110–111
 loss control considerations during, 89, 90
 opening roofs, 186–187, 188
 stages of fire development, 91
 in townhouses, 15
 weather, 111–112
sprinkler systems and, 250–251
in townhouses, 15
types of. See specific types
vertical. *See* vertical ventilation
in windowless buildings, 210
venturi effect, 90
Vermont case history, 11
vertical ventilation
 arched roofs, 175–176
 backdrafts affected by, 94
 establishing and supporting, 148
 existing openings, 153–156, 171, 173
 exit opening considerations, 148, 188
 exposures, 110–111
 firefighter safety during, 152
 flat roofs, 171–173
 hazardous conditions, 148–153
 in high-rise buildings, 199–200, 205–206
 horizontal ventilation compared to, 109
 in multistory buildings, 109
 opening roofs, 186–192
 pitched roofs, 162–163
 rain roofs, 100
 roof coverings affecting, 182
 structures and situations appropriate for, 109
 tools and equipment used for, 143–148, 163, 171, 172, 182

victims. *See also* property contents
 communicating with, 81
 evacuating, 222, 223, 241
 locating using thermal imagers, 79
 medical attention provided to, 80
Virginia case history, 11, 25
visibility
 backdraft indicators, 94
 emergency egress, 27, 28
 fans affecting, 137
 ventilation affecting, 107, 199
 while at LPG leak incidents, 223
 while on roofs, 148, 149, 171, 186, 207

W

walls
 collapse potential, 11, 12
 emergency egress through, 29
 forcible entry through (breaching)
 PPE used during, 66–67
 techniques for, 67, 68–71
 tools used for, 66, 68
 knockout (blowout) panels in, 69–70
 loss control and salvage operations, 268
 pre-incident planning identification, 66, 67, 119
 security measures built into, 43
 ventilation and, 119–122
warehouses
 case histories involving, 9, 11, 13
 fire spread, 95
 size-up, 16
Washington state case history, 9, 13
water service, controlling, 231–234. *See also* utilities, controlling
water supply
 mobile, 6, 283
 used in attacks
 loss control considerations, 266
 runoff from suppression systems, 251, 252
 salvage operations and, 84–85, 268–269
 water tanks affecting collapse potential, 105
weather
 high-rise buildings affected by, 202–203, 203–204
 humidity, 111
 size-up affected by, 6–7
 temperature, 111–112
 ventilation
 effectiveness, 131, 132, 172
 firefighter safety during, 153
 size-up, 111–112, 128
white ghost, 220
windows
 breaching walls near, 67
 coordinating opening with other operations, 82
 emergency egress through, 27–28
 forcible entry through, 62–66, 105
 grilles, 100, 105
 lost firefighters locating, 27
 pre-incident planning identification, 64
 security systems, 64–66, 124. *See also specific types*
 types of, 62–63
 ventilation, 100, 122–124, 132–135, 136, 156
wiring, 99–100, 101, 122. *See also* electrical systems

COMMENT SHEET

DATE _____ NAME _____

ADDRESS _____

ORGANIZATION REPRESENTED _____

CHAPTER TITLE _____ NUMBER _____

SECTION/PARAGRAPH/FIGURE _____ PAGE _____

1. Proposal (include proposed wording or identification of wording to be deleted),
   OR PROPOSED FIGURE:

2. Statement of Problem and Substantiation for Proposal:

RETURN TO: IFSTA Editor
Fire Protection Publications
Oklahoma State University
930 N. Willis
Stillwater, OK 74078-8045

SIGNATURE _____

Use this sheet to make any suggestions, recommendations, or comments. We need your input to make the manuals as up to date as possible. Your help is appreciated. Use additional pages if necessary.

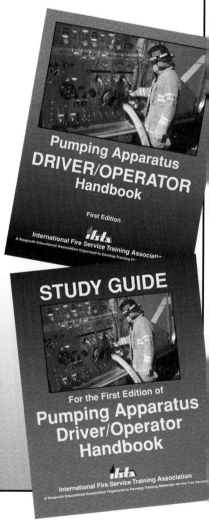